GOLD RUSH

GOLD
RUSH

**Inspiring Stories of More
Than 25 Companies in
Search of the World's
Most Precious Metal**

MICHAEL CALDWELL

CREATIVE CLASSICS INC.

Creative Classics Inc.
Vancouver, B.C.
Canada

Copyright ©2005 by Michael Caldwell

ISBN: 0-9692129-7-6

Caldwell, Michael H., 1946 -

GOLD RUSH...The Inspiring Stories of More Than 25 Companies in Search of the World's Most Precious Metal.

Printed by: Friesens Corporation, Altona, Manitoba, Canada

Foreword by: Will Purcell

Research: Greg Potter, Bonnie Bowman and Justin Smallbridge

TABLE OF CONTENTS

FOREWORD

A soft and heavy metal that is a good conductor of heat and electricity, gold has a variety of uses in modern industries, but it is the metal's yellow lustre that has made gold the most sought after commodity through the ages. Gold has been used as currency for nearly 10,000 years and the quest for the metal was a driving force behind the creation and destruction of many mighty empires and the discovery of new worlds. Once the realm of mighty nations, the cost of finding gold has dropped over the centuries. A small number of mining majors dominated the exploration landscape for many decades, but a large number of junior explorers have been having a much greater impact over the past quarter century. Gold has played a key role in the history of North America over the past 500 years and the metal will continue to exert a driving force upon the economy well into the next millennium, as a unique combination of major producers and junior explorers lead a new exploration phase, seeking the next big find in Canada and around the world.

The resource sector has experienced a boom and bust cycle that has played itself out many times over the past several hundred years. Lean times would come to an abrupt end with a big find in a virgin area, prompting a rush of explorers to the new district. Those discoveries were often the result of changing methods and technologies, a process that continues to this day.

The first forays by France and England into what is now Canada were spurred on by Spain's conquest of the Aztec, Maya and Inca empires, which was producing unprecedented treasures of gold. Jacques Cartier was the first European to venture far inland into what is now Quebec, but his exploration campaign was regarded as a failure back at home because he had failed to return with a bounty of gold. Several decades passed before France tried again.

English efforts fared no better. John Cabot had visions of gold when he set sail in 1497, but he failed to find a trace of the metal. Nearly a century later, Martin Frobisher thought he had made a big find on Baffin Island, and he launched a mining expedition in 1578. Frobisher's ore turned out to be nothing more than iron pyrite, in what may have been Canada's first big gold scam. Whatever the reason for Frobisher's mistake, Canada's reputation as a treasure trove of minerals took another big, albeit temporary, hit. Ironically, Martin Frobisher subsequently did find gold, but it was not as a miner. He turned to piracy later in life, recovering his treasure from the holds of Spanish ships returning from the New World.

Gold booms in the 19th century were prominent factors in the development of the more remote parts of North America. Precious metal finds in the southwestern parts of the United States had a lasting impact on California and Nevada, but discoveries farther north often left little in their wake. The Klondike rush that began in 1896 is undoubtedly the most famous gold find in Canadian history. Dawson City quickly swelled to become the largest city west of Winnipeg and north of Seattle. The Yukon boom withered away a few years later, taking most of Dawson with it, as the placer gold played out and word of a new find in Alaska reached the remote area, sending the gold hunters scurrying down the Yukon River toward Nome.

Things did not always play out that way. There have been many gold finds through the years, and although they did not capture the imagination in the way that the Klondike rush had, the discoveries often had a lasting impact on the local economies and the companies that brought the finds to production.

The desire for the yellow metal has changed little over the years and new deposits and reserves continue to be found. Some of the discoveries are in remote and relatively unexplored parts of the world, but novel approaches and recent technological advances have resulted in new finds in traditional gold belts, often within and near existing gold mines.

Gold exploration expenditures in Canada experienced an exponential growth during the latter part of the 1970s and the 1980s, and most of the exploration dollars were spent by junior companies. Some hefty jumps in the price of gold were contributing factors in the renaissance, but much of the interest stemmed from a big find in Northwestern Ontario that proved the worth of new techniques and provided a powerful measure of the potential profitability of a gold mine.

The area north of Lake Superior had been scouted for its gold potential for more than 100 years. There was a brief flurry of activity in the 1860s, when a prospector turned up signs of gold not far from the Hemlo district. Another prospecting find in the 1940s generated a minor staking rush in the area north of Superior, but once again, the play quickly died. Interest in the Hemlo area was reawakened in 1979, when two prospectors staked a large land position in the area and optioned the ground to willing explorers.

One of those companies was little Corona Corporation, run by David Bell. Previous efforts in the area had relied upon prospecting and geophysics, but there were no real indications of a gold deposit showing on the surface and geophysical surveys failed to produce any noticeable signature. Still, earlier exploration programs had reached the drilling stage, but in a bit of bad luck, the holes tested a barren region between two big ore zones.

Corona's initial program at Hemlo used a relatively new approach based upon soil geochemistry to hunt gold. Soil samples were collected below the surface, as close as possible to the top of the bedrock. The material collected was then sent for chemical analysis, in the hope of finding trace quantities of gold and other minerals associated with precious metal deposits. Corona quickly came up with an intriguing anomaly in its soil samples, and the Hemlo play was off and running.

Since the mid-1980s, the three main Hemlo gold mines have produced over 15 million ounces of gold from a main deposit that contains an estimated 22 million ounces, and the area still accounts for a healthy proportion of Canada's annual gold production. The site of Corona's big find is especially tantalizing for gold hunters, as it is clearly not in a remote and inaccessible part of the country. In fact, the shafts of the Williams and David Bell mines are clearly visible to travelers on the Trans-Canada Highway, a road that has carried many a prospector on the prowl for the next big find.

The Hemlo discovery helped spark a surge of activity that peaked in the latter half of the 1980s, culminating in 1987 when over $1-billion was spent on gold exploration, most of it by juniors hoping to duplicate the seemingly improbable success of Corona. Interest remained high through the end of the decade, but rising interest rates and a downturn in the economy triggered a bear market that forced most companies to scale back their exploration programs in the early 1990s.

Annual gold exploration budgets dropped below $200 million for a time, but rebounded during the mid-1990s, helped along by the rising price of gold, dropping interest rates and another round of new discoveries. Some finds were in relatively unexplored areas, sending prospectors scurrying to scoop up nearby ground, but the traditional gold districts accounted for many of the significant discoveries in the mid-1990s.

It is said that the best place to look for a new mine is within the shadow of a headframe, and that adage still proves true today. Placer Dome considers mine site exploration to be the most effective method of adding to its gold reserves, and the company has directed a significant portion of its exploration budget at expanding its reserves and seeking new deposits within an economic radius of existing mine sites. The program has been a successful one, as the company's mine site exploration program has added over 20 million ounces of gold to its reserves.

On occasion, the best place to look for a big new deposit is under one of your own. In 1995, Goldcorp Inc. made an unexpected find in the depths of its Red Lake mine, which had been in production since the late 1940s. The Red Lake region was a mature gold district, with production of more than 20 million ounces over several decades, and it seemed that Goldcorp's mine was nearing the latter stages of its life.

The conventional wisdom was that the material in the Red Lake mines gradually gave way to lower-grade sulphide rock at depth, but Goldcorp began producing some spectacular assays from its deep drilling program, with grades that averaged about nine ounces per tonne over mineable widths. The discovery of what was effectively a distinct new mine at the bottom of an old one baffled geologists, and adding to the mystery was the fact that it took nearly half a century to turn up.

Goldcorp ultimately proved up nearly three million tonnes of the material, and with an average grade of about two ounces per tonne, the high-grade zone contained more than six million ounces of gold. The find is not unique, as Placer also identified a rich new area within its own Red Lake mine, and the region again became a hot spot for gold exploration. The high-grade discoveries have prompted many junior explorers to take a new look at claims within other old gold camps across North America.

Gold juniors have been flexing their exploration muscles on other fronts. Small companies with a promising gold play have historically struck option deals with majors at an early stage, but in recent years, growing numbers of smaller companies have been able to push their projects through aggressive drilling programs on their own, and juniors have been optioning properties from much larger companies with increasing frequency of late.

Juniors have also been a growing force in remote corners of Canada and the world, tackling a number of potentially rich projects in areas such as the North, Africa and the former Soviet Union. The Hope Bay greenstone belt, near the Arctic coast, is typical of recent trends within the sector. Gold was discovered in the area by BHP in the early 1990s and over $80-million was spent on exploration. The company sold the project to Cambiex Exploration Inc., which promptly flipped a half share to Miramar Mining Corp. The two companies merged in 2002 and continue to explore and develop three promising deposits that are now thought to contain more than five million ounces of gold.

The last few years of the 20th Century brought tough times back to the resource sector. Hiccups in the world economy and a gold price that sagged below US$260 an ounce forced many companies to curtail their exploration expenditures. The crash took a bigger toll on exploration juniors and many of them headed for the exits. A long list of companies dropped their gold projects, becoming high-tech darlings overnight. Exploration budgets were slashed as new sources of cash proved to be as elusive as gold and Canadian gold exploration expenditures sagged to about $160 million in 2001. Still, a healthy proportion of that total was spent by juniors, despite the difficulties faced in coming up with the required cash.

Gold has recaptured a lot of its lustre over the past few years. Exploration programs are again reflecting a healthy optimism for the future of the Canadian resource sector, and junior explorers continue to be a major contributor to the resurgence. The price of gold has again surpassed the magical US$400 mark, and a steady stream of companies returning to the resource sector is a sure sign of the vibrant state of the industry and the market perceptions for its future.

Michael Caldwell takes a compelling look at twenty-eight Canadian producers and explorers and their inspiring stories, as the gold sector booms into this exciting new phase.

Will Purcell

AFCAN MINING CORPORATION

It may seem obvious that the name Afcan is a hybrid of Africa and Canada – in fact, the company still retains some joint ventured West African gold and nickel prospects to its credit. What is not so obvious, based on the name alone, is that the company's most promising riches are being mined in China where Afcan is quickly becoming an emerging gold producer to watch.

This makes sense, because what led up to its current incarnation is all over the map. Afcan's president and CEO David Netherway hails from Australia; Afcan's head office is in Montreal, Canada; and Netherway has worked in many parts of the world, to this day maintaining residences in three different countries. For this worldly explorer, a name is only a name. What's more important is what that name represents. In the case of Afcan, it represents a solid, experienced team under the direction of Netherway, an Australian mining engineer with 30 years of experience. It also represents their exciting China gold project that is breaking new ground, both literally and figuratively.

"I'm under pressure from some people to change the name," Netherway admits, "but I'm not too concerned about it.

"Maybe one day, but who cares? A name is a name as far as I'm concerned and people recognize it now, so I say let's keep it. Besides, we have re-branded the company with a new logo and website."

For Netherway, the name of his company is a mere triviality when compared to the serious promises contained within its portfolio. He has much more important things to think about and China tops the list.

With China recently receiving renewed industry notice, Afcan finds itself in an extremely favourable position, having finalized acquisition of the Tanjianshan (TJS) project in northwest China and already producing gold. Strategically placed and well funded with $6 million in cash as of April 2004, Netherway is satisfied and assured the company is in a strong position to move forward. It couldn't have happened without the confidence from financial backers who supported Afcan in its beginnings, which really meant they were placing their money and faith in Netherway and his known expertise. Now, Afcan enjoys the support of major institutional investors such as Sprott Asset Management, Royal Bank of Canada, JP Morgan, RAB Capital, LOM Securities, Research Works and AGF Precious Metal Fund.

But long before Afcan was a twinkle in Netherway's eye, and decades before China lured him with an offer he couldn't refuse, this Australian-born mining engineer was busy paying his dues elsewhere. Whether he was sinking a shaft in the desert, working deep underground in Australia, sweating it out in the jungles of Malaysia, or trekking three days with sherpas to reach a little zinc project 15,000 feet high in the mountains of Nepal, Netherway was getting around and gleaning invaluable experience and connections. He even did a short stint in the less exotic environs of northern Ontario, but declined a permanent job with Golder Associates because as he quickly discovered, "Canada was too cold".

As Netherway's expertise grew, the heavy lifting decreased and responsibilities increased, mostly coinciding with a move in 1984 to an exciting new locale – Africa – where he would end up spending 15 years, working primarily in Guinea and Ghana involved in the exploration, feasibility and construction of three gold mines.

Two years at the Ghana National Manganese Corporation kicked things off. In 1986, a conversation with "university mate" Jim Askew led to a collaboration on a successful gold project.

"Jim was off looking for projects and I had some friends in Ghana who had a gold project. Jim is pretty well known in the industry now, he's run lots of companies around the world, and when I told him about this project he said: 'Well, let's take a look'. So we did," said Netherway.

"I finished my contract with the Manganese company and we started working on this thing. It became the Iduapriem Gold Mine, and the Australian company was Golden Shamrock Mines. I ran West Africa and Jim ran the company in Australia. In 1992, we put it into production. It was a big mine."

Together, Netherway and Askew financed it, saw it through, and were very successful.

In 1994, Netherway moved to Conakry, the capital of Guinea, and while still running Golden Shamrock in West Africa, also ran the Siguiri project, which eventually became the Siguiri Gold Mine.

In 1996, they merged Golden Shamrock into the huge Ashanti Goldfields operation in a very respectable $300 million Australian deal.

Netherway only lasted six months at Ashanti in the capacity of Director General, managing Guinea.

"I wasn't going to stick around for that," he says, confiding, "I hate big companies."

Following that brief sojourn, he hooked up with Askew again and set up a private company called Mango Resources.

"I moved back to Ghana and picked up some properties for this company in Mali, in Sierra Leone, in Guinea."

During that time, Netherway also consulted for Nevsun's Ghana operation after receiving a panicked call that their chief geologist had dropped dead of a heart attack.

"Peter Hooper called me and said, 'Help'. So I ran Ghana for him for about a year and meanwhile I was also putting together these properties for Mango," explained Netherway.

Neither he nor Hooper could know at the time that this meeting would be fortuitous and rewarding for both of them much later on.

Around the end of 1997, Askew and Netherway sold Mango to a company called Prospex Mining, listed on the Vancouver stock exchange. They eventually took it over, with Netherway taking the helm as president and CEO and Askew as chairman. Following this "board revolution" and some money raising, Netherway picked up an option on a gold plant in Jamaica.

"I was looking for a property to put this little gold plant on, a gold property. I targeted all the small properties and one was called Jean Gobele in Guinea, which is now called Kiniero Gold Mine. It was owned by Semafo Inc."

Another merger took place, this time between Semafo and Prospex, with Semafo taking over all of Prospex assets. Netherway came on board as chief operating officer of Semafo in 1999, a job that would last until late 2001. Askew lurked around in the background, was on the board of Semafo for awhile, and then faded out of that particular picture. It wouldn't be long before he would reappear in Netherway's life, however.

During Netherway's tenure at Semafo, the Moroccans got involved and eventually took 53 percent of the company which they still own to this day.

"In the end, we didn't use the Jamaican plant. What we did was build the Kiniero Gold Mine. We got it up and running in 2002. It's producing and doing very well. So, Semafo was very useful during the bad times," says Netherway.

In 2001, Netherway left Semafo and went on the hunt for his own company. The time was right.

"I could see the gold price was going to go up, everything was ripe to have another start of a cycle again and I was looking for a junior company, a shell or something I could take on with a good project and run with it," explained Netherway.

Through past contacts, he was made aware of Afcan, which had been around for about 10 years as a listed company, but was sitting with no management and no money. It was perfect for Netherway's needs and true to his new company's name, he began by putting some West African projects into it.

"But I was looking for a very advanced gold project and all of a sudden, along came this China opportunity," Netherway said.

And who was there to hand it to him? None other than his old university mate, Jim Askew who was sitting on the board of Sino Gold Ltd., an Australian company.

"Sino wanted to sell this property and Jim said, 'I know just the person'.

"So I jumped on a plane, went to China and had a look, went to Sydney and negotiated the deal. That was in October 2002 and the rest is history."

The deal closed late February 2003, and Netherway was faced with the next inevitable step: raising money. He received some support from an ex-Semafo shareholder, but at the time nobody was really interested in knowing about China. Netherway dug in, literally.

"We got down there, started drilling and started turning this thing into something real."

Another fundraising in September brought Netherway and Peter Hooper together again, Hooper now being with Kingsdale Capital.

"They took us on. We went out to raise $3 million Canadian and I got offered $4.5 million in one day in Toronto. I went to the United Kingdom the next day and we got offered $5 million."

In no time at all, they had $10 million, and Netherway was grateful and appreciative for not only the money but the show of faith.

"That really changed things," he acknowledged. "Before that, the company traded by invitation. We knew most of our shareholders in Quebec and we traded a couple times a week...what we did was get John Embry on board with Sprott and he promoted us on television. Embry's the guru. If John says this is a good stock, everybody jumps in."

With Embry's seal of approval, Afcan's share price suddenly jumped from 20 cents up to 70 cents and was trading at 200,000 to 300,000 shares a day in October 2003.

"We closed at the end of September and then all this activity started as we were closing. We just never looked back," said Netherway.

It is April 2004 when Netherway sits down to talk about Afcan's history and current successes. At this time the stock is 32 cents, a relatively predictable dip as the market waits to hear more results and activity.

"It's completely undervalued right now," affirms Netherway, adding that he recently returned from another meeting with Embry, explaining Afcan's current status.

"We have a project that has an mineral potential value of $84 million, we currently have a market cap of less than $20 million (all US dollars), and we've got $6 million in the bank. So, they're valuing the project at less than $14 million and its got an upside of $84 million ... so it's all a bit silly at the moment."

There's nothing silly about the TJS project that encompasses 341 square kilometres in China's Qinghai province and boasts two mines that were in operation on the property. The smaller deposit to the north, Qinlongtan, was mined by the Chinese for oxide in an open pit slot. It has a resource estimate of 900,000 tonnes, which at a grade of 6.3 grams per tonne contains 178,000 ounces of gold. In addition there are heap leach pads, with an estimated 250,000 tonnes at a grade of 2 to 2.5 grams per tonne.

Sixteen kilometres to the south is a major project called Jinlonggou, which was being mined by the Chinese initially by open pit, later by underground methods. A sulphide plant was built about six years ago. Jinlonggou has a resource estimate of 2.5 million tonnes, which at a grade of 5.8 grams per tonne contains 473,000 ounces of gold. In addition, there are heap leach pads with an estimated 400,000 tonnes at a grade of 2.5 grams per tonne.

"So when we took over, we had a little operating mine," Netherway said. "We ran it last year and produced 3,500 ounces of gold from stock-pile."

Although it worked well, it was uneconomic and only broke even.

"But we kept the guys employed, we paid the government taxes, and kept everybody happy. There are 140 employees and we kept them busy, so that was good."

It was a nice beginning. What Afcan did next was take over a Chinese scoping study Sino had done on the project, with the aim to turn it into a Western bankable feasibility study.

"We had to get the resources up to Western standards, so we went drilling throughout the property last year."

And drill they did, putting in 61 diamond drill holes into the major deposit, 12 holes into the minor deposit and drilling the heap leach pads. Starting off with 650,000 ounces of inferred resources, Afcan turned it into 800,000 ounces, of which 600,000 is in the indicated category and the rest inferred. With a production start-up expected in late 2005,

Netherway sees the deposit increasing to an operation of over 100,000 ounces per year. Exploration potential is also high, supported by 23 large gold-in-soil anomalies along a 30 kilometre trend.

"We had a very successful campaign. We spent a million dollars on metallurgical testwork," said Netherway, adding that everything was being run out of Perth, Australia where their technical office is located.

"Perth is the center of the mining expertise in the world. Our people are based in Perth. It's easy for them to fly to China from there, it's the same time zone and only a 10-hour flight. It's worked very well."

By mid-November drilling was shut down due to winter conditions, and all the activity moved to Perth where the feasibility study was pulled together. A resource report was issued in March 2004.

"We've got the resource report, the flow sheet for the metallurgical test work, we've got the recovery up to 90 percent from 78 percent and now we have a very nice little project on our hands," says Netherway with obvious satisfaction.

What they're looking at, he says, is a project with a capital cost of $US30 million, an operating cost of $US186 an ounce, and production of 110,000 ounces a year on average. A 12-month construction period is expected.

"If we build it now, starting in the next few months, we'll be the largest foreign-owned gold producer in China. We'll probably be the fourth or fifth biggest gold mine in China," states Netherway with assurance.

The project is now ready to roll, barring the mining licences, which are expected to come from Beijing in late 2004. Afcan has already received a construction licence and been encouraged to "get on with it" but Netherway wants to wait for the mining licences. The licences are being transferred from the joint venture partners to QDML (Qinghai Dachaidan Mining Limited), the joint venture company.

"We own 85 percent of that joint venture. Our two partners are the local geology bureau of the Ministry of Lands and Natural Resources (7.5 per cent) and Dachaidan city council (7.5 per cent), the nearest town," explains Netherway.

Afcan breaks more new ground with this alliance, not only by being the first foreign gold company in the province but because QDML is the first true joint venture in China's gold sector.

"Again, we're a first," says Netherway.

"It's very important to us that we get the mining licences and then we have to raise the money to build this thing. We need somewhere between $15 and $30 million. We can build the front end of the plant for $15 million and then sell concentrate, or we can build everything we want for $30 million."

And building is what it's all about for Netherway. If he had a choice of being taken over or building his own, he'd prefer the latter.

"I want to grow the company. We're doing other things in China at the moment. We're signing other memorandums of understanding and deals and looking at other projects. We're trying to expand."

And there are a lot of upsides to this way of thinking. Drilling has begun, there are three rigs on site, and Netherway predicts increased resources quickly.

"We've found this flat lying structure that connects through to some of the other mines that were mining in the area. And this year we've got the money, the people, and the time to explore these."

One thing they don't have is a lot of nearby competition, barring a couple of other companies within the province.

"We've virtually got the province to ourselves. The province is the size of France and there are five million people down in one corner of it and we're at the other end," he says.

"And because the Geological Survey is our partner they know where all the other deposits are and they're keeping the deposits for us. Once we start construction, they will give us more projects."

Netherway, who has worked in many different countries, who keeps residences in Montreal, London, and South Africa, and jokes that he lives in an airplane, can't say enough about his newest environment, its people and advanced infrastructure. His globetrotting and vast scope of experiences certainly haven't dulled his delight at discovering and immersing himself in a new culture.

"China is absolutely amazing," he enthuses. "The infrastructure is incredible, we're in the middle of nowhere and I can use my cellphone almost anywhere in China. There are 300 million people learning English, everyone's got cellphones, the internet is free anywhere in China, and the country is booming."

Having the necessary infrastructure in place is especially valuable for Afcan, considering its isolated location at the southern end of the Gobi Desert and the northern end of the Tibetan plateau, sitting at 3,500 metres. The nearest town, Dachaidan, is 90 kilometres away, but that hasn't stopped technological progress from advancing to the area.

Late last year, while driving between Dachaidan and the site, Netherway noticed a trench running alongside the road all the way to the site turnoff and in. He called the local telephone company to see if they knew anything about it. They certainly did.

"Here's a fibreoptic cable sitting at the end of a pole 50 metres from the office!" exclaimed Netherway.

"So we have mobile telephones on site now and we have a fibreoptic high speed internet connection, at no cost to us. China Telecom put that in. They're huge."

Aside from up-to-date communications systems being in place, there's a brand new coal-fired power station under construction 35 kilometres away, and water is only one kilometre's distance from the site. Netherway still seems a bit in awe of all this luxury.

"It's incredible. Everything we need to build this thing is in China, or is going to be made in China. We need nothing from the outside, we're not going to import anything. It's not like Africa where you've got to import everything and bring the senior, experienced people in. We'll bring in a few ex-pats from Australia, but basically we'll run it as a Chinese operation."

Surrounding himself with good talent, Netherway wants to keep his company "lean and mean". The Montreal head office consists of only three fulltime employees, with old friend Peter Hooper soon to be joining the Afcan ranks as chief operating officer, with Netherway moving to Toronto to join him and the new chief financial officer in their new head office. The team also includes metallurgist Paul Skayman who is running the China operation and mining engineer Richard Li who has been with

Afcan for more than a year and spends most of his time in China.

"Paul built Kiniero Gold Mine and he was with us in the Golden Shamrock days. Richard worked for Sino for four years. The people are extremely important and I've got great people with me. We've got a good team here and in China."

For his part, Netherway travels to China as often as he can, usually every couple of months.

"I love it there," he says simply. "The Chinese are very friendly educated people. We have an office in the capital and we take an overnight sleeper train to the project. It costs peanuts – we're renting a three-bedroom apartment in the capital for $80 a month.

"It's wonderful. They really look after you there."

Although his work has always taken him far from his roots, Netherway uses his homeland as a comparison to illustrate the opportunities lying in wait in China.

"China is the fourth biggest gold producer in the world and it produces from 1300 mines. Australia is the third biggest gold producer in the world, about the same production, and it comes from 80 mines," he says.

"That's the opportunity in China. All the mines are small."

Although China is obviously the main attraction and focus for Afcan, there are certainly other projects on the go.

A nickel project in Guinea is joint ventured with FNX Mining, a well financed Sudbury-based company that is currently working on it. FNX is spending US $2 million to earn 100 percent, leaving Afcan with a 1.5 percent royalty. Sierra Leone properties were joint ventured with Ashanti Goldfields, now with a Canadian company called Axmin Inc. Axmin is spending US $2.25 million to earn 60 percent on this gold project. The Mali properties, with hard rock and alluvial potential, were joint ventured with Ashanti and are now available for joint venture. And Afcan has a phosphate property in Burkina Faso that they've proposed putting together with a zinc project in Burkina to make it more economical.

But his aim, Netherway says, is to joint venture everything in West Africa and concentrate on China where the opportunities are too great not to.

"West Africa is still up our sleeves, but is a distraction," he says. "China is the main thing now."

As excited as he is about getting something out of China, Netherway is conscious of Afcan's responsibility to its host province and eager to give back to the community.

"The key in operating in these countries is to be able to get on with the locals, to be very sympathetic to the local cultures and people, and encourage them as much as possible," he says.

Their relative isolation from major towns makes this a little more challenging than it might be otherwise, but where there's a will, there's a way.

"The biggest contribution we're making is creating employment, and we're training a lot of people, so that's good," Netherway notes.

"We're also putting US $50,000 into the local geology department of the university of the province and buying computers, hardware and software, and things like that. We want to help them develop geological students and give something back in that way."

But aside from academics and job creation, Netherway recognizes the importance of recreational outlets and would like to sponsor football teams or things of that nature in the local town. His main hurdle on site is the altitude.

"It's a bit of a problem up there because you can't do much that doesn't revolve around drinking," he concedes with a wry grin.

"You can play pool or play darts, but we're trying to dream up something else. In Ghana, in Africa, you can build a gym, a swimming pool, a tennis or squash court. That's the standard stuff you can put in because it gives people something to do.

"You can't do anything at 3,500 metres. You can't go out and kick a football, it's hard work. So, we're thinking about that at the moment. The guys have recently discovered sand boarding, and that is helping to keep them fit."

There's no doubt Netherway will come up with something creative and constructive. Keeping fit and amused are so much a part of his own nature and lifestyle, he will likely find some way to incorporate both to benefit everyone. Unfortunately the China location isn't suitable for two of Netherway's passions – running and sailing, the latter of which he enjoys every year.

"I built a 40-foot wooden yacht in Ghana, cruised to Guinea, and then brought it back to Ghana. I eventually got rid of it for a pittance, but it was fun," says Netherway.

"I'll have another one soon, but this job has to settle down, the company's got to get built."

And we're back to Netherway's passion for building – whether it's a boat or a company – it's what drives him.

"That's the thrill, building a company," he says. "Achieving these goals, raising money, finding gold, getting a good project and building that project into something real. And having great people with you.

"I want to build a mining company and I want to get production because it's security. It gives you money to be able to go exploring and build on that. I am not a promoter who will just promote a company, then sell it.'"

He thinks about this for a minute, and waves his hand dismissively at the mere mention of a corporate philosophy. Yes, there's an actual mission statement, he allows, but Netherway prefers his own.

"My philosophy in this business is that you've got to enjoy it," he says earnestly. "You've got to have fun."

It sounds simplistic, but consider the source. Coming from an astute mining professional with 30 years of experience behind him, many past successes and more to look forward to, no one can argue with that.

AURIZON
MINES LIMITED

Resource-industry venture capitalists often remark on the "treasure-hunting" aspect of the mining game. Inevitably – and quite understand-ably – their conversations are punctuated by phrases such as "taking a gamble," "the thrill of the chase" and "going for broke." David P. Hall, chairman, president and chief executive officer of Vancouver-based Aurizon Mines Ltd., comes from not an exploration background but a financial one. A chartered accountant, rather than a professional geolo-gist, Hall necessarily deals in solid, tangible facts, not gut instincts, blind hunches or educated assumptions. It is this shrewd and practical – some might say studied and cautious – business sense that has allowed his com-pany to flourish, rather than flounder, in times of economic turbulence.

"With Aurizon," says Hall, "we try and reduce the risk as much as we can for both ourselves and our shareholders. That's why we're more interested in advance stage assets, not pure grassroots exploration. We want assets where we can see that the potential has not been maximized, and that there is still more room to grow."

To that end, Aurizon has focussed its sights on the historic and high-ly prolific gold-producing Abitibi region of northwestern Quebec, where the company holds two significant projects: the Sleeping Giant Mine, of which the company owns 50 percent, and the Casa Berardi property, a 100 percent holding. Extending westward from Val d'Or, Quebec, the Abitibi region and its prodigious mineralization runs through the famous Rouyn-Noranda and Kirkland Lake properties all the way to Timmins, Ontario.

In total, the region has produced over 140 million ounces of gold since 1900. "It's an historic camp," says Hall, "and Casa Berardi lies about 100 kilometres north of the traditional belt. It has untold potential and is our number-one priority right now. We're working to get that to a stage where we can finance and start building a new mining operation there. Once we do that, we'll be looking at other advance stage opportunities in order to grow the company."

Born in Aberdeen, Scotland in 1946, Hall earned his Chartered Accountant qualification in his hometown and worked two years in Glasgow before leaving the country in 1972 to take a position in Bermuda for (what is now) PricewaterhouseCoopers. Relocating to Vancouver, British Columbia in 1975, he continued working for the global financial giant until 1981. At that time, he joined the Hughes-Lang Group, founded by Vancouver mining promoters Richard Hughes and Frank Lang, perhaps best known for discovering the Golden Giant Mine in Hemlo, Ontario in 1982.

"I had no experience with the mineral resource industry until I came to Vancouver," says the affable and soft-spoken Hall. "When I was with PricewaterhouseCoopers, however, I developed a smattering of mining companies in my client base such as Lornex and Cypress Anvil, and I became interested with the industry and the people in it. An opportunity presented itself to join the Hughes-Lang Group and I thought, 'Why not?'"

Remarkably, the Hughes-Lang Group housed close to 20 junior exploration mining companies under its one roof in the early 1980s. "That's the way that these exploration stables used to be run in those days," says Hall. "There were maybe a dozen of them in Vancouver, one of which operated roughly 70 companies." The practice came to a grinding halt with the stock market crash of October 1987. "The funding sources dried up as the equity markets closed, and these companies wanted to save costs," Hall explains. "The way to save costs was to cut down on the number of companies, consolidate the asset base and achieve administrative efficiencies."

The Hughes-Lang Group went through a period of rationalization and consolidation in the late 1980s and early 1990s, with its founders deciding to go their separate ways. Meanwhile, two of the companies within the group, both of which had advance stage projects in Quebec, were merged in 1988 to form Aurizon Mines Ltd. The company was listed on the Toronto Stock Exchange that same year (TSX:ARZ) and, in 2003, the American Exchange (AMEX: AZK).

"I started off as a controller for the Hughes-Lang Group," says Hall, "and then became the chief financial officer for Aurizon. When Dick Hughes left the group in 1991, I became president and CEO of Aurizon. I've been with the company a long time, and Aurizon's prime area of activity has always been Quebec." Notably, the company's initial acquisitions – the Sleeping Giant and Beaufor properties – would both go on to become producing gold mines.

"Dick and Frank initially started looking at Quebec in the early 1970s," Hall continues, "when Dave Barrett's NDP government was in power and British Columbia was becoming less friendly for mining. Our roots were in B.C. and our initial property was on Vancouver Island, but the group wanted to look at other areas, so they formed a relationship with Peter Ferderber in Quebec." Now an Aurizon director, Ferderber proved key to the acquisition of the Sleeping Giant and Beaufor properties. "While Peter did the initial scouting around and seeking out of assets, Frank and Dick raised the money for exploration," says Hall.

Discovered in 1984, the Sleeping Giant Mine was summarily developed and put into production in 1988. As a result of low gold prices and bad equity markets, however, Aurizon found itself in a position where it was mining out the reserves it had found, but not generating enough free cash flow to funnel back into the project, let alone explore for and develop new resources. "At that point," says Hall, "we decided to bring in a partner."

A decision was made to mine out the defined reserves at Sleeping Giant and cease operations in the summer of 1990, until a joint venture partnership could be negotiated. Enter Quebec-based international gold producer Cambior Inc., which was brought onboard to explore for new resources. "Cambior came along in 1991 and spent about $12 million to earn a 50 percent interest on some new gold zones," says Hall. "After being shut down for about an 18-month period, the Sleeping Giant property continued production and is still a producing mine. Under the terms of the deal with Cambior, they allowed us to continue to mine out the old reserves because those were pretty small – they were interested in the bigger picture. That gave us some cash in order to rebuild and grow again."

As fate would have it, one of the last phases of Aurizon's financing had been completed in October 1987, literally days before the stock market crash. "The financing was done in Swiss franc denominated convertible bonds for about $30 million," Hall explains. "It seems very strange to talk about it today, but the attraction of the Swiss franc denominated convertible bond issues in those days was that they had a very low coupon rate – five-and-seven-eighths percent – which by North American standards was low. The prevailing rate was up closer to the double digits.

"So that's how we did the financing," Hall continues, "and there was about a seven- or eight-year term on the bonds. But what happened was, when we made the decision to shut down Sleeping Giant, that triggered a write-down to the carrying value of the property, which breached a net equity covenant in the bonding indenture. That meant we were then in default under the terms of the bond indenture. This necessitated a trip to Geneva, Switzerland to meet with the bondholders. We were able to come to an arrangement where we would give them 17 to 18 cents on the dollar, about 95 percent of the cash in the company at that time, and some convertible shares. If Aurizon did not make it, the bondholders would have a preferential call on the assets in a liquidation. The bondholders became preferential shareholders. But after a certain period of time, those convertible shares would be converted into straight common stock. About 80 percent of bondholders went for that, so we sliced off 80 percent of $30 million of debt on our balance sheet.

"Once the company was able to keep Sleeping Giant," he says, "we were able to accumulate more cash because, as you're running down a mine, you're not doing things like exploration and development. You're basically just mining, pulling the ore, processing it and selling it, so your margin per ounce tends to increase. Thanks to that, we made quite a bit of money during the last few months of operation. That gave us enough cash to go back a year later, in the summer of 1992, and make a second proposal to the remaining 20 percent of the bondholders who didn't agree to the first proposal. We offered them somewhere around 37 or 38 cents on the dollar and they went for that. Finally, after going through a really tough period between the summer of 1990 and the summer of 1992, we were debt-free, and we still had some money in the bank."

While the financial wrangling was going on, Cambior Inc. had discovered and put into production two new zones at Sleeping Giant. Aurizon therefore found itself in the enviable position of not only having money in the bank, but a steadily accumulating cash flow courtesy of the mine. "With those two sources of cash," says Hall, "we were then able to start developing the Beaufor property that we held near Val d'Or, Quebec. We and our partner, Louvem Mines, developed that project to the point where, in 1996, we put it into production.

"By the mid-1990s," Hall continues, "we had a fairly successful company in terms of generating good cash flow and good earnings from our 50 percent interest in Sleeping Giant Mine and our 50 percent interest in the Beaufor property. However, we only had somewhere in the region of a quarter-million ounces of gold in reserves, so we weren't getting on the radar screens with the institutions because we were too small. That's when we made a decision in 1996 to go and find a project that would have a greater impact, in which we would hold a 100 percent interest, and which would be a company builder. We wanted a project that would have a dramatic impact on the production profile and the reserve potential of the company. In doing so, we decided to strengthen our technical team based in Quebec and, after looking at several opportunities, we agreed in the fall of 1997 to buy the Casa Berardi property."

Likewise located in northwestern Quebec, Casa Berardi had been discovered in the mid-1980s by a Vancouver junior exploration company called Golden Knight Resources Inc. "Inco had a big land package close to the Ontario border and they let Golden Knight farm in on it to do the exploration," says Hall. "During exploration, they found some gold-related zones. As a result, Inco built and developed the Casa Berardi Mine in 1988. In fact, it consisted of two mines – the East Mine, which sits very close to the surface infrastructure, and the West Mine, which went into production a year later and which is about five kilometres away. We presently have 37 kilometres of the Casa Berardi Fault structure in our land position, and that's one of the things that appealed to us – that we could get control of a large land position very quickly. The fact that the large prospective land position came with a considerable surface infrastructure was a bonus. There are various claims around it that have been staked by junior companies.

"By the time the Casa Berardi went into production," he continues, "the ownership was 60 percent for Inco and 40 percent for Golden Knight. Then in the early 1990s, Inco decided to concentrate on their base metals business and subsequently sold their gold assets to TVX Gold Mines. Thus, for the latter part of the mine's initial production life, the ownership was TVX 60 percent and Golden Knight 40 percent. The mine was in production from 1988 to 1997 and produced roughly 700,000 ounces of gold during that period of time. In 1997, it was shut down for various reasons and that's when we took a look at it and decided that there was some opportunity available for us. There were three things that attracted us: number one, we had the ability to acquire, control and explore a very large land position, covering 37 kilometres along the Casa Berardi Fault, a significant geological feature. Number two, there was very good infrastructure already in place that Inco had built, including a 2,200 metric tonne-a-day surface processing facility. So we had a mill, mining equipment, a power line, road access and tailings facilities – these things gave us a big leg up in terms of any new operation that was going to be there.

"The third thing," says Hall, "is that when we looked at the detailed records and at the exploration that had gone on at the project, we could see that it had never been specifically explored to depth. The West Mine went down to almost 400 metres and the East Mine went down to about 800 metres, but the project hadn't really been explored much beyond 300 metres. We knew that in the Abitibi gold region, these mines can historically go down to 1,000 metres, 3,000 metres, and so on. So we thought, it's a very good land position, it's a very solid infrastructure and it has a lot of exploration potential."

Aurizon duly signed a letter of intent with TVX and Golden Knight in October 1997 to buy the Casa Berardi project, immediately recognizing the profile and growth potential it would provide for the company. "It was a good time to buy a project but not a good time to finance," says Hall. "It was post-Bre-X and there was no appetite for financing junior gold companies. In essence, the equity markets were closed to us. The only way we could finance the purchase was to go to two of the major Quebec financial institutions. We arranged a $7 million non-investment bearing convertible debenture that allowed us to finance the acquisition of the Casa Berardi. It took us almost a year – we signed the letter of intent in October 1997, but we didn't close the acquisition until September 1998. It was tough to raise money in those days."

Under the terms of the acquisition, Aurizon was required to pay $2 million on closing, another $4 million payable after three years, and a net smelter royalty of two-to-four percent, tied to the price of gold but with a limited cap of $10 million. "Having acquired the property," says Hall, "we started exploring and drilling wide-spaced holes around the West Mine area and going down 1,000 metres – that's where we felt there was potential. The initial exploration was very successful and we found zones containing roughly 900,000 ounces of gold. We wanted to increase the gold inventory to roughly 1 million ounces – which would give us six or seven years of initial mine life – in the area of the West Mine, and that's what we got. We wanted to make sure that when we started up the surface infrastructure and began processing the ore that we could deliver a con-sistent flow of ore through the mill rather than having peaks and valleys of supply, which would result in a negative impact on our operating costs.

"During the initial phase of exploration, which ran from the fall of 1998 right through to late 1999," Hall continues, "we more than met our threshold. Having discovered the ounces, we put the mining engineers and planners to work and completed a feasibility study on the zones we had discovered. In the first quarter of 2000, a feasibility study indicated that it was economically viable to put the ounces we had found into pro-duction. We were estimated an initial mine life of approximately 7.5 years at an average production rate of roughly 200,000 ounces of gold a year, and capital expenditures of about $120 million. Unfortunately for us, this was at a time when gold was heading below US$300 an ounce and on its way to US$260 an ounce. As far as moving the project any further, all bets were off."

To complicate matters, Aurizon had issues at the Beaufor Mine, which was already in production, in August 2000. Having encountered problems from a safety perspective, the company opted to shut down the mine. "We had some work to do before would could reopen the mine safely," says Hall, "but having made the decision to shut down the mine, we immediately lost 50 percent of our cash flow.

"Therefore, we went through a period during 2000 and into the first months of 2001 when we had to batten down the hatches. We did studies on the Beaufor to determine what it would cost to do the renovation work and make it safe to put the mine back into production. The costs came to roughly $5 million, which we didn't have at the time. So in the spring of 2001, we had to make a decision to either sell part of the Casa Berardi project, or sell our 50 percent interest in the Beaufor Mine in order to survive. We chose the latter because we could see much more potential with Casa Berardi, given that it was a much bigger project. We sold our interest in Beaufor in the spring of 2001 to our partner Richmont Mines Inc. – which gave us some cash – and they continue to operate that mine today, from which we receive an ongoing royalty income of about $300,000 a year. That transaction enabled us to survive.

"At the same time," Hall continues, "we downsized dramatically, laid off most of our technical team, downsized our Vancouver corporate office from 12 people to five people, and did all the things we needed to do in order to live and fight another day."

Consequently, nothing significant happened on Casa Berardi for approximately two years. During that time, however, Aurizon maintained the property in good standing and preserved both the surface infrastructure and, more importantly, the underground workings. "We had to keep it pumped out and dry," says Hall, "and that was costing us $2.5 million a year – which is not an easy nut to crack.

"But we held on and held on," he continues. "We had various joint venture proposals from different majors in the fall of 2001 because the Casa Berardi is the type of project that, because of its potential, attracts and interests bigger companies. But any one of these joint ventures would mean having to give up our majority control of the project and settling for a minority interest. The board of directors decided that what we should do for the shareholders was to go forward with the project ourselves – if we could possibly hold on to it."

Aurizon indeed held on and, in the spring of 2002, gold prices began recovering. "Once gold started heading back towards US$300 an ounce, we were able to raise some money and go back and start drilling again at Casa Berardi," says Hall. "That allowed us to do two things: prove that Aurizon was still alive, and prove that we still had a project – Casa Berardi – that had substantial potential."

Subsequent drilling on the property successfully delineated more zones (Zones 118 to 123, in company parlance) between 400 and 1,000 metres in depth, and further east of where the company had initially drilled. "Once again," Hall says, beaming, "we proved this theory that the gold mineralization was at depth between 400 and 1,000 metres, and we extended the mineralization another kilometre to the east.

"Now," he continues, "we're in a period where gold has gone from US$250 an ounce to over US$400 an ounce. There is more interest in the sector and the equity markets have once again opened up their doors to junior companies like Aurizon. We were successful at tapping those markets and raising somewhere close to $50 million over the past two years. As a result, we've been able to spend more money not only on exploration, but also on underground development at Casa Berardi. We put in an underground access to Zone 113, which took us most of last year to do. We're at the point where, having drilled Zone 113 from surface with very wide-spaced holes, we're now drilling it at 25-by-25 metre grids to increase our confidence level in the continuity of the geology. The work is well underway and it has been very encouraging. We're going to take the results of that work, compile it and produce enough data to do a feasibility study on Casa Berardi that should be ready in the fourth quarter of 2004. Then we'll be looking at financing the project into production. In another two years – late 2006 or early 2007 – we should have an operation that will produce somewhere close to 200,000 ounces of gold annually and have an initial mine life of probably 10 years. There is a lot of untapped exploration potential at Casa Berardi."

In the meantime, there was still the matter of the $7 million acquisition deal that had been negotiated in the fall of 1998. "We still had our 100 percent interest," says Hall, "and our initial deal was $2 million on signing, another $4 million in three years, plus the net smelter royalty. Well, three years came along and that put us into 2001 – obviously there was no way we could raise the $4 million at that time, but we were able to negotiate a two-year extension on that payment by issuing a million shares to TVX.

"In June 2002," he continues, "another mining company that liked the results we'd been getting at Casa Berardi came along and offered TVX $5 million – $4 million for what was owed, plus $1 million for the royalty. Fortunately for us, under the terms of our agreement, TVX had to give us first right of refusal of matching the offer. So we elected to see if we could match that first right of refusal. As it turned out, we were able to raise the $5 million and that allowed us to pay off the debt that we owed and buy out the royalty. Now, I'm pleased to say, we have a 100 percent royalty – free interest in Casa Berardi."

The success of Aurizon led to the company securing the aforementioned listing on the American Stock Exchange in November 2003. "The Amex listing has done a great deal for us," says Hall. "Perhaps most importantly, it increases the company's profile in the United States – where there is obviously a much bigger population than in Canada – and traditionally we've always had a considerable U.S. shareholder base of about 25 to 30 percent. The American Stock Exchange has done a very good job of marketing themselves to the mining community and encouraging listings. We felt that getting a listing on their board would increase investor awareness of the company and liquidity of shares. Ultimately, that should result in an increase in share prices. Plus, American residents feel much more comfortable knowing that they can punch in Aurizon's ticker symbol and see it on the American Stock Exchange, rather than having to deal with a non – U.S. broker to buy Canadian stock."

As for investor confidence in the post-Bre-X world, Hall himself is confident. "The level of investor confidence in the mining industry is coming back due to the changes that were made post-Bre-X," he says. "The standards have picked up and the new rules on disclosure of exploration results have tightened things up exponentially. Furthermore, what we've seen happen in the past two years – post-Enron – is an increased focus on standards of corporate governance in general. Overall, things have improved dramatically."

Hall is quick to acknowledge that his handpicked team of colleagues have proved as integral to Aurizon's past – and future – as the overall turnaround in the mining industry. "We've got a good and loyal staff," he says. "Ian Walton, our executive vice-president and chief financial officer has been with us since 1982 and he has done an exemplary job through both the good times and tough times." Likewise a chartered accountant, Walton has been involved with public companies in the mining industry for over 20 years and is fully experienced in all aspects of mining finance, taxation and treasury functions.

"Our general manager in Quebec is a gentleman name Michel Gilbert," says Hall, "who, because of the downsizing the company went through, has had a lot of additional responsibilities imposed on him. He had to get into areas he wasn't familiar with, and he has really relished that challenge and done an amazing job." Gilbert, a geological engineer, has more than 20 years of exploration experience in Canada and Mexico, including nine years with Cambior Inc., Aurizon's partner at the Sleeping Giant Mine. He has been with Aurizon since 1996.

"There is also our longstanding and outstanding board," says Hall. "People like Frank Lang, who was our founding shareholder and who is still probably the largest individual shareholder in the company, and Peter Ferderber, the gentleman responsible for our involvement in Quebec, beginning 20 years ago. Peter had the foresight to see the potential there." Respectively, Lang was named Developer of the Year in 1987 for his role in the discovery of the Golden Giant mine at Hemlo, Ontario, while Ferderber was named Prospector of the Year in 1979 by the Prospectors and Developers Association of Canada for his discovery of the Belmoral Mine at Val d'Or, Quebec. Both men have been with Aurizon since its inception in 1988.

"Then there are our other directors," says Hall, "like our lead director Brian Moorhouse, our legal counsel Sargent Berner and founding director Bill Vance." Moorhouse is also president of Vega Management Corporation and has extensive experience in the financial markets. He was instrumental in raising significant equity funds for Aurizon's predecessor companies and has been an Aurizon director since 1988. Berner, meanwhile, is a partner of the Vancouver law firm of DuMoulin Black, which specializes in corporate, mining and securities law. Also a director of several junior resource companies, Berner has – like many of his colleagues – been with Aurizon since 1988. "People like these are critical when times are tough," says Hall. "You need that support behind you to get through those long, dark days when you don't think there is any light at the end of the tunnel.

"We also have excellent support – and valuable input from our two Quebec-based directors, Robert Normand and Richard Faucher, who joined Aurizon's board after the acquisition of Casa Berardi."

In total, Aurizon Mines Ltd. has six staff members in Vancouver and another 30 in Quebec, as well as about 100 underground and drilling contractors working year-round at the Casa Berardi site. "One of the things we've concentrated on over the past six months," says Hall, "was to assemble an experienced and talented team at Casa Berardi. We're talking about people with 25 years-plus experience in exploring, developing and operating mines in the Abitibi region. People who've worked for bigger companies like Barrick and Falconbridge and Inco and Cambior.

"The logistics of working in Quebec are very good," Hall continues. "One of the beauties about working there is that you have a tradition of mining that has been handed down from generation to generation. Thus, you have skilled labour within the area. When the Casa Berardi Mine was in production, it employed roughly 200 people and a lot of those people still maintain homesteads in the area.

"We think we've got extremely good opportunities going for us," says Hall. "As a result of the lean years that the resource industry went through and the cutbacks on exploration when you couldn't do anything, there aren't very many advance stage gold projects in North America – not to mention a property that has the infrastructure that we have. The Abitibi region is one of the top mining jurisdictions worldwide in terms of geology and investor friendliness. Not only that, but they have a skilled labour force and a cooperative government. The Quebec government is very pro-mining and they will bend over backwards to help you. In fact, they actually contributed money to the initial drill program we did at Casa Berardi."

Though not a geologist by training, David P. Hall slipped effortlessly into his role as president and chief executive officer of a mining company that not only weathered the beatings of a fickle market, but came out on top. "The mining business is a fantastic industry to be in," he enthuses, "mostly due to the people who are in it. They are by and large great to deal with and very supportive. There are some real characters among them, as well, which I truly enjoy.

"Sure, I could have gone off and done something else when the market faltered, but I felt we had a very good asset in Casa Berardi and I would have hated to jump ship during what was probably the bottom of the gold market. Besides,I had an obligation to our shareholders. We have a long list of loyal and longstanding shareholders who have been with us for many, many years. We had to stay the course in order to preserve and build something out of those tough situations. And that's exactly what we did."

BRALORNE GOLD MINES LIMITED

Every high-school history student has heard philosopher George Santayana's grand proclamation that, "Those who cannot remember the past are condemned to repeat it." Louis Wolfin and his son, David, respectively the CEO and the vice-president, finance, of Vancouver-based Bralorne Gold Mines Ltd., not only remember the past but fully intend on repeating it when it comes to operating the company's wholly owned mining property at Bralorne in southern British Columbia.

Located approximately 300 kilometres northeast of Vancouver in the Bridge River Valley, the region's Bralorne and Pioneer mines produced over 4 million ounces of gold between 1897 and 1971. When gold prices were fixed at $35 an ounce, however, production became economically unfeasible and the mining operations were summarily shut down. An equivalent amount of gold – worth roughly US$1.4 billion at today's gold prices – is believed to lie untapped at the site. And it is not just the Wolfins who think so.

"Two years ago," says David Wolfin, "we hired a professional geologist named Dr. Matt Ball, who came in third in the Goldcorp Challenge in 2000 – a recognized and well-respected gentleman, he did some 3-D modelling in the area and spent time studying all the old literature on the mines – volumes of documentation – and he estimated the area's potential to be 3.4 million ounces of gold. Matt has a Ph.D. in geology and is very conservative, so he felt comfortable saying 3.4 million. It could be much bigger than that.

"We asked Matt what the similarities were between Bralorne and the old Dickenson Mine," Wolfin continues, referring to the massive reserve now known as Goldcorp's Red Lake Mine, presently the largest producing gold mine in Canada. "He said that the Dickenson produced 3 million ounces and averaged a quarter-ounce of gold per tonne. Bralorne, on the other hand, produced over 4 million ounces and averaged a half-ounce of gold per tonne. Plus, there were 19,000 diamond-drill holes sunk at Dickenson but only 2,200 at Bralorne – approximately one-tenth the amount of drilling to find a bigger deposit. Bralorne is simply a better mine."

This property is also one of several underground mines – including the Pioneer and King mines – that make up the company's estimated 30,000 acres of mineral leases in the area. "We've been putting this land package together by acquiring leases through assorted companies over the years," says Winnipeg-born Louis Wolfin, who founded his own brokerage company in 1958 and began staking and exploring in the area in the early 1960s. "We commenced operations up at the old Congress Mine near Bralorne in those days and began developing a resource there. Eventually, we started to acquire more and more properties, and that brings us to where we are today."

Today, Bralorne Gold Mines Ltd. is in an envious position to say the least. "The company is debt free," stresses the elder Wolfin. "It has absolutely no debt whatsoever, it has a couple of million dollars in the bank, and it owns all of the properties. There are no royalties and no property payments to be made."

"All of which is significant," adds David Wolfin, who got his start in the mining industry at the age of 16, working summers in the mill at a mining operation in Mexico run by his father's company, Avino Silver and Gold Mines Ltd. "Usually, when you start up a mine, you're riddled with debt and it takes years to pay everything off. In our case, all the roads, the power, the water, the town from which to draw labour – we inherited it all."

Indeed, the Bralorne Mine stands as the richest and most productive gold mine in British Columbia's history. First staked in 1896, prospectors were initially attracted to the area in the late 1850s after following the river and creek beds north from San Francisco, searching for new mother lodes in the aftermath of the 1849 Gold Rush. Entering B.C. and working their way up the Fraser River, the first hearty souls reached the Bridge River Valley in 1858. By the following winter, an estimated 10,000 treasure hunters had passed through the town of Lillooet, panning and sluicing the valley's waterways.

In 1865, a government-sponsored exploration party led by one Andrew T. Jamieson reported that they had found "paying quantities of gold in various locations on the headwaters of the Bridge River." At the suggestion of an expedition member named Cadwallader, who was familiar with the region, the party beat their way through the bush and stumbled into a waterway (now known as Cadwallader Creek) and set up sluice boxes. In the scant time remaining before their two-month inspection tour ended, the men discovered that there was, indeed, gold mixed in with the gravel and dirt on the creek bottom.

Thirty-two years would pass before another prospector, Harry Atwood – who was sponsored (or "grubstaked") by William Allen, owner of Lillooet's Pioneer Hotel – made a strike at Cadwallader Creek in 1897, dutifully naming it "Pioneer" after his benefactor's inn. For the price of a $125 mail-order quartz mill, enterprising miner Fred Kinder acquired a half-interest in Allen's investment. When the mill finally arrived from California via horse-drawn wagon, it was not exactly what the two men had envisioned. As the mill was unloaded from the wagon and displayed in front of Allen's hotel, a crowd of locals laughed and jeered at the sight- one wag quipped that the rock crusher "was just big enough to make a good-sized coffee grinder." Undaunted, Kinder undertook the task of packing the device to the Pioneer site – only to discover it was capable of crushing a mere 100 pounds of rock a day, thus hardly qualifying as a lucrative investment.

Exit hotelier William Allen and enter mining entrepreneur Arthur Noel, who built-in exchange for half of the Pioneer property's net returns- an arrastre. The arrastre is essentially a crude water-powered drag-stone apparatus for pulverizing ores containing free gold, the primitive milling device was the first of its kind in Canada and subsequently garnered the pair an average of $10 a day in gold. The ore, however, had to be carried from the adit to the arrastre manually, ensuring that the men earned every penny of their money due to the backbreaking physical labour.

Nonetheless, they were able to earn a living and, when the partnership was dissolved, Kinder carried on alone – still packing the ore on his back- for another decade.

Though Noel had bowed out of the partnership with Kinder, he and four partners bought the property for $26,000 in 1911. When Noel and Frank Holten sold out their shares in 1915, the remaining partners – Peter and Andrew Ferguson, and Adolphus Williams – incorporated Pioneer Gold Mines Ltd. Over the next two years, the new company built a small mill and a power plant. By 1917, they had produced approximately $135,000 in gold bullion. Yet another decade was to pass, however, before any kind of significant work was carried out on the property.

The lull began in 1918, when several companies considered the Pioneer site for further exploration, but subsequently turned it down. Though the option on the property was picked up for $100,000 in 1920, the would-be owners failed to obtain an extension on the first payment. A Vancouver group headed by A.H. Wallbridge and A.E. Bull purchased a controlling interest in 1921, and spent $50,000 on Pioneer, but ceased operations two years later.

The turnaround finally came in 1928, when mining engineer David M. Sloan, at the request of Wallbridge and Bull, agreed to look at the property, which had yet to enter production despite demonstrating sub- stantial potential for over 25 years. Sloan came away convinced that the property would yield profit and approached prominent mining investors, hoping to secure money to sink into the venture; their financiers invari- ably advised them against it. Sloan refused to be dissuaded. He assumed Wallbridge and Bull's option and tried to raise operation capital. He came up with a paltry $4,000. Selling half of his 50 percent interest to one J.I. Babe, the two raised another $4,000. It wasn't much, but it was enough to put them into business. The Pioneer Mine finally entered production with a new mill capable of processing 100 tonnes a day, and Pioneer Gold Mines of British Columbia was incorporated in 1928.

Meanwhile, downstream from Pioneer, operations at the Bralorne property had taken a parallel course. First staked in 1896, the area was initially explored in earnest by three intrepid miners – William Young, Nat Coughlan and John Williams – who used pack horses and canoes to transport rudimentary mining gear into the Bridge River Valley from

Lillooet. As a history of the expedition recalls: "Taking their stuff up Seton Lake by canoe, they loaded it onto horses at the Mission and followed the trail over the mountain, being a dozen years too soon for the wagon road. Reaching the Bridge River, the prospectors transferred their implements to canoes and swam their horses across, repeating this 30 miles farther upstream at the Forks. It had been rough going all the way, but it became rougher still when they ascended the South Fork to the Hurley and the Hurley to Cadwallader Creek, breaking trail along rugged precipices and through heavy brush."

The trio persevered and ultimately their resolve was rewarded with the staking of the Lorne, Golden King and Marquis properties. These three, along with 49 other claims, would eventually form Bralorne Gold Mines's 1,200-acre land package. Until 1900, however, the respective owners of these dozens of claims worked independently. At the turn of the century, they agreed to unite and a representative was sent to Victoria to drum up financing. A syndicate was formed and a small stamp mill purchased for the property. Unfortunately, like the much-ridiculed "coffee grinder" upstream at the Pioneer, the Bralorne mill was not much better. The inefficient device was soon abandoned in favour of a primitive arrastre – the selfsame scenario that had played out at Pioneer – and the miners were able to recover approximately 60 percent of the free-milling gold that was produced.

The most prolific of the claims initially staked at Bralorne was the Lorne Mine. Between 1900 and 1916, the principal owner of the Lorne was William Sloan, a miner and geologist who had made a fortune during the Klondike Gold Rush and subsequently went on to become a member of British Columbia's provincial legislative assembly, as well as its minister of mines. Sloan hired engineers to survey the mine and their report was less that overwhelming. Ownership of the Lorne was then transferred to Arthur Noel (Fred Kinder's former partner at Pioneer). Noel installed a decent-sized mill consisting of five 750-pound stamps and a 1,500-foot water pipeline to power the mechanism. When the mill eventually wore out, Noel went back to using the arrastre. During his 12-year stint at the Lorne property, he accrued roughly $160,000 worth of gold.

The Lorne, however, had yet to become a bonafide producer. In 1928 – the same year Pioneer Gold Mines of British Columbia was incorporated – the Scobie Furlong Company purchased the Lorne and its adjacent properties for $300,000, resulting in the formation of Lorne Gold Mines Limited. Well-financed, the company had mine manager H.C. Wilmot drive a half-mile tunnel straight into the mountainside, searching for the King vein. Wilmot balked at the idea of veering from his course to look for offshoots and, consequently, daylight could still be seen entering from the portal at the 1,400-foot mark.

Concurrently, the Lorne Camp was being constructed above ground. The camp would eventually include a bunkhouse capable of housing 40 people, a two-storey mess hall with an office and storeroom on the ground floor, power and machinery shops, a sawmill, cottages and a stable for the horses.

In 1930, however, the Stobie Furlong Company ran into financial problems. Maddeningly, an estimated $1 million in gold ore had been identified but could not be reached without significant funding. The mine closed down, but most of the workers remained in the area, certain that work would recommence in short order. Provincial road construction projects provided interim employment, but Stobie Furlong eventually lost control of the property. By 1931, the Lorne had been taken over by the Balco Development and Investment Company, a corporation run by Austin Taylor, George Kidd, W.W. Boultbee and Neil McQueen. Once the mine had been acquired, the company renamed both their organization and the mine after the name of the property: Bralorne.

The new company financed the construction of a mill capable of processing 100 tonnes of ore per day – again, the same size as the Pioneer's mill at the time – and on March 1, 1932, Bralorne Mines poured its first gold ingot, weighing 393 ounces and valued at $6,217 (in 1932 dollars). Shareholders were thus paid their first – but hardly their last – dividend. The mine would earn them more than $14 million over the next decade-and-a-half.

By 1945, ore reserves were estimated to be in excess of 1 million tonnes, averaging better than half-an-ounce of gold per tonne. The Bralorne Mine was named, "the greatest lode operation in the world," and in 1948 its stock market value was listed as $5 million.

In the meantime, a settlement had sprung up at the Pioneer town site southeast of Bralorne where, in 1928, the first school and post office were opened, and the first wedding took place. Between 1930 and 1933, houses, stores and an 80-by-50-foot recreational hall were built. The latter, a two-storey structure, offered mine workers a selection of restaurants, a library, theatre, poolroom, barbershop and dressing rooms, in addition to a 4,000-square-foot dance floor on the second storey. In 1937, the Bank of Toronto opened a branch office in Pioneer, and that summer a robbery attempt was made on the mine's refinery.

It was not the only robbery to hit the area: the Bank of Toronto was robbed shortly after its opening and again in 1942. During the second heist, the bank manager was tied up and $2,000 lifted from the safe by a lone bandit. Search parties and a tracking dog were dispatched to find the culprit, who was later picked up walking along the railroad tracks by a Pacific Great Eastern Railway crew. He wasn't the only one after Pioneer's gold.

Ten years earlier, in 1932, Andrew Ferguson sued Pioneer Gold Mines. As aforementioned, Ferguson, along with his brother Peter and three other partners, had purchased the Pioneer Mine from Fred Kinder in 1911 for $26,000. Now destitute, Ferguson charged that: "From January 1921 to July 1924, the defendants, being in full control, fraudulently conspired to refrain from mining and producing gold so as to bankrupt the company." Ferguson likewise alleged that Pioneer Gold Mines of British Columbia had never paid him the agreed upon asking price of $50,000 when the company bought out his conglomerate.

Upon losing his first lawsuit, Ferguson carried his case to the Appeals Court of British Columbia, which ruled that Pioneer Gold Mines was guilty of a deliberate breach of faith; however, because Ferguson had not sought to set aside the 1924 sale, the defendants were not held liable. The Privy Council in London subsequently dismissed the suit on the technicality that Ferguson was not the proper party to bring the action; the Privy Council did, however, allow for a new trial. Before another trial could take place, an out-of-court settlement was reached in 1937 – five years after the suit was first launched. The details were never made public.

It is worth noting that in the summer of 1934 – in the midst of Ferguson's legal travails – Pioneer Gold Mines announced it had yielded more than $1 million dollars in profits during the previous six-month period. "It was the 1924 option and sale to the new company that squeezed out the original shareholders," Ferguson's legal counsel told The Vancouver Province newspaper. Once the owner of three New Westminster estates, Andrew Ferguson ended up a recluse and died at age 81 in a tiny upstairs suite in Kerrisdale.

David Sloan, the mining engineer who turned the Pioneer into a profitable venture, did much better than Ferguson but died much younger, after sustaining injuries in a plane crash en route to the site on July 30, 1935. The accident subsequently caused the deaths of all four passengers onboard, including the pilot and R.W. Brock, Dean of Applied Science at the University of British Columbia (and namesake of the campus's Brock Hall). Brock's wife, like Sloan, survived the initial crash and, thanks to a group of loggers who dragged them from the wreckage – as well as a team of doctors and nurses who happened to be staying at nearby Rainbow Lodge – were raced to Squamish by train and to Horseshoe Bay by boat, arriving within eight hours of the accident. Brock's wife, however, died in the ambulance a few minutes later. Sloan succumbed to his injuries on August 5, 1935.

That same year, the Pioneer – considered one of the world's richest gold mines – operated at 550 tonnes per day with an average grade of one ounce of gold per tonne. At its peak, workers found "clumps of gold as big as a man's fist," according to several accounts. Ore grades, which averaged more than half-an-ounce of gold per tonne, were sometimes measured in multi-ounces of gold per tonne. Yet between the mid-1930s and 1950, the mine was hit by several workers' strikes, including one that lasted five months in 1940 and another that lasted four months in 1946. Methane gas caused a mine explosion in 1947, while severe rains and mudslides flooded out roads and isolated the community for 10 days in 1950, during which time supplies had to be air-lifted in. In 1959, the Bralorne and Pioneer mines merged as Bralorne Mines Limited. The historic and fruitful Pioneer Mine ceased production the following year.

In 1971, the Bralorne Mine – known by this time as the "last producing gold mine in British Columbia" – was shut down after its owners, Bralorne Can-Fer Resources Limited, realized they could not operate profitably with gold prices frozen at $35 an ounce. Although Bralorne had won a reprieve the previous year, when the federal government approved the short-term Gold Mining Assistance Act to keep marginally profitable operations in operation, the subsidy – which amounted to $10 for each ounce of gold produced – was not enough to save Bralorne. Between 1932 and 1971 – the great era of the Bralorne and Pioneer gold mines – the properties had produced 4 million ounces of gold, paid $145 million in revenue, yielded $32 million in dividends, and employed 10,000 miners. By the time mining operations ceased, workers had tunneled a mile in, a mile deep, and the underground workings spread for over 100 miles.

"The value of gold pegged at $35 an ounce hasn't changed, while costs have spiralled," mine manager Ed Hall said at the time. "We have managed to keep alive by modernizing and by changing to lower cost methods, but we've come to the point where no more can be done. We have been gradually cutting back on production for the past four years and are now actually down to about one-third. On the bottom level there is some spectacular ore, but there are not enough working places in the mine with that grade of ore. To keep operating we would have to have a tremendously rich ore body. We would have to develop more ore and this would mean sinking another shaft at great expense. There is no way we could get our money back. The bottom of the mine is about 2,000 feet below sea level. Our main adit goes in about 3,400 feet. Going deeper would be very costly. Rock pressure is tremendous at the bottom. Rock temperature is about 130 degrees, making it one of the hottest mines in Canada. So our ventilation system is running at the limits of capacity." It was a no-win situation. For safety reasons, most of the mine shafts were dynamited or sealed by concrete, and the mine buildings burned down.

Two years later in 1973, the price of gold soared to a record high and Bralorne Resources considered reopening the mines. After an expensive survey of the remaining ore reserves, however, it was decided that enactment of the Mineral Royalties Act by the New Democratic provincial government made the resumption of operations economically unfeasible. In what would have been a somewhat pathetic coda, independent businessmen discussed leasing the main Bralorne shaft to grow mushrooms in the late-1970s – the abandoned mine offering ample heat and humidity for mushroom farming. Mercifully, more enlightened minds prevailed.

During the 1980s, E & B Explorations and Corona Corporation acquired the Bralorne Mine and attempted to revive interest in its properties and reopen its shafts. "Corona went in and spent millions of dollars building a camp – complete with bunkhouses, cookhouses and assay labs," says David Wolfin, "before pulling out of the region in 1990 when they found the Eskay Creek Mine. They were splitting the Bralorne project with other companies and finally decided it was too small because they didn't own the surrounding ground." The Wolfins' company, Avino Silver & Gold Mines Ltd., did.

In fact, the outstanding gold mineralization on Avino's adjoining Loco property convinced the Wolfins to make a play for Bralorne and, in 1991, Avino acquired a 100 percent interest in the property and located several vein extensions on properties peripheral to the Bralorne claims. These added considerably to the property's mineral potential and provided the catalyst for further exploration and development. Two years later, Bralorne-Pioneer Gold Mines negotiated an option to earn a 50 percent interest in the entire Bralorne project. In 2002, the company acquired a 100 percent interest in the Bralorne project.

"When they closed the mine," says Louis Wolfin, "they were still mining one-and-a-half ounces of gold down below. There have been a number of reports written over the years showing where all of this is, but it was the price of gold that forced the mine out of business." Adds David Wolfin: "In those days – 30 years ago – they had to hoist the ore several times to get it to the surface, and they couldn't make money at $35 an ounce. If we were to go down to depth, we could do what Goldcorp did at Red Lake – put in a shaft and start mining at $100 an ounce. But that's costly. What we want to do first is prove as much as we can near the surface and see where we go.

"We've found the extensions on the adjoining property," he continues, "and we've taken geologists up there who were flabbergasted that a town that was once home to 10,000 people never discovered them. There was 30 feet of overburden there, and the geologists looked for the obvious outcrops. Then we went in with a backhoe with a 30-foot arm and lifted up the rock and found the extensions. Now we can go through the old tunnels to access the properties further, and we don't have the expense of having to tunnel through hundreds and hundreds of feet of waste rock – it's already been done for us!"

Indeed, modern exploration techniques have revealed extensive zones of new gold mineralization, much of it identical to the high-grade gold found in the past. The Peter Vein, for example, returned assays of up to a very rich 16 ounces of gold per tonne on surface. Meanwhile, underground exploration at the Peter Zone has encountered an average grade of 0.38 ounces of gold per tonne over a strike length of 215 feet with an average width of 3.4 feet. Significantly, the Peter Zone correlates with a similar zone intersected 300 metres below surface that assayed 0.40 ounces of gold per tonne over a width of 6.0 feet and a strike length of 100 feet. All of which indicates that the Peter Zone may be expanded substantially.

In fact, consulting geologist Dr. Matt Ball has identified several areas on the Loco property in the northern part of the claim group that host promising exploration targets for expansion of Bralorne gold mineralization, including the Peter, Big Solly, Zone B., Millchuck, Maddy and Cosmopolitan veins. Dr. Ball notes that the pattern of veins in the Loco area mimics that of the Bralorne-Pioneer veins, making them "a structural extension of the Bralorne-Pioneer system," he says.

"These veins," says David Wolfin, "are not totally vertical – the Bralorne dipped down about a mile in depth, and we can assume that these ones do, too. When you talk about the dimensions – just the simple dimensions of these things – they're very significant. Any geologist will tell you that we're sitting on something huge. We've heard that from many geologists, so we're going on the dimensions and the fact that we know it's identical metallugically. All of the mineralization has been tested and it's all the same.

"The big question," he continues, "is, why haven't we developed the reserves at this point? That's because right after we found them, we got control of the whole thing, so our whole mandate changed considerably. The priorities now are to get it permitted, get it up and running and get a positive cash flow. Then we'll go back and develop these areas."

In 2003, the company raised over $5.4 million, allowing it to retire all debts up to date and complete an upgrade of the mill, utilizing crushers, conveyors and other equipment transported from the Zeballos Mine on Vancouver Island. Then on April 8, 2004, Bralorne-Pioneer Gold Mines Ltd. made a symbolic gesture by pouring the first bar of gold from the mine since its 1971 closure. At a private ceremony attended by Bralorne-Pioneer employees and residents of the Bridge River Valley, the 40-ounce bar – produced from material lying above ground since the mine's demise – is proof that the mine's mill is now operational. Working year-round, seven days a week, the company had employed 42 employees on site until recently, when that number increased to 60 (including 16 new hires from the town of Bralorne itself, as well as nearby Gold Bridge, representing what today constitutes approximately a third of the valley's permanent population).

"I've been at this for over 40 years," says Bralorne-Pioneer president William "Bill" Kocken, "and I've worked at a gold mine similar to this one, but I've never seen anything quite like it. It's all there and it's all paid for. We can break even with 100 tonnes a day if we get 0.22 ounces of gold per tonne, but we're hoping for a higher gold content – closer to the 0.5 or 0.6 ounces of gold per tonne that was produced in the past."

"We've been so busy getting the permits and refitting the mill," says David Wolfin, "that now is the time we're going to get positive cash flow. We're going to go back and start exploring. We've purchased a drill rig and we're going to start drilling up there and expand on what is already there. Right now, we're producing 100 tonnes a day – we're permitted for 500 tonnes a day, but Bill has set the mill up for 150 tonnes a day. We didn't want our mill so big that we couldn't feed it. We wanted to start small and then, when we feel comfortable and our technical team is in place, we will look to start expanding. We've already got most of the technical team together – miners, metallugists, underground engineers, mining engineers – and we're ready to start moving."

"It is a beautiful area," says Louis Wolfin, beaming. "And I think it has a bright future."

CANDENTE RESOURCE CORPORATION

Corporate offices tend to be just that: corporate. Hushed no-nonsense environments as staid and formal as the pressed dress shirts and cinched neckties of their inhabitants. They evoke a presence rather than a warmth; an entity rather than a personality. Not so at the Vancouver offices of Candente Resource Corp., where visitors are greeted by a brilliant splash of natural light as inviting in tone and cheerful in character as the company's personnel.

Perched above the city's Hornby Street in the heart of the financial district, Candente's home base reflects the company's personable, hands-on business philosophy and embraces its passion for finding precious metals in vibrant locations. Lively displays of Peruvian art – oil paintings, pottery and glassware – adorn the walls and brighten the milieu with colours both earthen and fiery. The company's corporate logo, a gold medallion embossed with the image of an ancient warrior, replicates a native artifact and was, in fact, created by a Peruvian goldsmith. Of the eight Vancouver staff members, six are women – including cofounder, president and CEO Joanne C. Freeze – and there is a decidedly "feminine touch" to the office detail and ambiance. It is clearly a conducive workplace, the type of environment in which people are proud to be productive.

Much of Candente's corporate identity can be attributed directly to Joanne Freeze herself, known to colleagues, industry peers, staffers and shareholders alike as "Joey." Articulate, sensible and immediately engaging, a cascading mane of blonde curls framing her easy and outgoing smile, Joey Freeze exudes natural sincerity. She speaks as freely and fluidly about geology as she does her business partners, and she is unswervingly loyal to the ideas and ideals of both. It is this rare combination of corporate savvy, technical know-how and feminine grace that inspires associates throughout the mining community to speak of her in glowing and ebullient terms. They should: the company has four advanced projects underway in Peru (with other properties available for joint venture) and a strategic partnership with Goldcorp in Newfoundland, Canada. Candente Resource Corp. (DNT: TSX-V) is well-positioned, well-financed and well-aware that its precious and base metal properties could be of world-class stature.

Born in Calgary, Alberta, Joanne Freeze came to the resource industry naturally – her father worked in the oil business. The family had to relocate from time to time and Joey spent her teen years in Tulsa, Oklahoma, before finishing high school in Chicago, Illinois. "I graduated from the same school as Rock Hudson, Ann-Margaret and Charlton Heston," she says with a chuckle. She went on to earn her B.A. in geography at the University of Western Ontario in 1978 and, in the summer of 1979, landed her first field job, exploring for coal in northeastern B.C.

In 1981, she received her B.Sc. in geology from the University of British Columbia and, after working in coal exploration for two more years, embarked on a four-year expedition with Art Troup of the Hughes-Lang Group, hunting for gold in B.C., the Yukon and the northern United States. A member of the Association of Professional Engineers and Geoscientists of British Columbia, Freeze took a position with Glen White Geophysics before becoming an independent consultant, evaluating projects for numerous major and junior international mining companies, including Queenstake Resources Ltd., Mountain Province Mining Inc., Placer Dome Inc., Dia Met Minerals Corp., Hughes-Lang Group, Utah Mines Ltd. (BHP), and Arequipa Resources Ltd. While working in Peru for Arequipa – a Vancouver-based company headed by the ubiquitous Catherine McLeod-Seltzer – she met future business partner and Candente Resource Corp. co-founder Fredy J. Huanqui, a Peruvian born-and-educated professional geologist very experienced in gold exploration in Peru, who would become Candente's VP Business Development, Latin

America.

"On August 1, 1995," says Freeze, "we were looking at two projects that Arequipa was financing and wanted me to write reports on-the Paron property, on which drilling was already underway, and the California Quatro property, which they were planning to drill. I was standing in the field on the second property with Fredy, who was working as a senior geologist for Arequipa. While everybody was wandering elsewhere, Fredy and I were talking about the merits of the project. He said, 'Well if you like this one, you'll really like one over there. It is called Pierina, named after my daughter.' He'd named the property after his daughter because the last time he'd been instrumental in a discovery people had forgotten he'd had anything to do with it. He said, 'This way they'll remember me.'"

Huanqui liked the property because he knew the alteration and was familiar with similar types of gold mineralization in the country and immediately recognized its potential. As far as Arequipa was concerned, however: "It wasn't as important to them at the time," says Freeze. "It was just another gold target." Despite the number of geologists who had walked the Pierina property, none had bothered to take any samples and surface observations revealed only barren rock. Besides, unlike many other gold properties in Peru, neither the Incas nor the Spaniards had mined the area. "The gold is contained in what is called vuggy silica – a grayish-white rock – and is therefore invisible to the naked eye," says Freeze. "Because there were no old workings, you would never know that there was any gold at Pierina."

Huanqui, however, was persistent. "November 1995 rolled around and Fredy kept showing me more data and getting more excited about it," says Freeze, "so I phoned Catherine McLeod-Seltzer and said, 'I'm com-ing back to Canada for a couple of months. There is this property called Pierina that your Peruvian geologist really likes – why don't you let me go see it so I won't have to fly back later if you decide you need a report on it?' Besides, I thought to myself, I want to see the property for myself." McLeod-Seltzer considered Freeze's offer and called her back the fol-lowing day. "She said, 'OK, we can handle three days of your time,' so I went up to Pierina and of course I really liked it. Though I wasn't sure where all the controls were and I didn't realize how big it was, I still really liked it." And for good reason – Pierina surface samples were grading up to eight grams of gold per tonne.

A month later, Freeze and her family – husband Art, also a geologist, and the couple's two children Dylan and Samantha – were enjoying a Christmas skiing holiday in Whistler, B.C. On January 1, 1996, she called McLeod-Seltzer from the resort community to wish her a Happy New Year. "I phoned and said, 'Happy New Year! This is where you can find me,' and Catherine said, 'Thanks very much but we don't need a report right now – we'll let you know when we do.' Four days later, I got a call back from Catherine saying, 'How fast can you write that report?' Arequipa's stock had been at about $1 a share back in August 1995 when Fredy first told me about Pierina. By the beginning of January 1996, it had hit $3 and was moving up. By the time I wrote the report in February 1996, it was in the $5 range."

Arequipa completed a $5 million financing at approximately $5 per share and Freeze returned to Peru to assist in exploration on the property. "I was lucky enough to stay on with Arequipa as the due diligence person," she says. "I was just helping in any way that I could in order to stay on the project. The nice thing about the job as the due diligence person for public companies is that I wasn't working on the boring stuff – I was working with somebody who had found something big enough and exciting enough to raise money on, so it had to be a certain way along. Through that experience, I got to know Peru very well. Even though I was not in an instrumental role, I was in an interesting role and I was assisting in the discovery of the mine."

In the summer of 1996, two adits were driven into the central part of the deposit prior to drilling. The tunnels subsequently yielded significant geological information. "At the end of August 1996," Freeze says, "Arequipa sold the Pierina property to Barrick Gold for US$700 million (approximately CDN$1 billion). It really is an amazing success story – in 13 months, Pierina went from being one of 19 properties owned by Arequipa in the Cordillera Negra Mountain range to being recognized as a world-class deposit. People in the industry had never heard of anything being staked and sold so quickly, let alone becoming a mine for under $10 million. It was unheard of. In fact, Payback Hill, contained over 1 million ounces of gold in one little knob. Until then, people were insisting it was a scam.

"Lots of very good geologists didn't think it was going to be anything very big, but because such good systematic surface work had been done by digging all the pits and two adits, Barrick was able to know how laterally extensive the deposit was. By the time Arequipa drilled the nine holes, Barrick was quite sure they had at least 5 million ounces as they'd also demonstrated the uniformity of the deposit. Pierina was one of those very few discoveries." As it turned out, Pierina contained in excess of 7.5 million ounces of gold and has since been put into production by Barrick Gold Corp.

Huanqui subsequently went to work for Barrick, while Freeze continued consulting. Then, in the fall of 1996, a friend and colleague suggested Freeze and Huanqui start their own company based on their collective knowledge and previous success. "At first," says Freeze, "I thought, 'Nah, I've got two young kids and whatnot,' but opportunities like that don't come along every day. Plus, I felt very strongly about Fredy's abilities and the potential of the geology in Peru. After careful consideration, we decided to go ahead and take the plunge."

Though the initial suggestion was to launch the new company on the strength of one especially hot property, Huanqui nixed the idea. Freeze explains: "Fredy, who has a great understanding of the business, just looked at me like I was loco. He said, 'I've been working for Barrick, you've been consulting for all these Canadian junior companies, and we're going to start a new company and immediately show up with a hot property on the table? The lawsuits will be unending.' Of course, he was right, so we decided if we were going to do this, we were going to have to raise our own seed capital and do our own regional exploration. Obviously we would use the knowledge we had, but we also knew that we would have to go out and start from scratch. That's exactly what we did."

Freeze and Huanqui officially founded Candente Resource Corp./Cia Minera Oro Candente S.A. in June 1997 (the company's name derives from a Spanish term meaning "red hot" or "too hot to touch"). With initial funding, regional exploration began immediately and the company was soon acquiring properties of merit. "We didn't go public until May 2000 because the mineral exploration market was not good," Freeze says. "People were not interested in putting money into gold exploration, and it was hard to convince investors to invest in gold at a time when they didn't want gold. But even when gold prices were at their lowest, companies operating in Peru as low-cost producers were still making very good money. In any event, we raised about $1 million in seed capital and managed to conduct our business quietly until May 2000."

In an office in the colourful and residential Miraflores district of Lima, Candente's Peruvian team presently consists of 10 fulltime employees, as well as assorted geological consultants working under the direction of the energetic Huanqui. "Working with Fredy has been very dynamic and I feel very fortunate," says Freeze. "He really understands what it takes to find a mine. We have always liked Peru and it was very important to us that we operate in Peru as a Peruvian company. Winning the confidence of the community has always been our number-one priority. It doesn't matter how much gold is in the ground, if the people who live near it don't want you to take it out, then you won't. They have the ultimate say."

Though the country has seen its share of strife and political turmoil, by the time President Alejandro Toledo Manrique assumed leadership in July 2001, the standard of living had greatly increased and economic growth was estimated at almost five percent in 2002. "When the new president came in, he heartily supported foreign investment," says Freeze. "Peru is now ranked by the Fraser Institute as the fourth best place in the world to be working in mineral exploration. You can get a lot done there for very little money, so there is presently quite a frenzy among junior resource companies clamouring to get into the country. Foreign investment is welcome and several international companies have invested a lot of money building the biggest mines in the world. Yanacocha is one of the biggest open-pit gold mines in the world, and Antamina is the largest copper-zinc mine. These are huge. The interesting thing about the Yanacocha is that in 1994, people thought it had 3 million to 5 million ounces of gold – they now know it has in excess of 35 million ounces. They've been mining 2 million ounces a year and it's growing."

Ironically enough, Peru's gold has been waiting to be discovered for millennia. Though both the Incas and Spaniards found gold in the country, neither mined the precious metal in sizeable quantities. "When I first went to Peru," says Freeze, "the country was known for silver. Now it is known for gold. Over the past 10 years, it has become the sixth largest gold producer in the world and the largest in South America. The Yanacocha and Pierina mines together make up 60 percent of Peru's gold production, while Barrick's Alto Chicama project will account for another 7 million ounces." Indeed, the Yanacocha epithermal gold deposit is one of the largest heap-leachable gold mines in the world. In 2003, production costs were at $88 per ounce and reserves were estimated to contain in excess of 35 million ounces of gold. "Peru is a profitable country for gold at almost any level," says Freeze. Candente is anticipating that at least some of its own properties could prove equally productive.

"Fredy deals with the people and he has many associations in Peru that make sure we have all the correct papers that we need," says Freeze. "I can't stress how important he is. I might be president, but he is my partner. I promised Fredy when we started this company that this time the gringos and Peruvians were going to be on 'equal ground' and make the same amount of money. When there hasn't been money for salaries, neither of us have received one. Whatever happens, we do everything equally. He is very trusting of me and vice-versa, which is great."

At present, Candente is focussing its efforts on two advanced projects in Peru: CaÒariaco SX-EX copper and Alto Dorado gold. In April 2001, Candente acquired a 100 percent interest in the CaÒariaco porphyry copper property in Northern Peru. An advanced-stage exploration project with potential for a significant leachable copper resource suitable for low-cost SX-EW processing, the property's key features include high-grade drill intercepts by previous operators demonstrating grades of 0.80 to 1.25 percent copper; a leachable zone open both laterally and vertically; and a larger potential resource comprised of a mixed enriched/primary assemblage with potential for eventual low-strip ratio production utilizing either flotation or a recently developed sulfide leach process.

Approximately 3,000 metres of diamond (core) drilling are planned for the CaÒariaco property this year, which will be carried out by Kluane Drilling of Vancouver, B.C., which uses a portable rig requiring no roads and minimal site disturbance. The property is located 110 kilometres by air from port facilities and a major city. Current road access is 150 kilometres, but a major paved highway lies 15 kilometres north of the property. In addition, the deposit lies at the north end of the Cajamarca District, a major cluster of significant copper and gold deposits extending over 165 kilometres, which includes the La Granja, Tantahuatay and Yanacocha deposits.

The Alto Dorado property hosts both high sulphidation epithermal gold and gold-copper porphyry styles of mineralization. Situated halfway between the remarkable Yanacocha deposit to the north and the equally significant Pierina deposit to the south, the property is 36 kilometres south-southeast of Barrick Gold's Alto Chicama property, where in excess of 7 million ounces of gold has been discovered. Alto Dorado covers 6,000 hectares within the same belt of Tertiary-age volcanic rocks as its neighbouring world-class gold deposits. Gold grades ranging from 0.5 to 3.6 grams per tonne occur both on the surface and in drill holes in vuggy silica, granular silica and alunite breccia fragments in the northeastern portion of the property. The surface expression of these breccias covers an area over one-kilometre long and 150-metres wide.

The Coeur d'Alene, Idaho-based Hecla Mining Company carried out exploration work on the property between 1996 and 1998, including extensive mapping, geochemical sampling, trenching, road building, and reverse circulation drilling. Thirteen holes were drilled to depths of up to 150 metres below surface and several intercepted mineralized intervals grading 0.25 grams per tonne gold and 0.20 percent copper with individual assays ranging up to 1.42 grams per tonne gold and 0.37 percent copper. The best intersection in target the Toril Zone measures 18 metres with grades of 0.5 to 1.5 grams per tonne gold. Approximately 3,000 metres of core drilling are planned for the Alto Dorado property this year. Drill targets have been delineated by geological mapping, rock chip sampling, trenching and geophysical surveys comprising 204 line kilometres of magnetics and 100 line kilometres of time domain electromagnetic soundings surveys. An additional 50 line kilometres of induced polarization surveys will delineate further drill targets. Similar geophysical surveys have previously been used in Peru to assist in the discovery of ore bodies with mineralization similar to that being found on the Alto Dorado Property.

In addition, Candente currently has two projects in northern Peru under joint venture with Orex Ventures Inc.: the Las Sorpresas gold-silver and El Tigre gold properties. Orex has the right to earn a 51 percent interest in each of these properties by incurring exploration expenditures of

US$2.5 million over three-and-a-half years. Las Sorpresas covers 2,827 hectares and borders the southern edge of the Yanacocha gold mine owned by Newmont (51 percent) and Buenaventura (43 percent). Gold targets on the Las Sorpresas property include both the oxide style of gold mineralization currently being mined at Yanacocha and the higher-grade sulphide mineralization being discovered at depth at Yanacocha. On the El Tigre Property, in excess of 1,000 surface soils and rock samples (collected by previous companies) show anomalous gold occurring over two kilometres in length and one kilometre in width. Mineralization is considered to be low sulphidation (El Penon type). El Penon produces gold at $44 per ounce for Meridian Gold in Chile, which makes this an excellent exploration target type. Exploration will be operated by Candente's Peruvian exploration team led by Fredy Huanqui and employed by subsidiary Cia. Minera Oro Candente S.A. ("Oro Candente"). Exploration programs are being designed so as not to disturb or interrupt current land use and to provide employment when possible to the local community.

The company is equally enthusiastic about its holdings in Newfoundland, Canada. "It was Larry who introduced us to the mineral opportunities in Newfoundland," says Freeze, referring to Larry Kornze, Candente's Director of Business Development, whose golden touch played a key role in the discovery of Nevada's Carlin Trend and Goldstrike Mine. "He showed me some samples from Newfoundland's Botwood Basin and pointed out that they were similar to Carlin-style gold mineralization. 'This could be another Carlin,' he said. 'In which case there is simply too much gold to ignore – we've got to be there.' With that in mind, Candente acquired the Staghorn, Linear, Island Pond, and Virgin Arm properties.

In March 2004, Candente entered into a strategic partnership agreement with Goldcorp Inc. to conduct exploration in Newfoundland. Goldcorp became a major shareholder (five percent) in the company in February 2003 by purchasing 1.7 million shares. This was the first step in the strategic partnership, which fundamentally facilitated Goldcorp access to Candente's expertise in both gold exploration and Newfoundland itself. The agreement allows Goldcorp to earn a 70 percent interest in either or both of the Staghorn and Linear gold properties by assuming all of Candente's expenditure obligations and completing bankable feasibility studies by 2010. The agreement also grants Goldcorp a right of first offer on other properties currently held or acquired in the future by Candente in Newfoundland subject to termination on certain events and time periods. This partnership with a premier gold producer not only validates Candente's belief that Newfoundland has excellent potential for hosting economic gold deposits, but it removes a good portion of the risk for Candente and its shareholders, with Goldcorp making the expenditures to bankable feasibility in order to gain their interest.

The Staghorn is the company's most advanced project in Newfoundland, located in the southwestern portion of the island, approximately 60 kilometres southeast of the seaport of Stephenville where commercial air service is available. The earliest recorded gold discoveries in the area were reported by Hudson Bay Mining in 1981 and BP Selco in 1988. In the fall of 2002, Candente carried out a property examination which included a small sampling program and delineated anomalous gold values from mineralized rock float ranging from 117 to 16,765 parts per billion over an area measuring 450 by 150 metres. Several other gold mineralized areas were identified with values ranging from 4,000 to 25,000 parts per billion gold.

Following these discoveries, Candente optioned the property in December 2002 and continued further exploration during the summer of 2003 to present. High chargeability zones on the property were identified by a recently completed induced polarization survey and occur over a 3.2 kilometre length. Gold has been identified to date at several locations over 2.5 kilometres of the same trend. The high chargeability zones appear to be associated with gold mineralization as they both occur within the same structural trend.

Gold mineralization of 0.5 to 25.7 grams per tonne is evident in three main trenched zones in bedrock, angular rock float, soils and heavy mineral concentrate samples. Gold values ranging from 0.5 to 13.5 grams per tonne (several in the 1.5 to 5 grams per tonne range) occur in the main zone in rocks comprising one-metre channels in trenches, selected samples and angular float in pits over a 70-by-30-metre area. Outside the trenched area overburden masks outcrop exposure over much of the property. The styles of mineralization, host rocks, structural setting and geochemical signature found to date on the Staghorn Property are all typical of intrusion hosted-orogenic deposits such as the 175 million ounce gold deposit at Muruntau and 19 million ounce gold deposit at Kumtor in Central Asia.

Joey Freeze still seems slightly "in awe" of her good fortune when it comes to attracting key personnel. Chief financial officer Peter de Visser is the principle of de Visser, Gray and Company, Chartered Accountants, a Vancouver-based accounting firm servicing public junior mining companies since 1987. In addition to acting as financial advisor to public companies, de Visser has had experience as a director of junior companies since 1992. A Canadian Chartered Accountant, he is a member of the Technical Subcommittee of the B.C. Institute of Chartered Accountants to the B.C. Securities Commission. "Peter has been instrumental in making sure we started the company with a solid structure and foundation and he handled the original aspects of interacting with the financial community and raising capital," says Freeze. "I've learned so many things from him, I can't begin to name them all. In all honesty, I came in as a geologist and really knew nothing about how to get a public company where we are today."

Both Larry Kornze and Candente advisory board member Frank L. Nelson "came on board soon after we had gone public," says Freeze, "and we are very grateful and happy to have them." Kornze, who recently retired from Barrick Gold Corporation as general manager of exploration for Mexico and Central America, had been with Barrick since 1985 and was instrumental in discovering millions of ounces of gold found in the Carlin Trend in Nevada. As Barrick's U.S. exploration manager, he was responsible for several discoveries at the Goldstrike Mine in Elko, Nevada, including the Betze, Meikle, Deepstar, Screamer and Rodeo deposits. Goldstrike is Barrick's flagship mine and, in 2000 alone, produced approximately 2.4 million ounces of gold. A 34-year veteran of international gold exploration, Kornze has also held various positions with Newmont Mining Corporation and Getty Mining Co.

At an industry investor conference in Vancouver, Kornze heard Freeze speak and became intrigued with Peru and the variety of Candente's properties. He considered the company's Alto Dorado data encouraging and was impressed by the size-potential of the CaÒariaco project. "Larry is an amazing asset," says Freeze. "Not only does he know gold, but he's a great guy and he's very supportive. He is recognized in our industry, easily approachable and has no ego." And though Kornze finds junior exploration companies an exciting area of interest, he will only associate himself with good people and good properties. Two years after joining the Candente board, he smiles when asked about the company's president. "Joey is a really great person," he says. "I didn't realize it at the time, but in addition to being honest and hard-working, she just puts so much extra effort into everything she does. It's a really big plus."

American geologist Frank J. Nelson joined Candente's advisory board as a consultant, bringing 36 years of experience to the company in all phases of base and precious metal exploration in North, South and Central America, as well as Australia, Asia and Europe. After more than 30 years with Freeport Exploration Company, he left his position as vice-president international exploration in 1999 to act as a consultant for Candente. He is credited with the discovery of two world-class mineral deposits: Mount Keith, a disseminated nickel sulphide deposit located in Western Australia; and Ertsberg East (Grasberg District), a copper-gold-silver skarn in Irian Jaya, Indonesia.

"These are fantastic people to have on our team because they know what it takes to find mines," says Freeze. "We just happened to meet them at conferences and through other people, and they really liked what we were doing. You always want to do business with people that other people know. Prior to working with us at Candente, Fredy, Larry and Frank were, as individuals, instrumental in the discoveries of more than 50 million ounces of gold."

Likewise bolstering the company's technical team is Michael Casselman, who joined Candente in February 2004, bringing with him over 35 years of Canadian and international mineral-industry experience. Casselman leads the exploration teams in both Peru and Newfoundland, and contributes managerial, technical, logistical, environmental and community-relations expertise. His 30-year tenure with Cominco Ltd. (from which he retired in 1999) began in 1969, where he was directly involved with the Highland Valley Copper Mine in British Columbia, from exploration to production. He also supervised exploration at the mine and in the surrounding district in the 1980s. In the mid-1990s, Casselman relocated to Santiago, Chile, where he led extensive copper exploration programs.

Happily retired by 2004, Casselman was enjoying a leisurely lifestyle, playing golf, hockey and spending time with his grandson, even taking up landscape painting. When asked why he came out of retirement to join Candente as the full-time Manager, Exploration, he laughs: "Actually, I was initially approached to help on a part-time consulting basis, just some assistance here and there. I like to call it the 'escalating job' – the duties just kind of snuck up on me. That's Joey!" In fact, Casselman has recently taken on even more responsibility when he accepted Candente's offer to become a Director.

Casselman pauses thoughtfully before adding, "In all seriousness, Joey runs a tight, well-managed company with good people and interesting targets – more than interesting. When I had my first opportunity to review technical data, it most definitely confirmed what I was led to believe from previous literature and discussions. In Peru, Alto Dorado and CaÒariaco are excellent targets and there is tremendous room for something both large and economic. In Newfoundland, the quality of data and targets are real with, what I feel, is a better than good chance of something significant in terms of ore-grade mineralization and economic tonnage. That's when I decided this company was something I would really like to be a part of – each region could have a deposit."

That is certainly what the folks at Candente Resource Corp. believe. "We now have a respectable profile in the investment community and a portfolio of excellent properties," says Freeze. "With two main projects being drilled this year, several more in the pipeline and a strong balance sheet, Candente is looking forward to a long and prosperous future."

So are its investors.

CASSIDY GOLD
CORPORATION

When people in the mining business concentrate their attention on a particular region, their primary responsibility is often to themselves and their company's shareholders. Few end up in politics. Political smarts and acumen are often key elements of any smart mining company manager's skill set, and that's more important when working outside North America. But even the greatest political finesse is frequently second to something else: engineering know-how, perhaps, or maybe geological savvy or a briefcase full of MBA brilliance.

Cassidy Gold Corp.'s experience is different. As it went looking for gold in Guinea, West Africa, the government there saw expertise and knowledge about mining throughout the world, as well as more particular in Canada, and knew they could get more out of their own work at improving their domestic mining industries if they got Cassidy's help in drafting mining codes and promoting what they have to offer to the rest of the world.

"A lot of mineral wealth is generated in Mali and Ghana, and as we go ahead, locals are becoming more comfortable with the mining companies coming in," says Cassidy president James Gillis. "At first, I think, they thought, 'Well, these guys are just coming in and taking all our gold.' But then they went through a transition stage. Ghana is the big leader based on British law and led by Angolagoldashanti, exploiting a deposit – the Obuassi since 1897; very rich mine – of 50 million ounces altogether; a million profitable ounces is a big mine. Gradually, more and more mines were found there, so that now, they have a good number of mines. Their French-speaking neighbours Mali and Burkina Faso have a lot of exploration going on. As the giant Sadiola and Morila mines have provided examples to encourage exploration."

When people think about gold and Africa, they almost always think of the massive discoveries and huge mines in the southern part of the continent. But as Cassidy is proving, West Africa is poised on the brink of becoming a very important gold center for Africa as the twenty-first century continues. While mining is not new in that part of the continent, the methods and means are very basic, as are the exploration methods people rely on.

For example, termite mounds are important in locating gold. Termites dig deep into the earth to retrieve the clay soil their mounds are built on and built with. Their search for wet clay as raw termite mound material takes the insects down to the water table. If the mounds are red, that can mean sulphides. Sulphides, in turn, can mean gold. Artisanal miners then dig narrow shafts – barely wide enough for one person – under the termite mounds, where they begin hewing out clay which they then sift for gold. They mine only what can be removed with the most basic tools. This technique means a lot of gold is left under the surface, its location already pinpointed.

"Then we come in and with all this free trenching, this surface gold," Gillis says. "They can only go so far. We can find the deeper source of the surface gold." Most recently, Cassidy discovered large tracts of significant artisanal mining on its Kouroussa and Siquiri properties in Guinea, in addition to the Koe Koe area it was already working on with drilling equipment.

Gillis believes that mine development is one of the fastest ways to bring West Africa up to speed with its more advanced continental neighbours as well as the rest of the world's economic community. He cites the development of Canada's economy in its early stages, as well as exploration sorties by large mining companies into Chile seeking copper as examples of the ways mining companies can help nations make their economies more robust and effective.

"These mines are creating great wealth, and they're the best way of moving ahead," Gillis says. "Every mine causes all sorts of trickle-down effects. When mining companies went to Chile and developed a couple of big copper mines, the next thing you know, the inflation rate is well under control and they've got the red carpet out for mining companies."

But there comes a point where junior mining companies need to exercise caution. Nations with well-developed mining infrastructure and regulations often seek to heavily regulate exploration and production, as well as tax any successful operation – often too heavily for the company's shareholders to make a reasonable return on their investment. That process drives international exploration. But even there, some regions are hospitable, and others offer more risk than the potential reward is worth. While geological risk can be cut substantially with geological experience and expertise, political risk must be carefully assessed as well. Fixing your company's exploration and development plans on a particular region means using the infrastructure you set up among several different projects or operations, which obviously makes a lot more sense than spreading exploration resources too thin among a range of disparate projects throughout the world.

"You build infrastructure in those areas and it's of tremendous benefit to all parties – locals, explorers and government," Gillis explains. "You can look at four, five, or ten properties because you've got the equipment and personnel available to support the evaluation process. Sound mining laws, security of title and transferability of title all add to your ability to move forward and justify spending your shareholders' money because you've good odds."

Finding a part of the world that's underexplored is a key part of this strategy. Guinea is very much underexplored and it is just emerging. A tremendous opportunity for mine finders. The government's department of mines and geology is in the process of enhancing a very good and operable mining code to make it one of the best, most transparent and reliable in the world. This process will attract more exploration companies from around the world. This, in turn, will improve the country's potential to find the mines which will, in turn, further improve all necessary infrastructure supporting even more exploration. Even the most hospitable regulatory climate or government can't help a mining company if its opportunities are overworked or played out or too crowded. But some areas have too many regulatory hurdles, too much government interference, too little familiarity with how to balance domestic, indigenous interests with those of the very mining companies necessary to develop the local resources.

"I couldn't go to Russia with a junior mining company," Gillis says. "It's difficult there. A lot of senior exploration companies have had a hard time there even though there is tremendous potential. China is a great place too. It's wide open. A junior exploration company would have a hard time. In Africa, where we work, they're very open and helpful to juniors because they know that they desperately need to find mines. It's critical and the government is doing everything it possibly can to attract and support junior explorers because they know we're the ones who can find the mines."

Gillis says he knows that as the properties in West Africa develop further, there will doubtless be some rivalries between tribal groups and villages at the immediate local level. But the initial positive reaction that usually greets his teams of explorers and geologists start relationships off on a good footing and it's up to his crews to make every effort to maintain this good standing. Each successful project improves the situation of each group or village, their neighbours will be more likely to welcome geologists and explorers and other people from mining companies, having seen how their arrival has benefited local people. And if a mine is found the company and the government of Guinea will identify and develop working relationships that maximize the economic and social benefits of responsible resource development.

Also driving exploration is the changing economic climate elsewhere in Africa. South Africa, for example, is struggling with currency exchange rates. The high rand is cutting into profits at established gold mines and depressing impetus for further exploration and development. Developers may feel as though patience makes more sense – don't develop a mine until currency exchange rates even out and potential profitability returns to an acceptable level.

"All the outfits that made their fortunes in South Africa – like Goldfields and Anglo Gold – are moving into West Africa and East Africa," Gillis says. "It's getting to be interesting. It's an exciting place to be." Not to mention that having been there before an influx of bigger companies looking to escape less-than-spectacular currency exchange rates likely means a subtle but distinct advantage for a junior exploration company that's already demonstrated its trustworthiness."

Cassidy's major properties include Kouroussa, in Guinea, which Gillis describes as "an absolute dream property." The company first sought opportunity in Guinea as Gillis and his colleagues became more frustrated with the mining climate in Canada in general and British Columbia in particular. "We were pretty much fed up with British Columbia – and perhaps with Canada – as a place to give our shareholders a chance at the big rise," he says. "It came to my attention that there was a property in Guinea. I sent a geologist over to take a look at it – Pierre Trudel, a good geologist, mining engineer, and top-notch guy. He came back and said, 'Well guess what, Jim that's a mine. It's a great opportunity.'" Kouroussa had gone through two companies by that point; these companies had tried to explore the resource and move it closer to development. But a combination of a poor money-raising climate and a sudden capital shortage in the wake of the Bre-X scandal and individual financial difficulties meant they'd lost the property.

When Gillis and Cassidy had the chance to get the property, he was initially reluctant. "At first, I said, 'Yeah, right.' It took about six months, because it took a while to convince me that it was a good opportunity and an acceptable risk." But the more Gillis learned about the Kouroussa property, the more encouraged – and eventually excited – he became.

"After 22 years of exploring in British Columbia and busting my pick, time and time again, this was just a real pleasant surprise, to drill five holes, four of which hit right off the bat. It was difficult at first – took us five months to drill 519 metres. Right now we're doing 150 metres a day. The only drill we could get initially was from a company in the U.K. – this really terrible old drill. We finally got it – US$108 a metre they charged us. They dragged the thing in – it was falling apart as it came in. They're drilling away and pounding down. You've got to give them credit for being absolutely incredibly good drillers to make that machine work as well as it did."

Cassidy's people in Guinea worked to get a reverse circulation (RC) drill to the site. The drill Cassidy Gold Corp. located was already working in Guinea for another company. "We talked to the owners and they said they could do the job for us but that it would be expensive," Gillis remembers. "If we couldn't pay the rate they would just move their rig back to Australia, which was where it came from originally. A reverse circulation drill was the ideal way to drill the large gold anomaly we had identified on the Kouroussa property, but these drills are very difficult to come by in Guinea. The owners of this RC rig knew that we were desperate to drill before the rainy season began in late June. This was in early June. They also knew that in the grand scheme of things this was not a big deal contract for them. The price of mobilization and metreage kept going up. Toward the end of the drill's trek toward the Cassidy project, the RC owners were up to US$40,000 just for mobilization, even though they were going right by our property anyway. Cassidy management was awaiting results from the 519-metre diamond drill program just completed. If they could get some good numbers they would have enough info to refinance and get ready for the next season. If not, they would have no choice but to pay for the RC rig in an attempt to get the good results necessary to get the next round of financing. If both drills then showed poor results, the company would have a real problem raising the necessary funds for this project.

"Sure enough, when the guy bringing this big RC machine is about ten kilometres away, we get the assays. They were just really good. One number was 373 grams per tonne . . . and that's awesome. We had this assay checked from the reject, which means from the same crushed-up material left over from the original sample, and it came back at 412 grams. We knew what we had. We phoned the owners of the other drill, and said, 'Head it back to Perth, boys. We won't be needing it here.' Now things have settled down at Kouroussa. We've contracted Boart Longyear for the drilling and are very happy with the professional proficient work they provide. The drillers are the best in the world and they keep a Super "38" Longyear drill rig tuned up and producing 150 metres a day, on average."

Guinea became a French protectorate in 1849 and a colony in 1891. The Republic of Guinea was granted independence in 1958 and has held free and democratic elections since 1993. French is the official language and French civil law forms the basis for the country's legal system. The Guinea Mining Code needs work but it has an acceptable system of reconnaissance, exploration, exploitation permits and mining concessions. The government retains a 15 percent carried interest in any developed mines. Mining concessions are granted for 25-year periods with 10-year extensions. In seeking opportunities where mining is encouraged, Cassidy Gold has found in Guinea a welcoming spirit of cooperation combined with a potential like nowhere else on earth.

Located 570 kilometres east of the capital Conakry, on a paved highway, the original Kouroussa permit area encompasses 240 square kilometres of open, subdued, Birimian terrane. On July 24, 2003, the company acquired two additional permits, totaling about 400 square kilometres. The first, Tambiko, is 207 square kilometres and contiguous with the Kouroussa permit to the east. The second new permit is the 191-square kilometre Siguiri permit, which is contiguous to the southwest with the mining concession of Société Ashanti de Guinée. Originally attracted to the Kouroussa area by the intensive artisanal workings combined with extensive highly anomalous gold geochemistry, Cassidy's exploration team has succeeded in identifying a minimum of three strong gold quartz vein systems with an initial minimal drilling project and is now drilling off a resource at one of them and waiting to drill the other two.

The full extent and antiquity of the artisanal mining in the Koe Koe area has only recently been recognized, particularly with respect to the sheer quantities of material moved and area of cuirasse undermined. The Kouroussa concession has yielded substantial quantities of gold over a very long period. Recent owners concentrated on the southern portion of the property, and in particular the Koe Koe and Sodyanfe artisanal sites.

A total of 2,776 soil samples were collected over 3.2 square kilometres averaging 342 ppb gold resolved into three separate anomalies. One kilometre northwest lies the Sodyanfe anomaly, encompassing a comparable area with 213 samples averaging 0.49 grams of gold per tonne, and ranging up to 8.63 grams of gold per tonne. The third anomaly, also in the Koe Koe grid area, lies along a creek bed known as the Koe Koe River. Now Cassidy has found a number of additional digging areas and has completed large soil geochemical surveys thereby outlining many additional drill targets.

Gillis acknowledges the added difficulty that the Bre-X scandal created for every company seeking to develop a gold resource, especially one outside North America. Some of investors' reluctance came from Bre-X, some of it came from a misperception about the Vancouver Stock Exchange.

"But there would never have been a Bre-X scandal if that company had been on the Vancouver Stock Exchange," Gillis says. "The Vancouver Stock Exchange was very good at recognizing bad actors and at enforcing rules that they had implemented to protect investors. What happened, though, was the Alberta Stock Exchange, peopled by a bunch of less sophisticated bureaucrats, had no idea about the modus operandi of these ragamuffins. So all of these less-than-legitimate mining companies were just spawning over there. Vancouver had tightened up so these guys couldn't get away with sensational claims without immediate and sure verification protocol imposed by the VSE. I've always been saddened by the downfall of the VSE because the result was the loss of risk investor money that won't be drilling holes. You've got to drill. Why won't people give us any risk money? Because of the scammers. In the Bre-X case it was because the Alberta Stock Exchange was not staffed with people experienced to reduce the risk of these large-scale scandals."

In addition to the general problems the Bre-X scandal caused for the securities business, the markets and people in mining all over the country and the world, Cassidy and Gillis suffered in immediate and particular ways as well. "It wiped us out; caused us six years of inability to raise money," he says matter-of-factly.

"That's six years of less exploration, six years of decreased mine finding." But the future is particularly bright for gold right now, something that investment and institutional money managers can see, and the reason that Cassidy and other gold exploration and mining companies are again able to raise money. "Now, because gold is around the $400 range," Gillis says, "we can finance again. Gold has a place in the future. There's a top-notch analyst in the United States, Doug Casey, who told everyone to buy ten mining or mineral exploration companies and put 'em away and forget about 'em, because sooner or later, everybody's going to be buying them and most people don't know what to buy. So they will just buy any gold company. They'll all go up.

"We've got 30 million shares out, which is not a large amount, although I'm a big believer in having lots of stock out. If you have lots of stock out you automatically offer a more stable and fair market. There's a lot of companies now in the gold mining industry with 100 million to 500 million shares out."

Gillis got into the mining business by a route that started with a love for minerals and exploration. "I started off in the British Columbia forest service, then went from there to the railroad – worked for the railroad for fifteen years. But all the time I was working there as an engineer, I would also be out prospecting, because it was interesting, you know? When I was a kid, I loved rocks. My brother loved airplanes. My brother is now a captain with Singapore Air, flying 747-400s and I'm out looking for rocks."

Gillis and Cassidy got into Africa through Moussa Traore, a Guinean national who is now a Canadian citizen living in Montreal. "Moussa got me to meet the Minister of Mines, Dr. Alpha Mady Soumah. We have a tremendous rapport, even though he speaks only French, and I speak very little. That 15-minute meeting turned into about nine hours. We went out for dinner, we had a real good talk. I didn't realize there are people in the world like Moussa. He went through hell getting his education, came over here to Canada, became a citizen, worked for the immigration department. He has been a tremendous ally to me. That worked out really well, one thing led to another and when I then flew to Guinea, the first three days were with the ministry. They asked me what they could do to help promote Guinea. They wondered, 'Why is Mali doing so well? Why is Ghana doing so well?' The Minister suggested a forum to obtain advice from the mining industry. He realized that they needed to do what was required to attract mining investment to Guinea. The Minister and his staff decided to get all the information possible to enhance the mining infrastructure in Guinea. The Minister already knew what to do and is quite sophisticated as well but it was really necessary to implement an excellent structure and then tell the world to come and try it out. I was mandated to do what I could to help. I had already told them they knew all that had to be done. Just make it work – that was the hard part. Once in place and staffed, the mining code had to be advertised. The first foray will be into Canada to show all attending the Prospectors and Developers Association conventions that Guinea has tremendous mineral wealth, that it is supportive of mining investment and the rules work and can be relied on in reality. Then they will attract the world's mineral exploration companies with all of their modern exploration techniques. They will develop and they will be able to support the people who will manage the mineral title offices. We'll all grow together."

Gillis demonstrates the way his company and the people of Kouroussa work together with a videotape of some of the members of Cassidy's team working alongside artisanal miners in Guinea. "They are hardworking people. I tried to lift one of those buckets and I couldn't move it. They put this on their heads, and walk seven kilometres."

As important as the people of Guinea are, and as much as the artisanal mining they do matters, turning that kind of small-scale work into something that can keep a mining company going and give investors a good return on their investment while also helping the Guineans requires a careful, one-step-at-a-time approach. That's where the Cassidy Guinea team comes in.

"The people involved are critical," Gillis says. "Our key players include Chris Wild, a geological engineer and vice president of exploration who oversees our entire operation." He cites the African team as being particularly intrepid. "In the field we have Jean-Jacques Lefebvre. He's an M.Sc. geologist – structural engineer – he worked for the mine to the north for four years. He's had a tremendous amount of experience there, and he's also worked on a mine in Mali. He was born in the Congo, and speaks fluent French and English. He's a top-notch guy and he really knows his way around – tremendous respect in Africa and all over the world. With him is Marthé Archambault. She is a master-of-science economic geologist as well, with lots of experience in Africa.

Marc-André Boudreau is our new chief project geologist. Tough but fair. He knows his way around in Africa and is a good exploration geologist – very energetic and knows how to get things done. He loves this property because there seems to be gold everywhere he looks. He has a tremendous amount of common sense and he's extremely tough. He really knows his way around over there."

The most immediate challenge is getting the initial Kouroussa resource into production and turning a profit as well as generating cash flow. That, Gillis maintains, will give the company "something to hang its hat on" with Guinea, the government there, the local people and investors in North America and throughout the world. It should also provide sufficient funds for the company to reduce its reliance on capital raised from the markets.

The Guinean government's biggest challenge right now is to make the country attractive for mineral exploration. Cassidy's challenge is to develop a productive mine. A mine to the south of Kouroussa was put into production in two years for a total capital cost of US$12 million. "In Guinea," he says, "I would say we could be in production within two years once we get a deposit-to-reserve status. When you get into the flow of Africa, it's good. If more mining companies come in, that builds the infrastructure. Then we'll have drills and cats and water trucks. And we'll have geologists and drillers. That is most important. It is good for Guinea, it's good for everybody.

"We do have a mission statement: 'Cassidy's mission is to create a successful mineral exploration company through geological experience and efficient management, where success is measured by the identification and development of high-quality mineral exploration projects. The acquisition of grassroots properties in new or underexplored areas which have potential to provide significant return on investment in the event of a mineral discovery is the focus of our geological and management team.'"

Cassidy Gold and its people are fulfilling their mission in admirable fashion.

EMGOLD MINING CORPORATION

The circular object Bill Witte holds in his hand is intriguing, to say the least. Smaller than a hockey puck, it has an organic earthen hue, like that of fine, unglazed pottery, yet it is anything but fragile. It's lighter! To the touch, however, this particular piece of ceramic has more in common with marble than baked clay. It is clearly no ordinary ceramic.

In fact, it is a sample of a 'super high-quality ceramic', Witte says, three-to-five times stronger than any ceramic material currently available on the market. Even without glazing, it is impermeable to water and doesn't fall apart when exposed to the elements. Environmentally friendly, the technology that produces the ceramic is capable of not only cleaning up mine wastes but transforming them into useful and profitable byproducts. It is no coincidence that this same technology – plus an awful lot of recyclable waste material – is being secured by William J. 'Bill' Witte, president, CEO and director of Vancouver-based exploration company Emgold Mining Corporation (EMR: TSX-V).

"I gave a presentation at the Harvard Club in New York," says Witte, an instantly likeable, incredibly knowledgeable and brazenly entrepreneurial fifth-generation Californian – now a Canadian – who has parlayed his extensive geological and metallurgical background into singular ventures distinguished by captivating histories and untapped potential. "One guy wanted to test the sample to make sure it didn't absorb water, so he dropped it into a tall, fluted glass – then had no way of getting it out, short of spilling the water all over the table or breaking the glass." Witte chuckles. "That provided entertainment for 40 brokers for about 10 minutes."

Born in Los Angeles in 1955, Witte was raised in Encino, California, earning his first degree in Civil Engineering from the University of Nevada, Reno, and his second degree in Mechanical Engineering from the University of Arizona. "I moved to Toronto in 1978," he says. "The idea was to come up here and have a bit of an 'international experience' for a couple of years. As it turned out, I fell in love with the place. Canada has been very good to me and I'm now a Canadian citizen." With almost 30 years of mining, engineering, business and entrepreneurial experience to his credit, Witte is a registered professional engineer in the province of British Columbia and has worked in all aspects of mine exploration, process research-and-development and operations, as well as in the fields of engineering, construction and corporate management. He has been responsible for assorted aspects of over 200 mining and technology projects around the world and has successfully developed numerous profitable mining ventures. All of which brings us to the ceramic samples cradled in the palm of his hand and scattered across his desk. "I used to have a lot more," he says self-effacingly, "but people keep walking off with them."

More than mere curios to amuse Ivy Leaguers or office visitors, the ceramic samples are comprised of waste materials from Emgold's flagship property, the Idaho-Maryland Mine, the second-largest underground gold producer in the history of California. In addition to having an agreement with the mine's mineral rights holders (that includes a mining lease and an option to purchase the entire 2,750-acre property), Emgold likewise has the worldwide rights to the nascent ceramics technology that made the samples possible. It is a one-two punch that puts Emgold in a league of its own. Theoretically, the technology will allow mining operations to not only stay in business in the event of substantial market dips but to continue generating profits, as well.

"The amazing thing about this ceramics technology," says Witte, "is that it eliminates the need for long-term storage of waste rock and tailings. We've done numerous engineering studies defining how we can best develop the mine using a variety of different scenarios. Obviously, the impact of having to store development rock and tailings forever is a very limiting thing, especially when you're mining within a city, which is the case with the Idaho-Maryland Mine. The fact is, the Idaho-Maryland might become an industrial mineral property before it becomes a gold mine." Or rather, before it becomes a gold mine again.

Discovered in 1851, the Idaho-Maryland mine, located within the city limits of Grass Valley, California – a tranquil town of 12,000 in the scenic Sierra Nevada foothills, roughly halfway between Sacramento and Reno – was in operation from 1862 to 1956, during which time it produced roughly 2.4 million ounces of gold. "This mine was in production during the time when California was becoming a state," says Witte, "as well as before, during and after the Civil War, which is why several parts of the mine are named after people and places immortalized during the war – Grant, Lincoln, Brunswick, Appomattox. People from both the North and the South came to work there and they named particular sections after different individuals and events.

"What is interesting about the mine," Witte continues, "is that until 1935, it was actually a bunch of different operations with different owners. They were very secretive about what they were doing, there was a lot of contract mining, and they were subleasing various parts of the mine. There was nothing cohesive about it other than the reporting of some gold to the appropriate jurisdictional government agency."

Between 1862 and 1893 alone, the Idaho-Maryland mine produced 1 million ounces of gold from one specific area of the mine. In 1894, however, the mine's wooden head frame burned to the ground, leaving the various owners to haggle over who owned what and who was responsible for paying for the damage. "They'd already made a ton of money," says Witte, "and from that point on, there were other people who became interested and started developing another part of the mine. The overall structure is about 9,000 feet long – it's really quite phenomenal."

The Idaho-Maryland Mine is a structurally-controlled, mesothermal gold deposit located in the northern portion of the Sierra Nevada Foothills Gold Belt. The fifth largest gold producing area in the history of the United States, the region produced 17 million ounces of gold during the century immediately following the California Gold Rush of 1849. "Everything ran pretty much until 1956," says Witte. "At that time, the price of gold was fixed at $35 per ounce, while the mine was running at an operating cost of between $60 and $110 per ounce. The local power company (Pacific Gas and Electric) pulled the plug on the mine because of lack of payment." All of the mines in the Sierra Nevada Foothills district closed in 1957.

In the meantime, however, the Empire Mine opened up next door to the Idaho-Maryland, their respective head frames two miles apart. A colossal underground producer, the Empire Mine was systematically mined during its entire operation. "It is essentially the mine that made the Newmont Mining Corporation what it is today," says Witte. "Newmont still owns the underground mineral rights to the Empire Mine, but they gave the surface rights to the state of California, where there is now a park with a wonderful museum.

"The original owner of the Empire Mine," Witte continues, "was a guy by the name of William Bower Bourn and he had an old cottage built there in the 1880s. It is still there and it is beautiful, just unbelievable. The entire house is lined with pure cedar, no knots, nothing like that. You walk in and the smell is still there. They've got all the original furnishings and they don't allow you to touch the walls. Docents dress up and they give tours in 1890s costumes and pretend they are living in that era. It's part of the heritage of Grass Valley, whose town motto is, 'The Heart of the Gold Industry.' They're very proud of their history and there are a lot of people involved with it."

The Idaho-Maryland Mine, on the other hand, was privately held and kept an extremely low profile. "Nobody really knows very much about it," says Witte. "The biggest difference between the Idaho-Maryland Mine and the Empire Mine is that the Empire Mine was systemically developed down to the 5,000-foot level, while the Idaho-Maryland Mine was not systemically developed and was only developed down to the 3,280-foot level. Consequently, I believe there is a lot of room to develop this thing."

That is, if you can figure out its inner workings, which have until recently tended to be more complicated above ground than below. "The Idaho-Maryland was very tightly owned," says Witte. "Very confusing and very secretive until about 1925, which was when a fellow by the name of Errol McBoyle – the mining engineer who actually worked at the Empire Mine – went to work at what has become the Idaho-Maryland. He really fell in love with the mine, particularly the Brunswick Shaft, so he spent 10 years of his life from 1925 to 1935 amalgamating the ownership

of the mine. Production was really quite minimal during that period of
time. Then in 1935, McBoyle did some major financing and built a new
'modern' mill, which was commissioned in 1937." Production skyrocketed.

Among other accomplishments, Errol McBoyle built the Sierra
Nevada Memorial Miners Hospital in Grass Valley and, in 1932, built the
Nevada County Airport. This latter labour, however, was as much self-
serving as philanthropic. "At one time, McBoyle was the second-highest
taxpayer in California," says Witte, "and he did a lot of good things. He
was one of the first people to buy a brand new Lougheed Electra to fly
gold from Grass Valley to Mills Field – now the San Francisco
International Airport – and down to the mint in San Francisco. But
because he didn't want to become the number-one taxpayer in California,
he was also using the plane to fly gold bullion down to Mexico illegally.
While there are no records of this per se, there are certain manifests existing that indicate he had very small cargoes that were very heavy. The reason he bought this particular aircraft is because it was the fastest commercial aircraft available at the time and faster than anything the U.S.
Customs people had in the air."

During the thirteenth excursion to Mexico – unluckily enough – the
Customs officials finally caught up with McBoyle's plane and forced the
plane to the ground somewhere in Arizona. "They told the pilot that he
could keep his license and fly the plane back to Grass Valley," says Witte,
"but the Customs men were keeping the cargo. That was the last we heard
about the Lougheed Electra."

Then along came World War Two. Convinced that the war was going
to be a short one, McBoyle paid to keep the mine pumped out and free of
flooding. Unfortunately, the war dragged out far longer than he anticipated and the mine's treasury was summarily pumped dry, as well. To com-
pound matters, McBoyle had undergone a series of personal devastations,
and suffered a series of strokes during the war and subsequently died in
late-1949.

Following McBoyle's death, the mine went to his wife, by default,
and her boyfriend tried to run the mine. They had no clue what they were
doing, however, and the already depleted treasury dried up altogether. "It
turned into an ugly situation," says Witte. "They didn't have anything

under control and things did not go very well. The cost of production went through the roof and, because they were so undercapitalized, they couldn't replace a lot of the aging equipment. Furthermore, they didn't have a lot of seasoned miners – a lot of the people who had worked in the mine went off to World War Two and came back to get college educations and better paying jobs elsewhere. As a result, a lot of new miners had to be trained on the job and it just didn't go very well."

In 1939, a man named Jack Clark was hired as a safety engineer at the Idaho-Maryland Mine. He became the mine superintendent in 1947 and stayed until it closed in 1956. "He's alive and well and is writing a book on the Idaho-Maryland," says Witte. "Jack has dedicated a good part of his retired life to researching the Idaho-Maryland and he has been unbelievably helpful to us. He has been an invaluable resource of information and he's a super nice guy."

Interviewed by The San Francisco Chronicle in June 2003, the then-82-year-old Clark – who reckons he has walked every foot of the Idaho - Maryland's 71 miles of subterranean tunnels – declared: "The gold's still there – you just have to know where to look." Clark believes that, once the mine is restored, it could produce at least 110,000 ounces of gold annually – worth more than US$40 million at current gold prices.

Since 1956, however, it has remained unmined. "At that time," says Witte, "the entire property went into bankruptcy and they had an auction. A businessman in Grass Valley named William Ghidotti acquired all of the tremendous surface position, all the facilities and all of the mineral rights. Ghidotti didn't really know what to do with the mine, so he sold off all the hardware and the buildings – everything. The only things remaining on surface are the two silos at the Brunswick shaft, the shaft that goes down to 3,280 feet.

"Ghidotti and his wife Marian didn't have any children," Witte continues, "but they were very wealthy and great philanthropists. So they set up a series of trusts for educational scholarships and decided they were going to have three people whom they trusted administer these funds after their deaths. One of them was their chartered public accountant, William Toms, who is the lead person in charge of the trusts, plus two lady friends (one was their land title agent) who played bridge with the Ghidottis: Mary Bouma and Erica Erickson. The Ghidottis really believed in these three people, so they gave the Idaho-Maryland Mine to them in payment for looking after these trusts when they passed away. They formed the BET Group, using the initials of their last names, and they own the Idaho-Maryland Mine today."

The problem was, the BET Group didn't exactly know what to do with the mine, either. Then, in the mid-1970s a geologist named Ross Guenther, who was working for a large mining company, was given the job of identifying potential gold properties in California and Nevada. "Ross's first course of action was to go to all the government literature and start looking around," says Witte, referring to the man who is now Emgold's project manager and director. "He kept running into a lot of information about the Empire Mine, but every once in awhile there would be something about the Idaho-Maryland Mine. Inevitably, he started thinking, 'Wow, that was a huge gold producer – what happened to it?'

"Eventually Ross Guenther left the company he was working for but kept bumping into little bits and pieces about the Idaho-Maryland Mine," Witte continues. "Unfortunately, it was never anything very substantial. Now, Ross is very entrepreneurial and he got involved with real estate, as well as a lot of other mining operations. So one day he is at the title company office in Grass Valley and meets this woman who is working there. He tells her he is a geologist and she says, 'Oh, you might be interested in a bunch of stuff I've got in my basement about a mine called the Idaho-Maryland.' Ross asked how much information was stored there. She said, 'It fills up my entire basement.' Naturally, after all this time, Ross thought, 'Yeah, right.' But he went over to her house and down into her basement and there it all was. It was Erica Erickson's basement and there were 11 tonnes of historic information stored there. It was catalogued, everything was in binders and drawers – he couldn't believe it. He was just amazed at the amount of information that was in there. The log books that reference all of this data take up dozens of shelves by themselves."

It was the mid-1980s and Guenther found a San Francisco investment group looking for a property to develop. He duly brought them the Idaho-Maryland project and spent a fair amount of time negotiating with the BET Group and the San Francisco company, which had optioned the property but didn't do anything with it. Guenther eventually became frustrated by the whole affair, and it was during this period that he met a man named Bob Crompton, who had a VSE-listed shell company. Guenther renegotiated the terms and conditions with the BET Group yet again and reacquired the rights to the Idaho-Maryland Mine in1988. By this point, of course, the mine's 71 miles of underground workings were flooded.

Crompton, therefore, came up with the somewhat novel idea of sampling the water to determine whether or not it was drinkable. Appreciating that the water would have to be pumped out one way or another to get to the underground workings, Guenther agreed. They discovered that the water was not only fit for human consumption, it was of an extraordinary quality. A feasibility study was undertaken with the idea of putting in a water-bottling plant. "It was a good idea," says Witte. "By bottling the water and selling it, they would have been able to pay for underground exploration. The only problem was, at that time, there wasn't a great deal of demand for bottled water. He was a little bit ahead of his time – five or six years later, California was in really bad shape for water."

In the midst of it all, Frank Lang, a Vancouver-based resource industry veteran with a long history of mine-finding (including the 1982 Hemlo discovery, which produces 500,000 ounces of gold annually), was sitting on the board of the company that had acquired the Idaho-Maryland Mine. "Ultimately, the water-bottling scheme wasn't going to work," says Witte, "because to do any serious mining, they would have had to pump out a lot of water. Besides, in order to bottle it, they would have had plastic or glass bottles all over the place and ended up with a real storage problem. At that point, Frank Lang said, 'Okay, I'm interested in further development of the Idaho-Maryland.' So, yet again, Ross Guenther renegotiated the terms and conditions with the BET Group. Frank had a group of companies that he amalgamated and formed Emperor Gold, which acquired the Idaho-Maryland Mine. From 1993 to 1996, things were really going gangbusters – the company spent about $7 million on the property and acquired a use permit to de-water the mine and do underground exploration work with the idea of raising more capital and hopefully putting it into production by 1997 or '98."

During this period, Bill Witte himself got involved, becoming a shareholder in 1993 "because I believed in what Ross had put together and I believed in Frank – plus, it was just a really great story. So I was continually asking them questions and I kept sort of pestering them throughout this whole time." Emperor Gold, meanwhile, changed its name to Emgold after finding out that Robert Friedland (of Voisey's Bay fame) already had a company of that name. The company's new name, however, wouldn't bring them any luck when fate struck hard.

"Emgold had arranged a very large financing of roughly $42 million," says Witte. "Two weeks before the closing, Bre-X hit, the price of gold tanked and all the investors just ran for the hills. The company thought it was going to have all this money and they had been gearing up to commence a series of operations. They had received the permit to do all the de-watering and exploration, and all of a sudden – poof! – the money just disappeared. So between 1997 and 1999, it became a matter of trying to hang onto the property because it was next to impossible to raise money."

Almost inevitably, the company went into default with the BET Group and effectively lost the property. "The only thing we had left was the permit," says Witte. "It was at that point in 1999 that Frank Lang, Emgold's chairman and director, asked me to join the board of the company. Then, with Ross Guenther, we spent the next year-and-a-half renegotiating the terms of the lease-option agreement. In 2002, we finally consummated the deal and we actually got the property for half the amount we had previously negotiated. In addition to that, we also got a much larger land position."

Reinvigorated, the first thing Emgold did was take a fresh look at the Idaho-Maryland project. "We took all of this information that was uncovered and put it into a Vulcan mine model (computer program) and produced a cross-section identifying rectangular slabs that are all almost vertical," says Witte. "When the mine shut down, there were 55 production targets that had been identified. Out of that 55, about 30 of them have a grade of greater than half-an-ounce per tonne. AMEC completed a 43-101 Technical Report and went through the data and came up with a mineral resource summary that we updated in April 2003. This report consists of measured and indicated mineral reserves of 1,666,000 tonnes grading 0.28 ounces gold per tonne, containing 472,000 ounces of gold; and inferred mineral reserves of 2,477,000 tonnes of 0.38 ounces gold per tonne, containing 934,000 ounces of gold.

The company next came up with a general development plan and took it on the road, attending conferences and conventions and raising funds.

The result was a multiple-stage plan. "First of all," says Witte, "we're doing surface drilling, looking at targets in an area that really hasn't been explored since 1893. Last summer we made a major discovery of a new gold zone that is an extension of a 1 million-ounce stope. We've had an intercept of about 10.1 feet grading about 0.86 ounces per tonne, and there are parts of that where we have 2.2 ounces per tonne, so there is definitely something very significant there.

"At that point, we had to do another financing," he continues, "and we now have $7.5 million in the bank and are drilling in new areas. The drill program is all from surface and is designed to test and develop our knowledge of the structure. Eventually, once we get our permit, we can put in a decline and do underground exploration, but most of the structures are dipping very steeply. Due to the geometry when we're drilling from surface, we can only clip bits and pieces. If we were drilling underground, on the other hand, we would have huge targets. So right now, we're drilling for structure. Once we get underground, we'll drill for grade."

To that end, Emgold had to apply for a permit from the City of Grass Valley to drill from four distinct sites – right inside the city itself. "It's not something you see everyday," Witte says, "but because we have just these four sites, we can't drill any old place. Consequently, we're drilling in an industrial park where there are a lot of buildings, parking lots and infrastructure. Obviously, most businesses wouldn't be thrilled about us setting up drill rigs in the reception areas of their offices, so we've had to use different means. The drill rig for the first site, for example, is in the backyard of a trailer-manufacturing plant. The dip is minus 25 degrees, which is extremely shallow. Because we're dealing with deeply dipping structures and we want to hit these things to find the true width, we've had to do some major gymnastics and geometry exercises in order to hit some of these targets. It is a challenge we're facing."

In 2002, the board appointed Bill Witte president and "it was just pure dumb luck," he says, "that the price of gold started going back up and we started frenetically raising money. We've raised $12 million over the past year-and-a-half, we're doing exploration on a couple of properties in B.C. that we acquired during the negotiations for the Idaho-Maryland Mine, plus we've got ongoing exploration happening, as well as the ceramics plant. We're in pretty good shape these days."

In addition to the Idaho-Maryland project, which the company plans to carry through to the production stage, Emgold Mining Corporation has three prospective gold properties in British Columbia. The Rozan Gold Property, located north of Ymir in southwestern B.C., lies adjacent to Sultan Minerals' Kena Property. The company is presently developing plans for further exploration and the initiation of a diamond drilling program. The Stewart and Jazz Properties, likewise located north of Ymir, are gold prospects that have yielded high gold geochemical results.

Besides the Idaho-Maryland Mine, however, Emgold's primary focus at the moment is the aforementioned ceramics business. Through the company's wholly-owned subsidiary, Golden Bear Ceramics Company, Emgold has an exclusive worldwide license agreement with Ceramext LLC to develop and use the Ceramext™ Process to convert mine tailings, fly ash and other waste materials into high-strength, low-porosity, industrial ceramics, including floor and roof tiles, brick and construction materials, as well as other industrial and commercial products. The patented, energy-efficient technology utilizes a vacuum hot-extrusion process to convert a wide variety of raw materials – including coal, lignite and biomass fly ash, slag, clays, volcanic ash and mine tailings – into super-strength ceramic building materials.

"The idea for the ceramic plant was the result of something that occurred while we were in the process of negotiating for the Idaho-Maryland Mine," says Witte. "Ross Guenther and his brother, who is a Ph.D. civil engineer in Washington, were at a family get-together and they were talking about some of the environmental problems that were being experienced in the United States. Ross, being a geologist, got to talking about rock, how it is made and how – if you could take some of this waste and apply geological principles – you might be able to produce something. That is where the ceramics technology was born.

"It is an amazing technology," Witte continues, enthusiastically. "It is elegant, simple and patented. Essentially, what happened was that Ross and his brother were discussing the problem of ash being produced by coal-fired power plants and how it was filling up landfill sites all over the U.S. They started doing some test work and discovered that this material is three-to-five times stronger than any other ceramic material on the market. Ross mentioned this to me and I said, 'Have you tried it on any of the

Idaho-Maryland tailings?' Though most of the tailings were sold for backfill because, metallugically, Idaho-Maryland tailings are very clean – effectively, you've only got gold and quartz – there are some tailings left on one of the parcels of land we acquired, probably a few thousand tonnes scattered over this one particular property. Ross went ahead and tried it out and, sure enough, it worked."

Emgold acquired the rights to the technology and Guenther hired a team of Ph.D. ceramics engineers to continue work on the process. "After these guys had signed the secrecy agreements and were working on the technology, they started banging their heads," Witte says with a deep-hearted laugh. "They kept saying, 'This is so simple – why didn't we think of this? Why did it take a geologist to come up with something so simple yet elegant? And, besides, what does he know about ceramics?'"

Emgold is currently setting up a demonstration plant and will be doing a feasibility study for use of the technology on the Idaho-Maryland Mine. "The feasibility study will evaluate putting in a decline to get underground to do exploration and production," Witte says, "and we're going to take all of the waste rock, crush, grind it and run it through the ceramics plants." Though the actual extrusion machine has been patented, the engineering team is continually developing patents as they go along. "Some of the components being used in the extruder weren't even available a few years ago," says Witte. "It is a high-temperature technology and we're using components that have been used in the space-shuttle program. We've hired extruder and heat-transfer engineers, and we're putting it all together and hope to have it up and running within the year."

They couldn't have come up with a better technology at a better time. "Right now in California, floor and roofing tiles are selling for approximately $400 to $500 a tonne," says Witte. "It will cost us roughly between $150 and $165 a tonne to produce our tile. That is a profit of about $300 per tonne from the waste. With gold at $400 an ounce, that's the equivalent of three-quarters of an ounce of gold. Our mindset on this thing is to eat the whole buffalo so that we don't have any waste products whatsoever."

In addition to the ceramics' industrial and commercial application, Emgold is confident that, given the right kind of tailings (that is to say, those containing no toxic or harmful chemicals), the process can be suitably modified to produce such everyday household and service-industry items as kitchen countertops, food trays, dishes and coffee cups. "We have a grand-opening ceremony scheduled," says Witte, "and California Governor Arnold Schwarzenegger wants to be there. There will be lots of publicity and community awareness involved and the community of Grass Valley is very supportive of the venture. To the best of my knowledge we're the first ones to do anything like this."

ENTRÉE GOLD INCORPORATED

Greg Crowe spends a lot of time in his comfortable, downtown Vancouver office even though he would rather be working in the unforgiving heat beneath the scorching Gobi desert sun. It's hard to imagine that he would prefer the vast, sparsely-populated plains to the company's head office. But by his own admission, instead of discussing his company dressed in a pressed white shirt, conservative tie and dark, pinstriped suit, Crowe prefers to be in functional fatigues out in the field. While there is obvious pride and infectious excitement as Crowe recounts his company's roots, genesis and prospects for growth, one still gets the impression that he would be even happier scrutinizing geological data and soil samples, looking for mineral deposits.

An impressive combination of geological know-how, passion for discovery and development and an astute business sense enables Greg Crowe to position Entrée Gold as one of the better-looking companies in the sector, and one that bears watching.

"What drives me?" he asks, pausing briefly to consider the question. "I just like the business. I get enjoyment out of watching things develop. I love mining, I love exploration and I miss getting out in the field as much as I'd like to. But that could be a function of the fact that things are working out well for Entrée."

As Crowe speaks, it is easy to picture him in the field; his sharp eyes and geological sixth sense somehow picking up the promise and presence of serious gold and copper deposits where others may see only a vast expanse of empty ground. At 50 years of age, Crowe is intense and focussed. He has an air of keen efficiency, tempered with a dedicated thoroughness that leaves little room for gaps or unanswered questions. At the same time, he's frank about what is not known, and what will require further study, investigation, or exploration to answer definitively.

Things are indeed working out thousands of kilometres from the office tower in which Crowe has landed in downtown Vancouver. The Entrée Gold offices on West Georgia Street are low-key, unprepossessing; quiet and efficient. Most days, only Crowe and perhaps three other people are in the office. It's a tight, capable team of professionals. Despite their modesty, the firm's offices are a vital part of the company's business: exploration in Mongolia of some very promising properties. Entrée Gold's three properties in southern Mongolia's Gobi Desert (Umnogibi Aimag province, to be precise) – just north of the Chinese border – are grouped together under the name 'Lookout Hill,' translated from the Mongolian name Shivee Tolgoi.

They are all mineral exploration concessions, purchased from a private Mongolian mining company. The three contiguous concessions, which host several exploration targets, cover 179,590 hectares in southern Mongolia's gold-copper porphyry belt and completely surround the approximately 8,500 hectare Turquoise Hill property being developed by Ivanhoe Mines Ltd. The areas of interest at Lookout Hill include the Copper Flats copper-gold target, the Zone III epithermal gold prospect, the X-Grid gold prospect and the Bayan Ovoo copper-oxide target. Copper Flats is immediately north of and along strike from the high-grade copper-gold Hugo Dummett Zone of Ivanhoe Mines. Zone III is 10 kilometres west-northwest of the Copper Flats area. X-Grid is two-and-a-half kilometres east of Turquoise Hill. Bayan Ovoo is located in the far western extremities of the property, 60 kilometres west of Copper Flats. All this is about 540 kilometres south of Mongolia's capital Ulaan Baatar.

Crowe, with two degrees in geology, explains why Lookout Hill is one of the world's most strategically-located exploration properties: "Ivanhoe Mines is developing what is thought to be one of the world's largest and richest porphyry copper-gold systems. They have been working on it now for over four years. Ivanhoe's Turquoise Hill concession is relatively small — approximately 8,500 hectares, or 10.5-by-8 kilometres in area — and hosts a northerly trending mineralized system that, to date, has been traced for over five-and-a-half kilometres in length. This system remains open along strike. Ivanhoe has outlined a resource that is estimated to contain in excess of 2.6 billion metric tonnes, which equates to over 14 million ounces of gold and 42 billion pounds of copper. The highest grade deposit on the property is called the Hugo Dummett Zone, located at the north end of that 5.5 kilometre long series of deposits. The zone's deposit hosts in excess of 1.4 billion metric tonnes, estimated to contain 6.4 million ounces of gold and 31 billion pounds of copper. Since this resource estimate, published in November 2003, Ivanhoe has done extensive drilling and is tracing the Hugo Dummett Zone further to the north, to the point where drilling is within 300 to 400 metres from our property. In addition, some of the richest gold and copper mineralization has been encountered in the northern portion of the Hugo Dummett Zone, adjacent to our Lookout Hill property."

Ivanhoe found one major deposit, but Crowe's instincts and geological expertise indicate there is potential for more. Following his instincts, as well as some encouraging testing and trenching results, Entrée secured a 100% royalty-free interest in all the land surrounding Ivanhoe's holdings, with all important indicators pointing to further findings of gold and copper in this particular piece of the Gobi Desert.

"Our property holdings amount to approximately 20 times the land package held by Ivanhoe Mines," Crowe says. "We acquired the property in the middle of 2002 and the work we've done was mostly completed in 2003. We've outlined several interesting areas of mineralization, including the Copper Flats zone, which is immediately north of the Ivanhoe system of mineralization. We've done extensive geological, geophysical, and geochemical work. The results strongly suggest a continuation of that system northwards onto our property, although we can't say for certain because there's no outcrop. It is a completely barren plain. Ivanhoe has had up to 22 drills on its property at any given time. What's really important about this property is that you're dealing with an extremely large regional system of mineralization, not one or two small deposits."

Entrée's work indicates that the region boasts a large, central copper-gold porphyry system with fractures running out from a central core. This is confirmed by tests performed, including geophysical and geochemical results. Although gold is what initially strikes investors'interest, the copper in Ivanhoe's deposit is economically more important. Copper has been trading at its highest in decades, for as much as $1.40 a pound. This is very different from just a few years ago, when copper prices dropped so low it was not economically feasible for even established major miners to pull it out of the ground.

"The new term for copper is 'red gold'," Crowe says. "Now I target only copper and/or gold mineral properties. Silver, platinum and zinc do not excite me. Gold performs well as a hedge against inflation, a haven in times of uncertainty and instability. They're complementary. They can balance each other, or they can work together."

Given its geographical proximity to China, Entrée's Lookout Hill property looks even more promising. "There's also the imminent demand for a lot more copper from China, as many of its sectors (such as housing and automotive) are growing exponentially," Crowe says.

Rebuilt from the ground up, Entrée Gold has come a long way in a very short time, and Crowe has been one of its chief architects. The company's predecessor was Timpete Mining, a junior mining outfit with properties in Central America. But as with many other junior mining companies, Timpete suffered in the downturn of the late 1990s. Some of its founders worked to resurrect the company in 2000 as a dot-com venture, renaming the company Entrée Resources. The dot-com crash meant trouble for Entrée Resources too. One of the key members of Entrée Resources' management team died early into the new century, and his heirs decided to sell the company.

At the same time, Ivanhoe Mines was developing its Mongolian property, having bought the Turquoise Hill asset from BHP, another major mining firm that wanted out. Ivanhoe kept a large block surrounding the area of drilling completed by BHP and then relinquished the rest of the property. The surrounding 179,590 hectares, which now comprises Entrée's Lookout Hill property, was subsequently picked up by a private Mongolian placer gold mining group – Mongol Gazar.

In March of 2002, the Mongolian owners of Lookout Hill were in search of a partner to help develop their property. They heard about the mining industry in Canada and attended the Prospectors and Developers' meeting held in Toronto in March. The Mongolians were introduced to a broker from Canaccord, Cary Pinkowski, who decided the property would be the perfect asset to put into a new company. Pinkowski consulted with another Canaccord broker, Keith Anderson Sr., and together they engaged a technical team and traveled to Mongolia to iron out the terms of a deal. Upon returning to Vancouver, Cary and his team said: "Now what do we do? We need a company." They found Entrée Resources as a possible shell for takeover and convinced Mark Bailey and Lindsay Bottomer to become directors. Crowe was brought on board in July 2002 to lead the charge.

"I've been in the business for 25 years," Crowe says. "I slowly worked myself up through a series of major companies and started to get involved with junior resource companies approximately 15 years ago. I was asked to join the Board of Directors for a couple of juniors and I enjoyed that side of things. For the last five or six years I've been accepting more senior roles, came on to be president of Entrée Gold."

Entrée also enlisted the assistance of Mark Bailey, 54, who like Crowe is a geologist with more than 26 years of experience. Mr. Bailey has been the president and CEO of TSX and AMEX-listed Minefinders Corporation Ltd. since 1995, and is highly respected for both his technical competence and aptitude in maximizing the effectiveness of exploration programs and budgets. While with Minefinders, he has been responsible for the discovery and ongoing development of resources now totaling more than 3 million ounces of gold and 165 million ounces of silver.

Director Lindsay Bottomer, also 54, has been a geologist for more than 30 years. For the past 15 years, he's been based in Vancouver working with Prime Equities (Pezim Group), Echo Bay Mines, and as a consultant to a number of junior resource companies. He is currently president of Southern Rio Resources and a director of Pacific North West Capital Corp. He was president of the BC & Yukon Chamber of Mines from 1998 to 2000.

James Harris is a corporate, securities, and business lawyer with over 20 years of experience in British Columbia and internationally. He has extensive experience with acquisition and disposition of assets; corporate structuring and restructuring; regulatory requirements and corporate filing; and corporate governance. Harris was also a founding member of the

Legal Advisory Committee of the former Vancouver Stock Exchange. Apart from his legal education, Mr. Harris has also completed a graduate course in business at the London School of Economics.

"The directors felt they still needed somebody to run the show," Crowe recalls, "And that's when I got the phone call – in late June of 2002. Within 10 days of coming on board, I flew over to Mongolia. I was in a strange country with these interesting people and had to negotiate and finalize the terms of an agreement. However, I never liked the terms: the Mongolian group retained a large interest in the property; Entrée could only earn a 60 percent interest. We had to spend $12.5 million in five years in exploration, issue up to four million shares of the company to the Mongolians, and, on top of that, there was an onerous net smelter return."

The net smelter return means that when a company puts an asset into production – starting with pulling ore out of the ground and refining it – every piece will have a gross metal value based on the trading prices of the metals of the day, irrespective of the economic viability of taking the ore out of the ground. The company has to pay the vendor a portion of the net smelter value (i.e. two, four or 10 percent) according to the agreement terms.

"It's not a good way to go," Crowe says. "A lot of companies try to get away from issuing smelter royalties by going to net profits royalties, which is a percentage of the profits after all the costs. I would say the net smelter royalty that we had was an unreasonable one, but what signing the original agreement did allow us to do was get a foothold on the property."

Nonetheless, Crowe and Entrée started exploration of their property in 2002, albeit brief. Southern Mongolia's hostile weather conditions means bitter, bone-chilling winters with temperatures dropping as low as minus 50 degrees Celsius, which truncates effective exploration. Following a break lasting until March of 2003, exploration resumed.

"In late 2003, we took another break with our exploration season," says Crowe. "We worked up until the end of November. But as temperatures went down to minus 30-50 degrees, we decided to pull out. We went back again in the middle of March to start our 2004 exploration season. Ivanhoe is able to work year round as they are in the advanced drilling stages of their exploration. Since Entrée's work to early-2004 has been strictly surface exploration, it is difficult to conduct these types of surface surveys in severe sub-freezing temperatures. Some of the survey equipment just doesn't work at minus 40 degrees."

Even with the advance stage of the Turquoise Hill project, Ivanhoe's share price stagnated between $3.00 and $3.30 per share until August of 2003. "Entrée's share price had reached a high of 70 cents to 75 cents in early 2003, and then we settled back at 25 cents," Crowe says. "Ivanhoe's stock price started to rise in August 2003, coinciding with an upturn in both gold and copper prices. Entrée's shares started to rise at about the same time.

"Fortunately, we had continued to communicate with the Mongolian owners of our Lookout Hill property. They had run into problems on their placer operations and, as a consequence, they needed money very quickly. In August we decided the time was right to try to renegotiate our deal. We almost came to an agreement, but then the Mongolian owner backed off. I returned to Vancouver and within a few weeks, I received a call saying the Mongolians were finally ready to do the new deal. I flew back to Mongolia, negotiated for a few more days and, with the aid of Cary Pinkowski, who helped convince the Mongolians of the merits of being involved in a publicly-trading junior resource company, we finally came to an agreement whereby Entrée would have a 100 percent royalty-free interest in Shivee Tolgoi and in a second property in the Kharmagtai area 120 kilometres to the north. The deal cost Entrée US$5.5 million and five million shares of the company, but it was worth it to obtain the 100% interest, royalty free. This became particularly apparent when, a few weeks later, Ivanhoe paid BHP US$37 million for a two percent net smelter royalty on their Turquoise Hill property."

Crowe continued saying, "In the meantime, both Ivanhoe shares and Entrée shares continued to increase in value. Ivanhoe was aggressively drilling and outlining new copper-and-gold rich mineralization in the Hugo Dummett Zone, close to their boundary with Entrée. With a 100 percent royalty-free ownership in the property, we were successful in raising CAD$14 million with the aid of Canaccord Capital and Salmon Partners. This financing was completed within two days in early October 2003 and was oversubscribed."

Discussing operations in Mongolia, Crowe says the exploration team has only one full-time employee, exploration manager Robert Cann.

"Everyone else is really on a part-time, long-term contract basis. We have an office there; and a full-time camp that breaks for three months. We have a local Mongolian manager who looks after everything and lives there full-time, year-round. He used to live just to the north of us in one of the round tents called 'gers.' He's an excellent manager, he commands the respect of all the Mongolians and he's a real asset. We also have five consulting North American expat geologists on site. On top of that, we have a full geophysical crew, which consists of four North Americans. In addition we employ up to 20 to 25 Mongolians who offer assistance as managers. They help with the geophysical programs, trenching, sampling and shipments, amongst other functions."

The people in Mongolia get along better with Crowe and his team than they might have with other miners from North America. Crowe's extensive experience in places as diverse as Asia, South Africa, Central and South America makes him more aware and sensitive to cultural differences and able to honour them. But his background in Canada enables him to see similarities where others might have missed them.

"We make sure that the people we hire and work with are respectful of other cultures. Language is probably the biggest difficulty. The Mongolians are used to foreigners, especially with the Russians having been in the country for several decades until 1991, and previous to that the Chinese.

"Because of the Russians, they're comfortable with Caucasian-looking people, and they're very friendly. But the culture, if you think back, has a lot of similarities to the northern part of our country. The Inuit probably came from Mongolia. We play up these similarities a lot and the Mongolians like it. They live in round tents called gers, Inuit live in igloos, they're of similar stature, they're nomadic."

There's also a steely core of resolve and a long, proud history. However, most Westerners believe in the stereotype of the 13th-century Mongols as barbaric plunderers content only to destroy, pillage and plunder. But the Mongols got this negative reputation because they were good at what they did – better than their foes the Persians, the Chinese and the Russians. The nasty reputation comes from Persian, Chinese, Russian and other accounts of the speed and ruthlessness with which the Mongols carved out the largest contiguous land empire in world history. It persists to this day, shaping Asian and Western images of the Mongols and of their earliest leader, Chinggis Khan. Equal to their effectiveness as empire-builders and conquerors, however, are the Mongols'contributions to 13th and 14th-century civilization. The Mongol Khans – Chinggis and his son and successor, Khubilai – also funded advances in medicine and astronomy. Their construction projects (extension of the Grand Canal toward Beijing, the building of a capital city that became present-day Beijing) and of summer palaces in Shangdu ('Xanadu') and Takht-i-Sulaiman, and the construction of roads and postal stations throughout their lands, promoted developments in science and engineering.

Internationally, the Mongol empire linked Europe and Asia and began an era of frequent and extended contacts between East and West. Once the Mongols had achieved relative stability and order in their newly acquired domains, they neither discouraged nor impeded relations with foreigners. Though they never abandoned their claims of universal rule, they were hospitable to foreign travelers, even those whose monarchs had not submitted to them. The Mongols encouraged travel in the part of Asia under their rule, permitting European merchants, craftsmen, and envoys to journey as far as China for the first time. Asian goods reached Europe along the caravan trails (earlier called the 'Silk Roads'), and the ensuing European demand for these products eventually inspired the search for a sea route to Asia. It could be argued that Mongol invasions indirectly led to European exploration eastward in the 15th century. The Mongols' openness toward foreigners and their influence meant a profound and lasting interchange of products, people, technology, and science throughout the Mongol domains.

In China, the Mongols increased the amount of paper money in circulation and guaranteed the value of that paper money by backing it with precious metals. Under Mongol rule, merchants had a higher status than they had in traditional China, and paper money made trade much easier than the goods-barter system that so many traders were still relying on at the time. The Mongols established merchant associations called Ortogh to promote caravan trade over long distances; merchants could pool their resources to support a single caravan. If a caravan failed, no single merchant would be put out of business. Losses, risk and profits would be shared, and the Mongols provided loans at reasonable interest rates to

Ortogh members.

More recently, Mongolia went through a severely trying period with the collapse of the Soviet Union and the rapid departure of the Russians, a presence that had been a fact of life in Mongolia for decades. In early 1991, within 48 hours, the country's economy went from being fairly robust – based on the ruble with support of the Russian military and business enterprise – to virtually bankrupt. It took six or seven years to turn the country around. Now there's a well-codified and enforced legal system. Entrée's lawyers in Mongolia have taken cases to trial for some of their other clients and have been satisfied with the legal rulings.

Most importantly, perhaps, there's a new mining code.

"They adopted components from the mining codes of Canada, Britain, Australia and the United States," Crowe says. "Now they have one of the most progressive mining codes in the world. Under these terms, we have 100 percent interest in our property. We have to pay fees to maintain our exploration licenses; they amount to about US$150,000 a year. These payments will escalate over the next four years. We have seven years to explore, after which we have to reduce or convert to a mining license. After that, we must enter negotiations with the federal government to secure forward-going taxation rates through a stability agreement. Ivanhoe is currently in negotiations to enter a stability agreement because they've reached their seven-year point. We're in year three, going on four. We've got some time."

But even with these improvements and more capital for continuing exploration, there is another factor affecting the value and the share price of both Entrée Gold and Ivanhoe Mines: The two companies' close proximity of properties.

On the one hand, all the geological facts regarding the Ivanhoe operations in combination with the exploration work completed by Entrée, strongly suggest the potential for the continuation of Ivanhoe's copper and gold mineralized system onto Entrée's Lookout Hill property. Every positive development for Ivanhoe provides a boost for Entrée.

But a downturn in Ivanhoe's fortunes or its operations can have an adverse effect on Entrée's. One case in point is the market reaction to the Ivanhoe scoping study in January 2004. The frustration by investors when the study was not produced as quickly as hoped, and then a negative reaction to the study results once released.

"If you superimpose Ivanhoe's share price chart on top of ours, what you get is that they track almost identically," Crowe says. "They were trading at $3.50, up to a high in early November of $15.50, while we came up to a high of just over $3.00. In November, Ivanhoe started getting some bad press; mostly from U.S. based analysts who opined that it was overvalued. Their stock price came off, and so did ours. Until we start developing our own assets, we are tied to the fortunes of Ivanhoe. Both ourselves and our investors came to that realization. In early December 2003, Ivanhoe was supposed to come up with a scoping study. In January, they came out with the results – which the market didn't like at all – and that took us down to around a dollar. We've since rallied up to $1.25, $1.50 – in that range. They went to a low of $6.00. They've since rallied up to the $7.50, $8.00 range."

Ivanhoe's development in Mongolia is important to Entrée in another, more concrete, way. Ivanhoe's explorations and development is a couple of stages further ahead of Entrée's. But Ivanhoe has also had to start further back in the understanding of the mineralized system and has a long way to go to get its assets to the point where they're profitably productive. "The amount of money they're going to have to put in capital is probably close to a billion dollars to bring that mine in: establishing a mill, processing facilities, infrastructure, roads – all that is capital-intensive," Crowe says. "If we were to try to develop a similar asset on our own, we would definitely need assistance. We have the advantage in that where we have some potential gold assets, and mining gold is somewhat less capital-intensive than copper. As for transportation: we don't have to ship a concentrate for gold. We can process and refine gold right on the site and get 99.999 percent gold ore and then fly it out, so we have that advantage."

As with almost every other company in the mining sector concentrating on gold, Crowe and his colleagues might be expected to have seen their company's fortunes or reputation dented by another outfit, the notorious Bre-X, which saw its claims of a vast motherlode of gold in Borneo proven false in 1997. But Crowe says most intelligent investors can tell the difference between the work Entrée is doing – and the results of its explorations so far – from the patent fraud at the heart of Bre-X.

"A lot of investors are followers. No matter what you do, you're not going to educate the followers; they're just going to follow. The other ones already know. They got out of the sector at the end of the '90s, because they knew the end was nigh. Not only was there Bre-X, there was also a collapse of base metal prices which came quickly on the heels of the collapse of the Southeast Asian currencies. The smart investors have come back and we now have one of the biggest metal booms. People are leery about the U.S. currency being the backing of the world economy. It's an important component, but it's not the only one. You need something to back a currency. If it's not going to be gold, what's it going to be? Oil? I wouldn't want it to be oil. Platinum? Too hard to come by. Gold is precious enough that it can command a high price, it's relatively stable and a good hedge against turmoil and at the same time it's plentiful enough that you can explore and find it."

Intelligent investors can tell the difference between Bre-X and legitimate, responsible operators. Gold also has a 'glamour factor' that draws people and sharpens their interest. Crowe understands that. "When gold is trading at $250 an ounce and copper is trading at 60 cents a pound, there is no glamour. Right now it's the other way around. Gold's been up over $400 an ounce – up as high as $450 – the glamour is back on gold. With copper trading as high as $1.40 some days, the glamour is back on copper."

But for a company like Entrée, being able to start producing minerals means another choice: whether to bring in a partner, such as a large major, to help develop the property. Right now, there's nothing like that on the horizon, but it's a possibility. Until many drill holes confirm the potential size and extent of the mineral deposits under the surface, the best course of action can't be known.

"In addition to the possible extension to the Hugo Dummett copper-gold system onto our Lookout Hill property, we also have potential stand-alone gold projects," Crowe says. "We're a little early to be considered a takeover target. They may have been able to take us over, and maybe they would have been wise to do so, when we were trading under 25 cents a share and we had a market capitalization of around $6 million. However, at the peak, we had a market capitalization of over $150 million and we were just too expensive a target for a group like Ivanhoe to take over at the time. Now we've come off, we've got our capitalization at around $50 to $60 million. We know sharks are out there and we're the guppies and we know they've noticed us. But they haven't bitten us yet."

The other option, of course, is a joint venture with a medium to large company. But at this time there are no plans for taking that step, although Crowe acknowledges that the question arises frequently. This requires addressing numerous unknowns that only drilling can help answer: the depth of the deposit, the grade of the minerals and other aspects. That process has now begun.

In the late spring of 2004, shortly after Entrée's exploration season resumed, its drilling equipment finally arrived. Midway through May, six holes were drilled. It's a long way from production, but it's one more step toward vindicating Greg Crowe's instincts about the Lookout Hill holdings and the copper and gold potential they represent.

"We have strong beliefs that all will be in our favour," Crowe says. "Ivanhoe has developed an economic series of bodies along a five-kilometre strike length, which is now only 300 to 400 metres from our property boundary. It's not much of a step. Could a company of our size think about putting a potential deposit of this magnitude into production? Realistically, not without help. Would we carry on and do it ourselves? It would have to be a very modified version of our company if we did. We could consider selling out to another group. As a director of the company, it would irresponsible of me and all of the directors not to consider reasonable offers. At that time we may have to approach our shareholders regarding voting on certain issues. But that's down the road and we don't know what's going to happen."

ETRUSCAN RESOURCES INCORPORATED

If any mining company deserves special notice for taking its social responsibility to heart, Etruscan would have to be at the top of that list.

Led by president & CEO Gerry McConnell, the Etruscan team has enthusiastically supported his vision and ongoing efforts to make Etruscan the standard for corporate responsibility in Niger, West Africa.

To that end, this diversified junior mining company based out of Windsor, Nova Scotia, has remained true to its social mandate. Ongoing projects include construction of a health clinic in Toure, named after former Nova Scotia premier John Savage and his wife Margaret, schools erected in Bossey Bangou and Koma Bangou, agricultural initiatives already in place and the drilling of literally countless water wells. Whether Etruscan is working on its own or in partnership with dedicated groups in Nova Scotia who share McConnell's passion, it's certain there's no end in sight for their deeds because there's no end in sight for the needs.

Perhaps Etruscan's vice president Anthony Hayes best encapsulates Etruscan's view when he says quite simply: "We consider ourselves guests in these countries."

These are the kind of guests who don't show up empty-handed or take their invitation for granted.

"Our corporate philosophy when we're working in these countries is that the resources do not belong to Etruscan. The resources belong to the people, we always have to put that front and centre in the way that we conduct ourselves in the country."

Hayes is sharing these insights in March 2004, as he takes a break from activities at the annual Prospectors & Developers Association convention in downtown Toronto. Joining him to discuss Etruscan's story is geologist Donald Burton, vice president exploration for Etruscan. Between the pair of them and their individual areas of expertise, they can relate Etruscan's journey and subsequent successes from both the financial and geological aspects as well as the company's commitment to the Nigeriens in whose country they are operating.

It is interesting to note that this natural resource company got its name from the Etruscan people, a mysterious civilization that settled in the Italian peninsula around 850 BC. They were a sophisticated people whose goldsmiths were known far and wide as artisans of great genius. So adept were they with this wondrous metal that 3,000 years later, the Illustrated Dictionary of Jewelry featured a full page on Etruscan gold jewelry.

As a broad overview, Etruscan is known as a company with a tremendous asset base in both gold and diamonds and a proven track record for knowing how to work in Africa. To that end, work is being done at a record rate. With respect to Etruscan's three main gold deposits, the short version reveals that Samira Hill should be pouring gold by mid-September 2004 and by 2005 is expected to be in full production at about 100,000 ounces. By 2006, Youga is projected to be producing gold to the tune of an additional 100,000 ounces and by 2007, Agbaou could also be up and running.

"When all three mines are running, they'll be collectively producing a little over 300,000 ounces of gold per year," says Hayes.

"So rather than running around trying to find a five-million-ounce gold deposit, we've done the same thing but we're using three smaller deposits."

If all that weren't enough, Etruscan also enjoys outstanding exploration and development opportunities in the gold sector with a portfolio of strategically located gold properties in Mali, the third largest gold producer in Africa and home to some of the lowest cost gold mines worldwide. Etruscan is well-positioned with two properties in South Mali (Finkolo and Nianembele) and three properties in the Mali West Shear Zone (Djelimangara, Kolomba, Sanoukou). Finkolo is located 15 kilometres from the five-million-ounce Syama gold deposit and Djelimangara is contiguous with AngloGold's Sadiola Hill property that hosts 10 million ounces.

But gold isn't the only coin in Etruscan's purse. With 35 diamond properties in the Ventersdorp, Mooi River and Lichtenburg districts of South Africa, the Tirisano diamond mine in production since 2002, one plant already built that will produce just under 30,000 carats and a second 50,000-carat plant expected to be running by the end of next year, the company's diamond side potential is huge.

Although Etruscan is currently receiving most of its notice for the gold prospects, it's the diamonds that could well end up being a dark horse for the company. Don Burton says it's simply a matter of doing the math.

"If we build five plants, each producing 50,000 carats, we'll be producing 250,000 carats per year which will start you on the way to being the second-largest diamond producer in South Africa, number one being de Beers.

"We can do it. If we're able to get US$50 million in capital we could build five plants next year. But it will happen in stages, it will be a growth process," Burton says.

That growth process had its earliest beginnings in the late 1980s when Etruscan shared an office and a management team with NovaGold, a company founded by McConnell. At that time, Burton was vice president of exploration for NovaGold.

As the two companies matured, it became apparent that Etruscan was focussing on Africa while NovaGold was seizing opportunities in North America. A formal split between the two companies occurred, and a core team including Burton, McConnell, Angus MacIsaac, and Glen Holmes remained with Etruscan.

"NovaGold now has its own separate management. Today it's a very successful explorer and gold developer, primarily in Alaska, the Yukon and B.C. Gerry remains a director in that company," explained Burton.

Initially excited about the Venezuelan gold rush occurring in the early-1990s, Etruscan decided to try and get in on that play and secure a land position in the desirable Kilometre 88 area. But according to Burton, timing is everything and they missed out. By the time they arrived, everything was all filled up.

"If you wanted a piece of land, you had to put a million dollars cash on the table and you'd get some tract of land in the jungle," said Burton.

Although disheartening at the time, that failure opened the door to success somewhere else – namely Africa.

"A contact from West Africa brought to our attention a project in Niger, which we didn't know anything about. He told us that the same geology everyone was going crazy about in Venezuela – called the Guyana shield – also existed in West Africa," said Burton.

The geology may have been similar, but the situation certainly wasn't. Whereas Venezuela was being overrun with mining companies, Niger was basically untouched.

"Nobody was working there," said Burton. "The government was just about to try to put a framework in place whereby foreign investors could come in and get permits."

Again, timing would prove to be everything but this time it would lie in Etruscan's favour.

"Etruscan made an application for the first gold permit in Niger and we successfully were chosen by the government to work on that permit. At that time, there was only one gold permit in the whole country and it was called Koma Bangou," said Burton.

It would take another year before the government had carved up the rest of the interesting geological areas into other permits, during which time Etruscan was busy working on the ground and identifying other potential areas of interest. When the government offered new areas for gold permits, Etruscan had selected an area called Samira as the important property to try and get. They partnered with the government on that permit.

Calling the property Samira Hill, because of a noticeable hill in the middle of the area, Etruscan got busy. A gold anomaly had been identified after regional surveys, but nobody knew how much was in store.

"We took this permit from its initial discovery starting in 1995, and worked for four years. In the end, we had identified that this deposit was in the order of two million ounces of gold," said Burton.

Extensive geological work demonstrated that the deposit was hosted in a unique rock package that the Etruscan team dubbed the Samira Horizon. And because they identified about 50 kilometres of this mineralized horizon, or gold belt, they proceeded to pick up more permits, including two in Niger and one in Burkina Faso.

"We knew we had at least two major deposits and, over the course of the four years, we identified five other deposits – just gold. Nothing else," said Burton.

After a drilling program on both Koma Bangou and Samira, they discovered the Koma Bangou gold resource was around 300,000 ounces, a respectable amount but not large enough to develop a commercial mine. It didn't help matters that the gold price at the time had plunged to $260 an ounce.

But in the meantime, Niger was attracting interest from major mining companies and Etruscan started getting some serious neighbours. Barrick set up shop right next door with a large permit, and Ashanti Goldfields, a large Ghana-based African gold mining company, held another large permit. Even Placer Dome got in on the action, by signing a major joint venture with Etruscan on the Samira property in 1998.

And because finances are now involved, this is where Hayes comes in.

"I was on the brokerage side, acting as underwriter for Etruscan and it was during that period that I raised more money so we didn't have to do a giveaway deal with Placer Dome – something juniors can get trapped into when they don't have sufficient funds," Hayes said.

The year was 1997 when both Hayes and Placer Dome joined forces with Etruscan, the Placer Dome joint venture being the first in Africa.

"Placer Dome spent about $14 million looking at this property," Burton says. "They came in because they saw the potential that Samira might have something in the order of five to 10 million ounces of gold."

Because of its size, Placer needed not only to see a lot of gold, but also wanted to see it in the oxide zone, near surface.

"They're not interested in going underground. They're looking for cheap, big surface mining operations and because we had 50 kilometres of this belt, they felt there was potential to find a big hit like that."

In the end, although Etruscan had delineated about two million ounces at Samira Hill, it was determined that a little over half would have to be extracted by underground mining. Both things considered, it didn't meet Placer's threshold and they bowed out in early 1999.

"So after spending $14 million, they gave us everything back and we had the benefit of all that work, which allowed us to immediately go into a feasibility study to take around to banks and see if we could raise money to build the mine," said Burton.

Etruscan determined that of the two million ounces of gold contained within the deposit, they would be able to extract around 700,000 ounces by open pit mining. After that, they'd be looking at hard rock and an underground mine would need to be put into operation.

"Placer Dome drilled the only deep holes on this deposit and they got very good results. They were getting 10 to 12 grams of gold over widths of 10 to 15 metres. It's good enough for an underground mine, but they weren't interested in that," said Burton, adding that there is currently only one underground mine in West Africa.

That mine, the Obausi mine in Ghana, began as open-pit and then went down at least 1,000 to 2,000 metres, by Burton's estimation.

"Just like we would mine in Canada. Today, that deposit is in the order of 20 million ounces of gold but it's not coming from pits," he said.

Feasibility study in hand, Etruscan got a financing offer for construction of its mine, but again, timing wasn't optimum. Gold was down under $300 and Etruscan's stock price was also down around 40 or 50 cents. On the basis of market conditions, the banks were only willing to lend them $16 million for a mine that would likely cost about $25 million to build. Rather than having to dilute the company, Etruscan decided to look for a partner with the financial capacity to get the mine into production.

Enter Semafo, a Toronto-listed junior based out of Montreal that had experience and was very active in West Africa, mainly Burkina Faso.

"They had exploration expertise but the main thing we needed was cash," said Burton. "They had about $25 million in the bank at the time, so they certainly had the money."

Since Etruscan had already done all the technical work and possessed the documentation, Semafo came in for 50 percent of the project in return for fully funding acquisition of the Libiri deposit right next door that Ashanti had previously worked on. A million ounce deposit, Libiri was too small for the giant Ashanti.

"It made good economic sense for us to purchase that deposit because it's only three kilometres away, they're both on the same belt, and we could develop both deposits at the same time," said Burton.

The plan was to build a processing plant at Samira, and truck the ore from Libiri to the plant. Everything seemed to be falling nicely into place with two promising and exciting deposits. There were no money worries with Semafo having fully funded all the working capital requirements and agreeing to arrange project financing This allowed Etruscan to keep its half interest without spending any money until production.

"That's really how Etruscan survived through a very difficult period," Burton pointed out.

But before they could get too cocky about things, there was another setback. Right around this time, a Moroccan group took over Semafo and gold was once again below $300.

"It was 2001, and all the partners in the project agreed we would not spend any more money on the project until the market improved and we could put this thing into production. We just put everything on hold," said Burton.

Hayes notes that Etruscan's stock was also at an all-time low, hovering around the bargain basement price of 25 cents.

"When I first got involved in 1986, the stock was three dollars," Hayes noted.

In fact, it was as high as $9 during that period when the only asset Etruscan had to show for itself was Samira Hill.

"Those were heady days back then, for all juniors. They were all trading really high and West Africa was very much in vogue with all the brokers," Burton said, illustrating the huge discrepancy between then and now.

"Today we have three projects the size of Samira Hill, plus a huge opportunity in diamonds in South Africa, and we're trading at $2.30 which is where the market is today."

But Etruscan didn't rack up all its current projects by spinning its wheels or sitting on its Niger projects while waiting for the market to improve. They sent a couple of their geologists who live full time in West Africa, out to scope new projects that might fit Etruscan. The geologists came back with two priority targets – one in Burkina Faso called Youga and another in Cote d'Ivoire (Ivory Coast) called Agbaou.

Youga was owned 50-50 by Ashanti and Echo Bay Mines, while the Agbaou permit was held by Diversified Minerals, an Australian company.

"We thought that if we somehow could get our hands on them, they'd be perfect," said Burton.

Because Ashanti wasn't willing to sell at that time, all efforts were directed at Agbaou and securing a permit from the government.

"There was enough work done on it that told us there was at least 1.1 million ounces of gold there – not big enough for the big guys, but just the right size for what we were trying to do. It was a long, drawn-out process with the government for the application, which took two-and-a-half years," said Burton.

"The government was also quite busy with the civil war that was going on," pointed out Hayes.

"Yes," agreed Burton, "It kind of interrupted things."

But pushing on through the strife, the permit was officially granted to Etruscan in November 2003. It was a year that started off on a positive note when Etruscan heard Ashanti was now willing to sell its Youga property. Ashanti put it up for bidding in a tender process and Etruscan was the successful bidder, paying US$6.5 million in cash.

"We completed that acquisition in January of this year," said Burton.

Suddenly, the picture had changed dramatically. Whereas before, Etruscan only had Samira Hill with 2-million ounces, they now had 1.1 million ounces at Agbaou, and another 1.3 million at Youga – from 2 million ounces to 4.3 million ounces of gold.

"Out of that 4.3 million, about 3 million ounces is attributable to

Etruscan," Burton explains, "Because we don't have 100 percent of that."

The breakdown is as follows: Etruscan has 40 percent of Samira (partnered with Semafo), but holds 85 percent of Agbaou and 90 percent of Youga, with the government taking its standard cut and Etruscan having control.

As things stand now, everything is nicely on track. Samira Hill is under construction and expected to be ready to pour gold in September 2004. When Etruscan purchased Youga, it was already permitted by the government to go into production. A little more drilling and, Burton estimates, construction on Youga can begin by January 2005 at the latest. The Cote d'Ivoire project is the least developed, with gold production expected in about three years' time. All three projects will be open-pit, but as Burton points out, more gold awaits them underneath every one of the deposits.

"It keeps going, but that's for later," he says.

The trick, according to Hayes, is to get into production first and secure cash flow.

"Once we're in production and we've got the debt paid back, then we can start going deeper and expanding," he says. "You can't keep going to the market because they get fed up and eventually they say, 'Well, you've got all this money, what are you doing with it?'"

For many juniors, the gold pipeline built by Etruscan would be quite enough to make them happy. But there's more to the Etruscan story than gold, and it's the diamonds that could very well end up dwarfing the significance of the gold prospects.

In 2001, Etruscan partnered up with another Canadian company called Mountain Lake Resources that had seven diamond properties in South Africa, about a two-hour drive west of Johannesburg. The properties contain alluvial diamond deposits, or diamond-bearing (diamondiferous) gravels, not hard rock. The final agreement saw Etruscan with 51 percent control.

"So, they had a good land position, had demonstrated that the diamonds in the gravel were good value, and would sell per carat for a good price. But they were unable to find a partner who would finance and develop a commercial operation with them," said Burton.

The problem, it seemed, was a lack of water in the dry, prairie-like landscape.

A large and well-known diamond mining company, Ashton Mining, had looked at the area and although they found the hundreds of millions of tonnes of gravel attractive, they weren't thrilled with the lack of water in the arid landscape. Because lots of water is necessary to wash the gravel, Ashton passed on partnering, believing it would be impossible to make a commercial mine without the water.

Taking that into consideration, Etruscan's first order of business was drilling for water. They knew that local farmers were drilling to 60 metres for water. They also knew they were looking at karst topography, whereby the area bedrock was dolamite, similar to limestone.

"That's a very good type of geology to find huge underground water reservoirs in," said Burton. "So we started drilling to 120 metres and we found lots of water."

Water problem solved, they decided to go ahead and build a commercial plant at an estimated cost of US$8 million. The banks they approached were pleased with the project and the gravel but wanted more confidence in the grade. The catch is, in order to determine grade, the gravel needs to be processed. Etruscan proposed processing 5,000 to 10,000 tonnes of gravel to satisfy the bank's requirements. But apparently, that wasn't enough.

"One bank said, 'We want 150,000 tonnes of gravel processed before we're even going to talk to you about giving you money.' Another group wanted 200,000 tonnes," said Burton.

It was a typical catch-22 – Etruscan needed money to build a plant, but the banks told them they need a plant to process the gravel and prove grade.

"It was crazy," said Burton simply.

Not to be deterred, the Etruscan team decided they would try to raise their own money and build their own plant.

"We raised US$2 million from existing shareholders who had faith in the project, and from directors and employees. We just internally pulled together and built a small plant. We have now processed close to one million tonnes of gravel through that plant."

There were three parameters Etruscan needed to prove for a business model that would 'make the whole diamond project work'. These included grade (how many diamonds in the gravel], size (of the diamonds) and value (how much money per carat).

As far as grade was concerned, Etruscan predicted the grade would be 2.8 carats per 100 cubic metres. Burton puts it in perspective:

"That would be like having five dump trucks come to your front lawn full of gravel, dump the gravel on your lawn, and you would have to find something the size of a pea. If you don't find that pea, you've lost money."

That's the risk, and that's precisely why huge volumes of gravel need to be processed to define a grade.

After processing the million tonnes, Etruscan discovered the grade to be 2.6, which, according to Burton, "may as well be the same as 2.8."

The average stone size predicted was one carat. The average stone size found so far is .98. Close enough.

The average value predicted was US$400 per carat. After selling almost 10,000 carats, the average value is $411.

"So those three parameters are bang on," says Burton.

The key to profitability however, is volume. The plant they built with the help of loyal supporters isn't capable of pushing through a large enough volume to make it profitable. A rebuild on the plant should enable it to push through about 28,000 carats per year – 'a reasonable size'. The engineering firm working on the refit has also engineered an optimum-sized plant that Burton estimates will cost about US$10 million to construct and be capable of producing 50,000 carats per year.

"We just raised money and we now have $15 million. So we could do that ourselves now. To build the second plant, we know that the banks in South Africa are willing to talk to us about loaning the money."

It's a good position to be in financially, but Etruscan certainly didn't forget about those shareholders who put their faith and money into the project when no banks would touch them.

"In return for taking all that risk, that group of investors who we call unit holders, they now own 24 percent of the project. So now Etruscan has 51 percent controlling interest in everything and Mountain Lake ends up with 25 percent. That's the partnership."

The partnership that began with Mountain Lake and seven properties has now evolved to include 35 properties in the district. The math can be staggering.

"If the three parameters hold up and we have the dominant land position in this district, we think right now we've probably tied up about one billion tonnes of gravels on all these properties," says Burton.

"Based on the US$400 a carat and the grade, one tonne of gravel should have a value in the ground of about US$6. That's what it would be worth. So we've got a billion tonnes of that. But for us to dig it out of the ground, run it through the plant, and recover the diamonds will cost us US$3 per tonne. Thus our target profit is US$3 a tonne."

The optimal production rate, according to Hayes, is 50,000 carats a year. When one considers the plant already built will produce 30,000 a year and the second plant expected to be up and running by the end of 2005 will produce 50,000 carats a year – Etruscan will obviously conquer the optimal production rate. In time, five plants producing up to 250,000 carats a year isn't unthinkable and could indeed enable Etruscan to become the second largest diamond producer in South Africa.

"It's going to be like a McDonald's franchise," jokes Burton.

All of which is why Etruscan's stock is undervalued at its current price, according to Hayes.

"We should probably be trading around $4.50 just for the gold we have. So you've got a company that's now trading at $2.30 and the gold assets should be worth twice that. But if the diamonds come in, it just becomes logarithmic. You should then be talking about $25, $30, $40 stock," says Hayes.

The Etruscan team takes it in stride, having seen their stock hit a low of 25 cents and a high of $9. As Hayes points out, if the value is recognized, the share price will increase.

"The diamonds are right now being valued in the marketplace because we know that Mountain Lake is trading at a particular price and they've got 25 percent of the diamonds. Just on the basis of what the market is paying for it, the Tirasano operation in Etruscan should be valued at 70 cents per Etruscan share.

"But that's only 20 million tonnes of diamondiferous gravels. If you start to look at a billion tonnes, then that would be a fifty-fold increase."

Despite his optimism and conviction, Hayes remains philosophical about it all.

"We could be looking at a $40 value, but whether or not the market pays for it, remains to be seen."

As it is with many mining companies in today's climate, cautious optimism rules the day. The Bre-X scandal still lurks in the back of everyone's mind and both Hayes and the rest of the Etruscan team clearly don't want to get ahead of themselves despite their confidence and delight with the way things are progressing. It is only now, Hayes says, that they're willing to step out and take a bit of credit.

"Post Bre-X, we took the position that we should do a lot and not talk as much as we did. Now we've done that and we're beginning to talk about it. In looking at what's out there today at the different gold shows, we're seeing what other companies are promising to deliver and we already have that and more. Yet our stock price is trading at one-fifth of the market capitalization of these other companies.

"We already have it, because we've done it...we just haven't talked about it."

There is, of course, one thing the Etruscan team has no problem talking about, nor should they. It's that passion and commitment to Africa and its people. When asked about Etruscan's corporate philosophy, it's the first thing they mention. There are undoubtedly many answers they could give when questioned about their philosophy – focus, determination, teamwork, to name a few. But although those traits are important and likely a given for any junior company to move forward or even stay on the map, they're not the traits that first spring to mind for Hayes when asked about his company's philosophy.

"It's a company with a big heart," he says, and not without a trace of pride.

"The philosophy you'll hear most often from Gerry and the employees is that we very much like working in West Africa and South Africa. We like the work, we like the people and the countries we're in. We're not there to resurrect colonial attitudes and I think we're very different in that way. We're proactive with the governments, we're very involved in the communities, and I think this is where we belong – our people and the team we've built up."

"Devastating" is how Hayes describes some of the things the Etruscan team has seen while working in Niger and that's what pushes them to make a difference in the quality of life for their employees and the communities.

"In Niger, they have a life expectancy of about 42 years. When John Savage went to Africa, there were people saying we could source some CAT scans and really good equipment for the hospitals, to which John very succinctly said: 'People don't understand that over there, they don't care about cancer because they're not going to live long enough to die from it.' That's the reality."

It's not CAT scanners or high tech equipment the local communities need, it's simple things taken for granted by most North Americans. Things like clean water and good sanitation.

"If you get clean water, it will clean up an awful lot of the illnesses, significantly reduce infant mortality and extend life," Hayes says.

Some of the primary diseases currently affecting the population are malaria, TB and AIDS, the latter estimated by Burton to be about a 30 percent infection rate.

"The primary killer for those in the bush is malaria and life-threatening respiratory illnesses, like lung infections," Burton says.

Aside from drilling wells for water and erecting the bush clinic and schools, Etruscan is also lending a hand in agriculture programs.

"There's not much you can grow there, but we have agricultural initiatives in some of the villages where we've sourced water pumps and fencing so they can protect an area to experiment growing different crops."

The initiative seems to be working, with at least one successful experiment already undertaken.

"They grew, for the first time, corn as we know it – corn on the cob. We've got the program going and it's very successful. We're trying to get them to develop a bit of an economy."

And that's the proactive part of Etruscan's philosophy, according to Hayes.

"We're helping people develop skills that can eventually develop into self sustaining industries which they themselves build."

It doesn't hurt that Etruscan's two highly-respected geologists, Werner Claessens and Pascal van Osta, have both lived and worked in West Africa for many years. Their skills and value to Etruscan reach far beyond their technical expertise, and they are an integral part of what Gerry McConnell describes as Etruscan's most important resource – "our people".

"Each of our geologists has lived in Africa, in all kinds of different places, for 15 to 20 years," said Hayes. "They know Africa very well, they know the protocol, how to deal with the ministries and the bureaucracy. It's one of the advantages that Etruscan has in West Africa – we've kept a core team of people living and working there, even through the bad times and the hard times.

"We have a solid reputation with all the governments we work with, and we're highly regarded both technically and socially throughout Francophone West Africa."

Etruscan has also proven by example that companies don't need a lot of money to lend a hand. More important, is the will.

"That social initiative in Niger was done without the benefit, yet, of having a mine operation," says Burton.

"We weren't producing gold, we weren't making money, but we felt compelled, just by the fact that we were working in the second-poorest country in the world, to try and do something to help."

With a solid team carrying out successful exploration and development under difficult conditions, Etruscan remains acutely aware of its own presence in Africa.

"Everybody is very much aware of how difficult it is to live and work in some of these countries," says Burton, "And we all think we can return good things for those people by doing what we do."

Armed with that philosophy and an impressive portfolio of gold and diamonds, it seems likely Etruscan will keep doing what it does for a long time to come.

At press time, Etruscan had successfully transitioned to a gold producer in September 2004 with the pouring of the first gold bar at the Samira Hill Gold Mine. The official opening of the mine was held on October 5, 2004. This milestone event for Etruscan and the State of Niger was attended by the President as well as the Prime Minister of Niger. Etruscan now looks forward to establishing gold production in the adjacent country of Burkina Faso at its Youga Gold Project.

EVERTON RESOURCES INCORPORATED

Always up for a challenge, Everton's president and chairman Andre Audet has recently added a new skill to his diverse portfolio of attributes- he's learned how to dance the merengue. While this accomplishment may not overly impress shareholders, Everton's portfolio of properties in the colourful and historic Dominican Republic certainly will.

Mining usually isn't the first image that springs to mind when visualizing the Dominican Republic. Generally thought of more as a tourist destination and host of last year's Pan Am Games, this country conjures visions of white sand beaches, rum and cigars, and the omnipresent music and merengue, the island's national dance. And although it is still lying somewhat under the radar as far as a mining hot spot is concerned, it won't be for long. While the coastline is awash in dancing and sunbathing, the Dominican Republic's interior has, in fact, had a mining history for hundreds of years. Falconbridge has been a fixture for at least 30 years and Placer Dome is currently evaluating Pueblo Viejo, one of the world's largest gold deposits with an estimated 17-million-ounce resource remaining. Everton has snapped up properties right next door to Pueblo Viejo, and Audet is satisfied they've secured the best land position available.

When Audet was first apprised of the great mining possibilities in the Dominican, he admits his knowledge of the island was limited to the culture and the stuff of tourist brochures.

"I didn't know it as a mining country. I knew it as a place with nice beaches, golf courses, good rum, great resorts, great cigars. But when we started looking at it, we said: 'Holy jeez, there's two world-class deposits on that island!'"

Sold on the fact that Falconbridge had been successfully and profitably mining nickel since the seventies, and knowing Placer Dome was spending a fortune on Pueblo Viejo, all the rest of it was a no-brainer for Audet. As he investigated other key factors, Audet discovered the country was politically stable and boasted the fastest growing economy in the Caribbean, with major investments coming into the island. Tourism ranks as the largest industry, followed by agriculture and an increasing influx of manufacturing concerns taking advantage of tax-free zones that have been set up. Satisfied the political and economical risk was low, Audet promptly said: "Okay, I'm sold...what ground is available?"

The obvious target was to secure properties near Pueblo Viejo, which were known, according to historical data, to host a 30-million ounce deposit. And to that end, the best nearby ground was held by a junior company called GlobeStar, based in Toronto. Three deals later-two with GlobeStar, one with Linear Gold that also held property beside Pueblo Viejo-and Everton now basically has a stranglehold on every property on strike to Pueblo Viejo. When Placer or any other major comes calling, Everton will be there to take the call.

Although he's thrilled with the Dominican and prospects therein, Audet didn't set out to become Everton's president. He was already pretty busy as president of Majescor, an Ottawa-based diamond mining company, and initially only lent his financial expertise to Everton as a director. According to Audet, he got involved with Everton because he had some time on his hands while waiting for results to come in for Majescor. Anyone else might be relieved to have some down time, but not Audet.

"The thing with diamonds is, it takes so bloody long to get results that I got bored. Sometimes it takes six months to get a story out," he said, speaking from GlobeStar's offices during a quick business trip to Toronto in August 2004.

While waiting around for Majescor's results to come in, Audet became a director of Everton and when the Dominican potential began to reveal itself, he became increasingly interested and excited, negotiating the deals with GlobeStar, raising money and generally spending a lot of time investigating the opportunities. This increasing involvement led to Audet becoming chairman last year, and eventually president in January 2004. Now president of two mining companies headquartered in Ottawa, Audet has access to great geological and financial talent, through which he has built a credible team to move forward in the Dominican. His job and expertise, he acknowledges, is in finance.

"I'm not a geologist. I'm the guy who raises the money and does the promotions, the marketing, and gets the story out there. I know the brokers, I know how to talk their language."

It's a language Audet's been speaking since 1987 when he left his job at the Royal Trust, secured his mutual fund and financial advisor licences and began working for Midland Doherty. As it happened, timing couldn't have been more ironic with Audet resigning on October 19, 1987, the day of the stock market crash. He says his boss at the bank laughed and said: "You want to leave a bank and work in the stock market? Don't you know the stock market is crashing?"

Audet chuckles as he recalls the moment.

"I said, 'Yeah, that's the best time...when stocks are low, right?'"

A couple of years later, Audet left Midland to work at BMO Nesbitt Burns from 1987 to 1999, moving up the ranks and eventually becoming vice president. It was during his tenure at Nesbitt, while working as a broker, that Audet began developing an expertise in junior mining. As he puts it, he got 'hooked' by the diamond discoveries in the Northwest Territories when he watched his stocks quickly move from 10 cents to 10 dollars.

"Obviously everything ended with Bre-X, but it was a great run. I saw the good side and the bad side and learned through those experiences."

Wanting to leave Nesbitt, Audet began looking for other opportunities through mining companies he had invested in and trusted.

"I started talking to different people I liked in the business, who were straight, honest and did good work."

In August 1999, he found what he was looking for and quit Nesbitt. Teaming up with Jacques Letendre (ex-De Beers) and Andre Gaumond (Virginia Gold Mines president), they created a new company called

Majescor as a vehicle for some interesting diamond results Gaumond had discovered through Virginia. Audet became president of Majescor, a position he still holds to this day. As fate would have it, Majescor shared an office with 3Net Media, a public internet company formed in 1999/2000 during the dot-com boom. Like many internet companies of the day, 3Net Media had originally been a junior mining company-in 3Net's case, it had been born out of Mount Hope Resources. But with the subsequent bursting of the dot-com bubble, 3Net turned to its neighbours at Majescor for some help in reverting back to a mining company. As they explained to Audet, their shareholders were specifically interested in gold properties. Audet obliged and began consulting with various geologists, one of whom suggested the Dominican Republic. That's when Audet began doing his homework on the Dominican Republic and discovered, much to his amazement, the great Falconbridge nickel story and the existence of Pueblo Viejo, one of the biggest undeveloped gold deposits in the world.

"Falconbridge is getting close to $6 billion in revenue since they mined it in the seventies and nickel has doubled in price over the last year, so they're making good money with that deposit," Audet pointed out.

Excited and coerced by the potential, the mining history and the country itself, Audet quickly found himself spending almost half his time working on behalf of 3Net. He decided to take it one step further and make it official, dissolving the internet division, doing a four-for-one consolidation from 20 million shares down to five, and authorizing a name change from 3Net Media to Everton Resources Inc. In short order, he negotiated the deals with GlobeStar and Linear Gold for prospective ground that hugged Placer's Pueblo Viejo land position, and the rest, as they say, is history.

Key in negotiating the deals was geologist Marc L'Heureux, who had worked with GlobeStar and Majescor, as well as Barrick and Falconbridge. He had been to the Dominican more than 20 times and was extremely familiar with the geology of the deposits. Subsequently, L'Heureux joined the Everton team and is now their vice president of exploration.

Once things got rolling, it didn't take long before Audet was asked to take over the presidency from Dwane Brousseau, 3Net's former president and an ex-RBC broker. Everton's quick evolution made it necessary to have someone with more mining and financial experience leading the charge.

"We needed someone who had been involved with more mining companies, who had contacts with brokers and institutions, so I became president and Dwane became our manager of investor relations in Vancouver," Audet explained.

"So, we still keep the same team. But once we started raising serious money, it was time to go with a little more experience on top. And it also helps that Majescor had a good successful run."

As an amusing side note, the name Everton has nothing whatsoever to do with mining and in fact, has everything to do with rugby. Audet says the name was chosen by one of 3Net's directors, Ian MacLean, a rugby player from Vancouver.

"Everton is a rugby team in the U.K., and we ended up naming the company after this team. I think they had a rivalry with Ian's team when they came to Canada."

When asked why they went with Everton, he smiles and shrugs: "It's a name. It's simple."

Everton may be known as a rugby team in the U.K., but Audet is banking on its future value as a hot mining company in Canada with formidable assets in the Dominican and Latin America. Kicking things off were the three deals in the Dominican, the first being with GlobeStar on what's known as the Bayaguana concession. For its part, Everton has to spend US$1.5 million to earn a 50 percent interest in the property that measures 15-by-5 kilometres.

"That property had a lot of money spent on it from Falconbridge and GlobeStar. It has exactly the same geology as Pueblo Viejo, which hosts 30 million ounces, and it already had a mineral inventory...300,000 ounces had already been drilled off by Falconbridge at the Cerro Kiosko deposit. There was also a big copper deposit called Dona Amanda which has about half-a-billion pounds of copper sitting on the property."

Although the price of copper was only 60 to 70 cents at the time of the deal, Audet notes it's now doubled in price, giving the deposit a better chance.

"There were also a few other good drill holes on the property, 24 metres at two percent copper that Falconbridge had drilled and never followed up, and there was a big gold soil anomaly. So it was a great property and we saw it as having a lot of potential."

GlobeStar came into possession of the properties when Falconbridge, the biggest mining company on the island, decided to sell off all its non-nickel assets.

Deal number two, again with GlobeStar, involved three properties contiguous to Pueblo Viejo. For a paltry US$1.1 million, Everton can earn up to 70 percent on those properties if they take it to bankable feasibility.

"It was a pretty cheap deal. We wanted a chance to go higher than 50 percent because, if we make a discovery, we want to be able to interest a major company."

Called Cuance, Los Hojanchos and Loma de Payabo, the properties encompass about 75 square kilometres and feature primarily gold, with some silver and zinc thrown in for good measure. They're practically within stone-throwing distance from Pueblo Viejo.

"These properties are a few kilometres away from this monster, Pueblo Viejo. They're all adjoining."

In Everton's third deal, they grabbed yet another property called Loma el Mate, right beside Pueblo Viejo, through a deal with Linear Gold, a Halifax-based junior. Everton can earn a 50 percent interest by spending half a million dollars over two years and issuing a couple hundred thousand shares.

If it isn't already obvious, Audet explains Everton's strategy.

"Okay, here's 30 million ounces," he says, pointing at Pueblo Viejo on a map. "Once Placer announces publicly it's going to go ahead, they're going to say: 'Who's around here?' And we're it."

Audet wanted to get positioned not only before Placer's expected announcement in December 2004, but also before the Dominican becomes a lot more visible and attractive.

"Right now, the Dominican is not on the radar screen. Everyone is in West Africa, Peru, China or Canada. But Pueblo Viejo is Placer's number one development project. They're keeping things really low key right now because they're acquiring more ground. But they can only stake in one area because we have all the rest."

As far as strategies are concerned, Audet is satisfied Everton's is going as planned.

"The strategy seems to be working because Placer Dome is becoming more aggressive in getting more land. But they're limited because we've got 60 percent of that deposit surrounded."

If that isn't enough to excite shareholders, Everton has also applied for seven poly-metallic concessions between Falconbridge and Pueblo Viejo and two large nickel concessions, all of which Audet expects to be granted from the government by the end of 2004.

"We're well funded to do all the work we need in the Dominican Republic until the end of the year," Audet says, adding that they'll likely be using the $1.2 million left in their treasury by the end of year.

"We're drilling like crazy right now, so the money is going fast."

A 20-hole drill program began in July, once Everton managed to wrestle a drill from Placer's grasp.

"Placer Dome was hogging all the drills on the island, but they finally let one loose and we've got it until the end of the year," says Audet with a grin.

Ten holes into the program, they hit some rather surprising results in the form of new copper porphyry discoveries located 300 metres from Dona Loretta. The reason it's considered a new discovery is because it's not directly beside Falconbridge's hole.

"We hit some really high grade copper that was 15 metres at over one percent copper and 90 metres at .6 percent copper. So the next phase, we'll do deeper drilling because some of the best results are at the bottom of the hole," Audet explained, adding that the idea is to go open-pit up to 300 metres.

Following that, the plan is to move the drill to the Dona Amanda copper deposit that's open in all directions, 45 million tonnes at .45 percent copper. Next up, the drilling is moving closer to Pueblo Viejo where six to eight holes will be drilled on Everton's Los Hojanchos property.

While GlobeStar is currently in the process of putting a mine into production at its Cerro de Maimon deposit, Everton isn't interested in going that route. Audet wants to keep things simpler, make a discovery and advance the properties, whether they be gold, copper or nickel, to the point where a major will be interested. And the majors are already sniffing around the Dominican Republic. Aside from Placer Dome that is already in there, other majors that have begun investigating the country's prospects include Newmont, Anglo Gold, Goldfields and BHP Billiton, the latter looking for copper.

"The majors have taken notice and they need commodities, they need copper," Audet says, pointing out that there's a reason both copper and nickel have doubled in price.

"The world needs commodities to build things, whether it's wiring or stainless steel or whatever. There's a big demand for commodities and the country has a successful history of producing giant deposits."

Even the juniors are starting to take notice and more and more are applying for concessions and looking at going public shortly. Although GlobeStar and Everton are currently the two most significant juniors in the Dominican, Audet expects it to bust wide open in the near future.

"It's brewing right now. We think it's really going to explode once Placer announces that Pueblo Viejo is going to be a big mine for them."

For his part, Audet is satisfied with Everton's position and welcomes the other juniors. From his perspective, an influx of companies only serves to attract more attention to the area. And as the saying goes, no publicity is bad publicity.

"The more the merrier!" Audet exclaims. "It's not a big island and we're pretty well maxed out on it. There's nothing else really."

All mining activity is basically centered around one area in the middle of the island, with the two huge deposits (one nickel, one gold) situated a scant five kilometres apart. Nothing is on the coast or near any of the tourist areas, yet the proximity to the capital, Santo Domingo, is only an hour away.

As far as a mining location goes, things couldn't be more civilized. No helicopters are needed to drop people onto the property, because they can drive right up to it. There's power, water, all the infrastructure necessary, and nobody has to live in tents in a bush camp – they can all drive home at the end of the working day. The Everton team rents a five-bedroom house in Bayaguana and most of the local employees live in Santo Domingo. The Dominican team was hired by GlobeStar from Falconbridge when it sold its non-nickel properties and, as such, they are Canadian-trained and have traveled all over the world working with Falconbridge. Everton couldn't have asked for a better group of workers, according to Audet.

"They're Dominican, but Canadian-trained as far as standards and doing the geology work. They're a great and very efficient group of people," Audet states, adding that they are also consistently under budget, something that's a refreshing change of pace.

"If you go to work in the Arctic, everything's over budget. But here, they're able to do the work very cheaply and efficiently. A dollar goes a long way."

All things considered, as Audet says, it's not a bad place to work. And when the work is done for the day, nobody goes home and watches television. The locals find other forms of entertainment, much of which includes one of their favourite social activities-dancing.

"Boy, they know how to live. They're a very happy people and they love dancing," Audet enthuses.

On his last trip to the Dominican, Audet was taken to a local haunt and tried his hand (or feet) at dancing the revered merengue. When asked how he fared, his face lights up.

"It was fun!" he exclaims, then confides, "I can get the rhythm in me. It just depends how much rum I drink."

And he laughs out loud, re-living his moment of grace. It's obvious this country and its people have made an impression on Audet, both from a business and a personal perspective. Fluently bilingual in French and English, his next goal is to tackle Spanish, something he will no doubt also master in short order. He has great respect for the people of his host country and an acute awareness of Everton's corporate responsibility to the local citizenry.

"It's nice to make money, but then what? You also want to enrich other people's lives," he says, adding that the more successful Everton becomes, the more they'll be able to contribute locally, by increased employment and social initiatives.

Recently, GlobeStar and Everton made 'hefty' donations through the Canadian government and embassy to help out after massive flooding occurred on the Haitian-Dominican border. Aside from employing locals whenever they can, they've been drilling wells for fresh water to aid the nearby villages. As they progress, more initiatives will fall into place. It's something that's always on Audet's mind.

"It's nice to be able to return the favour and enrich communities. We wouldn't have a company if it wasn't for this country. It's not all about money, it's about the impact you have on your fellow human beings also."

Audet acknowledges that although the Dominican is considered rich by Caribbean standards, it's a very poor country in the global context. The discovery of resources in third world countries can help create a middle class where none exists, Audet believes. In the Dominican for instance, people are either very rich or very poor, although he concedes everyone seems to be joyous, no matter what their circumstance.

"I say very poor, but no one is starving on the streets. They have the basics - water and sanitation - and they'll have a little house with no windows and no doors. The nice thing is that fruit and vegetables are growing wild everywhere, but it's not the same quality of life. They don't have cars or televisions, but these people are very proud and very happy. It's great to see. We, in Canada, could learn from the way they live their lives."

Now that he's learned how to dance the merengue, Audet might want to consider brushing up on the tango, Uruguay's national dance. That's precisely where Everton has set its sights next with a deal finalized in August 2004 on a large acquisition. True to form, Everton will be venturing into a country that's still somewhat under the radar, and scooping one of the best land packages in South America. This particular deal came to Audet's attention through his good friend and one of Everton's directors, Ron Little, president and CEO of Orezone Resources. Little was apprised of the opportunity through Dean Williams, a former senior geologist with Barrick Gold who had worked in Argentina and Chile. At the end of the day, Everton negotiated a deal with DelcoSur, a private company owned by Williams and his three partners. Audet is very optimistic about the Uruguayan land package that's reminiscent of a well-known area closer to home.

"Dean secured two-thirds of a greenstone belt that is the same size as the one between Val d'Or and Timmins in northern Ontario and Quebec. He says it's like coming into Val d'Or in the early fifties," Audet says, pointing out that 40 to 50 mines have been found on that stretch of Canadian geology.

So far, minimal work has been done on the Uruguay belt that measures 250 kilometres in length, two-thirds of which are now secured by Everton and DelcoSur. The deal requires spending US$2.5 million over three years with Everton needing to spend US$400,000 the first year.

"We can earn up to 85 percent in the properties that are part of DelcoSur. And we're also issuing some stock, about two million shares over three years," Audet explains, adding that they'll be raising money in the fall for that deal.

Audet likes to call Uruguay his Plan B and as far as backup plans go, it makes an enviable Plan A for any company.

"It's a huge land package and DelcoSur would be the operator, with a senior geologist from Barrick heading up the program, it's very sellable."

Which brings us to Everton's stock price that historically has risen from 10 cents initially to a high of 60 cents in December 2003 and is currently sitting at around 40 cents. With Everton's prime land positions in both the Dominican and Uruguay, Audet doesn't expect it will stay at that price for long. Undervalued would be an understatement.

"I don't know of any other junior that has a huge land package adjacent to 30 million ounces, that has 300,000 ounces of proven gold, half a billion pounds of copper and exposure to nickel. And we haven't even talked about our people yet."

Yes, the people. Audet is clear not only about the importance of having credible talent on board, but also that they are duly recognized and given due credit. First on the list is Everton's key geologist and vice president of exploration, Marc L'Heureux, whose resume includes such companies as Falconbridge, Barrick, Cambior and GlobeStar. Everton's vice president of corporate development, Brook Macdonald, was with Placer Dome for eight years and president of Placer's Latin American subsidiary in Venezuela.

"He's fluent in Spanish and connected to all of Latin America, having worked with people and companies in Peru, Brazil, Argentina, Chile, Guatemala, Costa Rica. He's a great addition, especially because Placer Dome will come knocking at our door if we get any sniff of gold in our drilling," Audet points out.

Rounding out the management team is Everton's chief financial officer Marc Carbonneau, a chartered accountant with more than 18 years as a controller.

The board is stacked with talent that includes Ron Little, Ian MacLean with Bema Gold, Alain Krushnisky, former vice president for Cambior, and John Paterson, a mining engineer and director of the Prospectors & Developers Association of Canada.

"We've put a lot of time and effort into building the team," Audet says, "We've got a great team now, and we're continuing to seek opportunities."

If all that financial and geological expertise wasn't enough, Everton is currently in the process of creating an advisory committee comprised of experts in every field-lawyers, marketing and mining professionals, accountants and others with particular experience in Latin America. It may seem like a lot of people, but as Audet emphasizes, there's a lot going on and no end in sight. Currently, the Everton team is also evaluating opportunities in Peru and Brazil.

"We've looked at many opportunities in Central America because of Brook's experience, and our focus is to become a significant junior mining company based in Latin America," Audet says, adding that by the end of the year they should know if the Dominican will deliver on a large gold or copper discovery.

Once the nickel concessions are granted, Everton plans on bringing in a partner like Inco, or some other significant nickel junior company to share the risk. As far as commodities are concerned, Audet believes they're in a bull market and demand will continue to grow. In terms of gold, Placer would likely be the most logical company to approach Everton in the Dominican. As Audet puts it, he can wear a copper, nickel or a gold hat, but his focus is gold.

"That's why we created the company, but we're not throwing away

the copper or nickel or zinc because we were able to secure those properties cheap. We might as well take it. The nickel was available and if we
didn't take it, someone else would. We'll option it to another company
and they can spend money on it for us. Copper isn't the main focus, but
BHP Billiton and others have been knocking at the door. We might as well
see if we can add value to it and then farm it out to a major."

Now that they've built a solid team, secured some promising properties and are out seeking new opportunities, Audet says the next step is to
raise some money in the fall and winter to complete the Uruguay deal and
do another phase of drilling on the copper, nickel and gold projects. A
quick couple million should do the trick, he says, adding that the company is now at the stage to attract institutional financing, thanks to the
upgrading of expertise in management and on the board. For now,
Everton can be found on the TSX-Venture exchange but expect to see
Everton moving to the big board next year.

It's all an adventure, according to Audet. The discovery is the big
reward for the shareholders, but the fun lies in the chase and all that it
entails. For Audet, much of the personal satisfaction he gains is from
exposure to other cultures, countries and their people, and the opportunity to give something back to those communities.

"You get to meet fascinating people, to go to great countries and
experience other cultures and to see other human beings who also want
the same thing," he says.

Uruguay will be hard pressed to equal the colourful experiences
Audet and company have enjoyed during their stay in the Dominican
Republic. Santo Domingo has a fascinating history as the oldest city in
the new world, and Audet cites the weather, the golfing and the people as
among the best in the world.

"And the rum is fabulous," he adds with a grin. "Rum, women and
song...and merengue dancing. It's a great country and a lot of fun."

It seems Audet couldn't be happier with the ways things are progressing for Everton and for himself. He still lives in Ottawa, where he
grew up and went to university, he's still married to "the same gal" he met
a year out of university, and he currently shares an office with Majescor
and Orezone. It's one big happy family.

"Yeah, I'm excited about everything," Audet affirms, adding with a smile.

FREEGOLD VENTURES LIMITED

As a young man working the family farm in Ontario, Harry Barr dreamed of what lay beyond the hay bales and fence posts. In concept at least, it is a familiar tale: that of the restless and inquisitive soul for whom the world holds untold promise. Defoe and Dickens wrote about such figures, as did Steinbeck and Hemingway. The difference is that Barr – president, CEO and director of Freegold Ventures Limited, CanAlaska Ventures Ltd. and Pacific North West Capital Corp. – is not a character culled from the pages of fiction. Well-known and respected throughout the international resource and venture-capital communities, his ambitions have been realized and his objectives achieved time-and-again over the past quarter century. He is the dreamer who made his dream come true.

Barr exudes an unassuming yet undeniable presence in his companies' glass-paneled offices in Vancouver's upscale Kerrisdale district, a healthy and sensible distance from the city's hustling and bustling downtown core. Surrounded by rough-hewn carvings of regional folk art and ornate replicas of wooden sailing ships, the 49-year-old Barr, sporting an open-necked golf shirt and casual attire, is the nucleus around which orbit a dozen handpicked colleagues. Noticeably absent is the staid hierarchical stuffiness that in turn defines and inhibits many a corporate enclave. The openness hinted at in the architectural design is reflected in the staff's convivial and productive rapport. The visitor gets the immediate impression that information and ideas are exchanged freely, that discussions are held and decisions made. There is no mistaking, however, that the former-collegiate football player with the brawny forearms, witty banter and disarming manner is the central component in a humming and buzzing matrix.

"My dad and now my brother Tom are among the biggest hay dealers in Eastern Canada," says Barr, who grew up in Ontario's Ottawa Valley, the eldest son of third-generation farmer Ken Barr. "My family originally came from Scotland and we've been working the same piece of ground since 1867. We were lucky enough to have a gravel pit on the property but it wasn't until the late-1990s, when I was attending a conference called Investing in the Americas in Miami, Florida, that I discovered something I probably should have known all along. The Ontario government was there to speak (which I thought was a little odd given the fact the conference was about South America) but when the spokesperson pointed out that gravel deposits in Ontario are classified as mines the light came on for me. Until then, I'd always referred to myself as a fourth-generation farmer and a first-generation miner. That's when I realized I was a fourth-generation miner, as well, because our gravel pit had always been an integral part of the farm. In years when things weren't going so well – or even when they were – the gravel would keep on rolling out of the pit, providing us with a good livelihood. The bottom line is that my family and I grew up around cattle, hay and grain, but bulldozers, backhoes and dump trucks were a big part of our lives. We all worked very hard at our family farm, which is something I am proud of. My dad was a tough taskmaster but he taught our family a lot about people, business in general and most of all he taught us about the value of a hard day's work."

A strong work ethic wasn't the only thing Harry Barr learned about, growing up in the flight path of the Ottawa International Airport, 110 kilometres from Canada's capital city. Likewise imbued with a spirited sense of adventure and wanderlust, he had long harboured "a dream of getting on one of those planes, rather than going back and forth plowing the field or whatever it was I happened to be doing," he says. "I started on that path when I left the farm to attend the University of Guelph. Though it was only four hours away, it was a much bigger world than I'd ever seen." Enrolling in agribusiness, Barr soon discovered other diversions. "Football came first and school came second, but partying and all the rest of university life seemed far more important than studying," he recalls with a chuckle. "The main thing was, the whole experience taught me there was a different life to be had outside of the farm."

Besides, far greater than anything he could glean in a classroom was the wisdom imparted to him by a favourite uncle named Mel Barr. "I referred to Mel as "John Wayne gone mad" he says jokingly, but in fact he was a brilliant entrepreneur. He grew up on the same farm as the rest of my family but, when he was in his twenties, he went out and started his own construction company. The next thing he did was buy a farm outside of Ottawa, at least 10 kilometres away from the outskirts of the city. People laughed at him. There was nothing there. What he knew, and they didn't know, was that it truly was a field of dreams." Quite literally from the ground up, Mel Barr built and established the subdivision of Barrhaven, now part of and home to 20,000 people.

"I idolized this man," Harry Barr says reverently. "He was always a wheeler and dealer who had his fingers in big deals in exciting and exotic places. In 1979, after selling off most of his subdivision and making many millions of dollars, he decided to become a gold miner in the jungles of Colombia. He was 73 years old at the time." In the meantime, Harry, 50 years his uncle's junior, had graduated university and become a successful real-estate salesman in Ottawa, working for one Fried Kemper, the first man in the city to wear the hallowed Century 21 'yellow jacket'. Kemper, still a broker of high-end real estate in the region, gained a somewhat infamous reputation as 'the other man' in the breakup of former-prime minister Pierre Elliot Trudeau and wife Margaret (she and Kemper later married, though subsequently divorced).

"When I was 23, Fried Kemper was the big wheel in town," says Barr, "confident, a great salesman and somewhat flamboyant. I really looked up to him. His father had been a successful entrepreneur and Fried was taking over the business. Fried hired me away from another company where I had a banner first year. I'd only been working with him a few weeks as a real-estate agent when my uncle Mel contacted me and told me I should be the manager of his placer gold mine in Colombia, South America. Then I didn't hear from him for a few months. Suddenly, in July 1979, his stepson showed up at my door on a Wednesday and said, 'Here's your ticket to Colombia. You're leaving Saturday morning and you're going to be the manager down there.' I hadn't even talked to my uncle for four or five months, but that's the way he was. A man who usually got his own way – no time to think or pack, you just had to go."

Fortunately for Barr, Kemper was not only sympathetic to his dilemma, he was downright supportive. "I went to Fried and said, 'Look, I've done very well with you, but my uncle has given me this ticket and wants me to go to Colombia.' He said, 'Colombia? Go! You can always come back here – you've got a job anytime – do you know how beautiful the women are down there?' If Fried had said, 'No, you've signed on here and you have a duty to stay,' I probably would never have gone, given my farm-boy ethics. But he said, 'Go,' and I already had the ticket, so I went."

Harry Barr spent three years in Colombia, from 1979 to 1981, as the mine's managing director, and made history by brokering a deal that allowed his company to obtain the right to mine precious metals with 100 percent ownership rights on the companies' leases, a privilege previously never before granted to a foreign mineral-exploration company. "Prior to that," says Barr, "the Colombian government granted rights similar to the way the Mexican government did in those days, which is to say the foreign company put in all the money but could only own 49 percent of the mineral rights. We changed that law."

The experience Barr gained working with his uncle lured him into the mining game. "The time I spent in Colombia really got me hooked on the business, I got the fever," he says. " It was a very interesting time. We ran a placer mine down there and I fell in love with the characters, the travel, the adventure, the challenge of raising the funds and learning to speak the language – all of it." Gold also reached its all-time high during that period. Though he remained with his uncle's company until 1985, he redirected his focus after meeting a kindred spirit at a Vancouver mining convention in 1983. Alaskan miner and entrepreneur Kelly Dolphin was speaking to an audience of 500 about the advantages of fine gold recovery via state-of-the-art gravity-recovery equipment when Barr first encountered him. Following Dolphin's presentation, the pair arranged to meet for breakfast the next morning. By the end that day, they had agreed to form their own company. "He became a very important person in my life," says Barr.

"When we met, Kelly was a young guy like me who had big dreams," Barr continues. "He ran a company for years out of Fairbanks, Alaska, called The Miner's Company. He specialized in the new equipment that was being used to extract fine gold using gravity-recovery – free of any chemicals – the faster and easier you can split the gold off in a gravity circuit the better it is for your bottom line. There were over 1,000 placer mines in Alaska at the time. When they changed the placer-mining laws a few years later it almost put Kelly out of business but it was the right time for me because I was able to convince him to join me in forming Freegold."

The pair officially became partners in May 1985, though the upstart Freegold Ventures Limited (TSX: ITF; OTCBB: FGOVF) was hindered by a slow market year. A broker who had initially offered financial services backed out, unwilling to gamble on a couple of youngsters with next-to-no track record. Barr and Dolphin persevered, soon heading to Alberta, where First Commonwealth Securities, which raised $750,000, financed them. It was the shot in the arm they needed – Freegold went from the talking stage to a public company in a scant three months.

"During our first two to three years," says Barr, "we looked at producing gold from tailings of former hard-rock gold producers mostly back east in Ontario. Tailings are basically the waste materials left over from old mines." The company's first project involved a tailings stockpile at Ontario's Campbell Red Lake Mine. Freegold drilled out the tailings and proved over 500,000 ounces of gold at a grade of 0.056 ounces per tonne. When Placer absorbed the Campbell Red Lake Mine during its takeover of Dome Mines (resulting in the formation of Placer Dome Inc., one of the world's largest and most successful gold mining companies), the new owners decided they didn't want a junior company rummaging around in their waste. After a year's worth of haggling, Freegold walked away with $150,000.

"To attract a major mining company in those days, a project had to have the potential to produce a million ounces of gold," says Barr. "At that point, we realized we'd better assemble a geological team that could help us find those kinds of projects. So we went to Alaska in a big way, from placer projects to open-pit and hard-rock underground projects – those became the type of projects we began to acquire. The buzzword from 1990 right up to today has been open-pit or bulk mineable deposits. It's lower-grade open-pit material, but there's a helluva lot of it and you can recover large amounts of gold out of these deposits. In the meantime, the quest for developing higher-grade underground projects almost disappeared, though there are still a lot of them around. It's funny, there was a trend to go back to underground projects simply because the price of gold went down so low the key criteria became grade. With the advent of gold prices under US$300 an ounce, a gram or two per tonne didn't matter. It still wasn't enough; the producers weren't making any real money. Over the past few years, the price of gold has driven people back to the logic they should have used even when gold prices were higher. The more grade you have, the less you have to mine, the more chance you have to make a good return for your shareholders."

To that end, Freegold secured the Golden Summit Project, a hard-rock gold property conveniently situated 20 miles from Fairbanks in proven 'Elephant Country' and, not coincidentally, less than five miles from Alaska's largest gold-producing mine, Fort Knox, which yielded in approximately 400,000 ounces of gold in 2003. Smack dab in the middle of the Fairbanks Mining District, where 10 million ounces of placer gold have been recovered since 1902, Freegold presently controls 18,000 acres, making it one of the largest landholders in the district. When gold prices went down at the end of 1997 says Barr, "nobody cared about our business. But we hung on over the last few years and like old prospectors we kept our core properties." Not a bad idea, considering that Alaska's estimated gold resources have risen from 1 million ounces in 1985 to over 75 million ounces in 2003.

"Most people think that if you are an Alaskan you must also live in an igloo," he says and laughs heartily. "In fact, you can order a pizza from where we are with a cell phone. There is a main road; there are power lines that run through our property. It's a big chunk of ground and most of the project has not been drilled. If you're a major mining company and you're really truly looking for gold and your stocks have doubled or tripled in the last year or two, you have to take a serious look at Freegold's Alaska projects. The near-term producers, with massive projects that are very close to production, could barely raise a dime a year ago. Now they're trading at all-time highs and need new projects to keep them going and replace the ounces they are mining."

Freegold Ventures Limited – the name derives itself from the rarely-found, free-milling gold that can be extracted without chemicals from crushed quartz – eventually moved from the Alberta exchange to the Vancouver Stock Exchange and, in the summer of 1998, the Toronto Stock Exchange. "Going back to when we started," says Barr, "there were some very tough years. The analogy I use today is, 'Can you imagine having an overhead of $5 million to $10 million a year with no cash flow to speak of?' We had to depend on our own savvy when trying to raise money through joint ventures with major mining companies. Junior mining companies only have very short windows to the equity market. A lot of the time you're raising money at whatever price you can get it at, just to keep things going, and that's what we've done over the years. Our specialty is packaging mineral properties and getting major mining companies to invest their money in them. The majors can earn part of the project but we keep a substantial amount for our shareholders so that should the project become a producing mine, we'll still have a large part of it. To prove we have a strong technical team, we remain the operator for the first few years and our head office usually receives 10 percent of the dollars that are going into the ground. This business model has allowed us to keep a large and experienced team of geologists, engineers, technicians and administrative people in place over the good and bad years. Having that team is even more important today because there is a severe lack of skilled people.

"We have the seven most famous, past-producing underground mines in the Fairbanks Mining District," Barr continues, "and not one of them has been drilled by us since 1942 – all work stopped because of the War Act of 1942 and nobody has looked at them since." Even though these mines produced one-ounce-plus per tonne at relatively shallow depths, Freegold and our previous industry partners were content to keep them on the backburner, concentrating instead on bulk mineable or open-pit targets on the Golden Summit Project. With such a massive project Freegold was searching for a well-financed producer to pick up the ball through a joint venture. That company arrived in January 2004 in the guise of Meridian Gold Inc., which entered into an option/joint venture agreement as part of the Golden Summit Project. A mid-tier gold producer with a first-rate track record of discovering, developing, and operating profitable gold mines throughout North and South America, Meridian's gold reserves were estimated at 4,281,000 ounces as of December 31st, 2002, while its production costs are among the lowest in the world at approximately US$60 per gold ounce.

"Seven million new ounces of gold have been found in Alaska every year since 1985," says Barr. "Most people don't understand Alaska's potential, and that's why we stay there. Explorers up there are making money for their shareholders and that is why we were prepared to hold onto our key projects over the last few years when investors were not interested in junior gold exploration companies. These types of projects can create an enormous upside for our shareholders and that allows us to do what we do best – go out and prospect for new properties and start again. I'm kind of like the old watch salesman who opens his coat to the 'big boys' and offers 20 different projects from which they can choose.

Which is why shortly after taking Freegold public, Dolphin and Barr embarked on a new venture: CanAlaska Ventures Ltd. (TSX Venture: CVV; OTCBB: CVVLF). "Alaska was Kelly's true love," says Barr, "and he introduced me to the great state of Alaska and all the mineral wealth that was there. Freegold's very first properties were in Alaska and we continue to work up there in a major way." Because Barr was Canadian and Dolphin was Alaskan, the new company's name – CanAlaska – suggested itself. CanAlaska Ventures Ltd. went public on the Vancouver Stock Exchange in 1988. One of the company's flagship properties, the Rainbow Hill Project, is located in the central part of the state, approximately 225 road miles from Fairbanks. A 90,285 ounce drill-inferred gold resource, Rainbow Hill is slated for a more extensive drill program in the summer to better define the lode gold deposits likely stemming from the nearby Gold Hill and Lucky Hill areas, sites of known lode sources. Furthermore, Rainbow Hill is upstream from a past-producing placer mine called Valdez Creek, which yielded more than 500,000 ounces of gold before ceasing production in 1996. CanAlaska has grown to be a diversified mineral exploration company with gold and base metal projects in Canada, Alaska and New Zealand.

In February 1995 Barr received a devastating blow when his partner of 10 years, Kelly Dolphin, was killed in a snowmobile accident near Fairbanks. An avid snowmobile racer, Dolphin had been preparing for a race on the outskirts of Fairbanks, when he and another snowmobile collided at an estimated 80 miles an hour. "We worked our guts out together and we were the best friends and partners in the world," says Barr. "He was like a brother to me. It was a really traumatic thing. He was only 35 years old and had a wonderful wife and two little kids. Kelly and I started Freegold and CanAlaska and we still have those companies today. We did a lot of work together and shared many great times. I still think about him almost every day. Kelly was one of a kind."

This personal setback was compounded two years later by a professional one when the infamous Bre-X scandal was revealed in late-March 1997, making headlines around the world and sapping investor confidence in the gold market overnight. "You got it," Barr says with a sigh. "After that fiasco, the price of gold fell to a 20-year low, the dot.coms took away all our money and turned into dot.bombs, and the general stock market blew up in 2000. Where have people been investing for the past three to four years? We know they were going to real estate across North America but, generally speaking, you couldn't get most of them to buy IBM let alone Freegold, CanAlaska and Pacific North West Capital. It didn't matter what resource you had."

What do you have to do to win back investor confidence? "You've gotta be a good storyteller through the good and bad times," Barr says beaming. "You wouldn't believe how many projects Freegold has had over the past 18 years, all based around the same premise – grassroots gold exploration. In November 2003, something hit me again. I wondered what we could do to revise our corporate strategy and, more importantly, what does the investing public want in a junior? The answer was that they want a minimum of three million drill-indicated ounces in the next three years because, with ounces in the ground, the mining analysts can value us. The majors and mid-tier gold producers, desperate for replacement ounces, will look at buying some of these projects, or maybe we'll be big enough that a mid-tier producer will say, 'We like you guys, we like your exploration team, we like your projects – they might not all be near production – but one is and a couple are two or three years away – so let's just buy the whole company.' That way, it allows our exploration team to start our search again. After all, we are explorers."

Barr and his team – 12 people in the Vancouver head office, five in a satellite office in Sudbury, Ontario, and between six and eight field operators working around the clock on various projects – have edged ever closer to that goal thanks in a large part to the efforts and expertise of a man Barr calls, 'The Wayne Gretzky of mineral exploration in Alaska'. Curtis Freeman, president of the Alaskan-based Avalon Development Corporation, has been Barr's principal consultant in the state for over 17 years. "He's the best," Barr says unequivocally. "We contract with him and his people and Curt and his team in Fairbanks report to our senior guys back here, and together we develop our Alaskan projects. I love working with the Curt. I can trust him to spend our shareholders' money wisely and where it is needed. He's not only a very honest guy; he is also a very smart guy. You've got to believe in the people you do business with or else you're finished.

"Over the years we have assembled the right team of people, both technically and administratively, and together we have done what it took to keep exploring mineral projects. That's how I see this business. It's a great lifestyle and I've met a lot of exceptional people. My partnerships last for years. Our financial team, our technical team and our administrative team, the investor relations'people, our lawyers and accountants have been with us for years. We work hard, have a lot of laughs here in the office and we get the job done."

Much of his colleagues' loyalty and dedication can be attributed directly to Barr and the business philosophy he has developed over years of hard-won experience. Barr elaborates, "When the market went through those bad years from 1997 until 2003, when everyone else was down and out and couldn't raise any money and didn't have the affiliation with major companies like we did, their offices were chopped down to one or two employees. We didn't have that problem. We had contracts with big companies that put many millions of dollars into our projects.

"The joint ventures that we've put in place over the years have really allowed this group of companies to grow," he continues. "When everybody else was downsizing and declining, we kept our big projects together and acquired new ones. But, it was hard to keep it all going. Because we're in the United States we're fighting the strength of the U.S. dollar – not long ago we sent CAD$3 million to Alaska but, with the exchange, only US$1.77 million arrived. So we were fighting a major dilemma, the strength of the dollar and the fact that nobody cared about gold for the most part over the past six or seven years. Flow through financing literally kept hundreds of juniors alive in Canada through the poor years but this finance mechanism was not available in Alaska. It was a very difficult time but luckily we persisted and we diversified. I've been asked the question several times before: 'Why do you have two or three companies?'and I always answer the same way: Because if I didn't I wouldn't be sitting here at this boardroom table today. Usually one company is struggling and the other company is doing a lot better. We started a third company – which was even more difficult – but the third one, believe it or not, was the one that helped drive the other two through some very bad times because we made an extremely significant discovery in the spring of 2000 when most other companies were on their knees. Suddenly, there was a new story for our group and that brought a lot of momentum to us. Sometimes that's why you'll see promoters running off to the next new story before they have finished off with their old projects. It's often easier to tell the new story to investors than the old one. New projects for our group have often raised sufficient money to work on the new projects and to keep the old projects going through bad times. The difference with our group is that when we start something new, we don't abandon the older, less-saleable projects because they always come back around when metal and investor confidence returns to our sector."

The 'new story' in Barr's book was the formation of Pacific North West Capital Corp. (TSX: PFN), a platinum and palladium exploration company focussing on the River Valley PGM Project, a 50-50 joint venture between Pacific North West Capital Corp. and Anglo American Platinum Corporation Limited (a.k.a. Anglo Platinum), the world's largest producer of platinum. The property, located approximately 70 kilometres northeast of Sudbury, Ontario, was estimated to contain over 1 million ounces of palladium, platinum and gold in three categories in the fall of 2002, with over 70 percent of the property yet to explore. Since July 1999, Anglo Platinum has spent over $12.6 million on River Valley. Drilling in 2003 and early-2004 discovered four more new areas on the project, over 9 kilometres and a third resource calculation is in progress. The River Valley project is the third stand-alone discovery of platinum group metals of any consequence in North America in the last 20 years and is a long way from being drilled off. Platinum, an increasingly in-demand resource in the marketplace, is a highly conductive metal used in the production of high-tech electronic devices, including computers, automobile catalytic converters, new-age fuel cells, and jewelry. As Barr readily offers, however, the new stories are only good in the short run. It still takes a discovery to make a company.

It is this practical and realistic understanding of the resource industry that has kept Harry Barr in business for 25 years. That, of course, combined with the excitement the industry creates and the people Barr has been able to work with over the years. The thrill of the chase must also have a payoff for your shareholders at the end of the hunt. These days, Barr is keeping closer to home, as it were, reluctant to extend himself further afield than necessary. "At one point, we were in nine countries around the world," he says, "and now we're down to three. In fact, we'll focus on North America for the foreseeable future, though we'll probably spend a fair amount of time and money in New Zealand over the next few years. The older everybody gets, the less exotic the far away places seem to be.

"Right now," he continues, "Alaska is our main focus for gold and North America is our favourite place for the platinum group and base metals. Though I started out in the jungles of Colombia, Alaska is where I would rather work at this stage of my life. We've seen investor confidence flow back into metals, and I see a good multi-year period coming up for the junior mining industry. You always have to look to the guys who stayed in the industry – we stayed in, we went through the bad times. Sure, we had some good luck through a major discovery that helped us keep going, but it also gave us the strength to keep things together. Now we've got money and interest from the investment community and the majors – they have much smaller exploration departments these days so they need our expertise. It doesn't mean they'll enter into a joint venture with us every time ... but we can quickly arrange a meeting with any of the majors based solely on our reputation.

"Most people in our industry say you're lucky if you make one major discovery in your life," Harry Barr says wistfully, "but I believe we can find another two to three before it's all over. In this business, you have to believe. There have been some terrific highs and some horrific lows for my shareholders and our management team over the years, but through it all, there has not been one minute of boredom. Of course, we're trying to run our lives a bit more moderately these days." He then adds with a smile, "but it's hard to do. After all, we are at the beginning of another big run in the exploration sector."

FRONTEER DEVELOPMENT GROUP INCORPORATED

Geology, like any scientific discipline, is traditionally associated with empirical fact-finding and detached objectivity. Even its most zealous practitioners tend to err on the side of caution and keep their passions in check until a discovery has been made, tested and proven. Dr. Mark O'Dea, president and CEO of Vancouver-based Fronteer Development Group, holds his own as an internationally renowned and respected geologist: he placed second in the prestigious Goldcorp Challenge in 2000, and Fronteer is one of Canada's top-10 junior exploration companies. Nevertheless, he allows himself a bit of subjective leeway when talking about one of his favourite subjects.

"Gold is simply an amazing metal," enthuses O'Dea, a youthful and athletic 36-year-old. "For the past 6,000 years, since the dawn of civilization, gold has been valued, admired and envied. It has been a symbol of gods, royalty, wealth and success. Wars have been fought, kingdoms lost, loves won, and hearts broken over it. In fact, it is woven into the fabric of the human psyche and is virtually part of our DNA as a species."

Stirring words from a modern scientist, but O'Dea has a special love for gold and has built a company of talented individuals around his passion for making new discoveries. With no fewer than four Ph.D. graduates on the company's management team, and carefully considered acquisitions in some of the world's most prolific and prospective gold regions,

Fronteer Development Group Inc. (FRG: TSX) is well-positioned and well-financed. The company's proven ability to meld scientific expertise with unbridled passion sets it ahead of the pack.

"It is interesting," says O'Dea. "Most people associate the use of gold with jewelry, religious icons and dentistry and, historically, this has certainly been the case. However, the physical properties of gold are unmatched by any other metal, making it indispensable for countless applications in our society today and for the future. We wouldn't have come so far so quickly if it weren't for gold. Every year, tens of thousands of lives are saved in car crashes because of the gold used in air-bag circuitry. Energy consumption has been reduced by up to 20 percent in modern skyscrapers thanks to the thin layers of gold used in their windows. And hundreds of thousands of people have had their vision improved as a result of the role that gold plays in laser eye surgery. These are just a few examples of our reliance on gold – a reliance that grows stronger every year."

This profusion of new, nontraditional uses for gold in technology and medicine has resulted in a growing worldwide demand for the precious metal. In fact, says O'Dea, "Demand for gold exceeds production by approximately 20 million ounces per year. It is pretty clear that if the world continues to advance technologically and grow in population, we need to find more gold." Fronteer is up for the task.

"Finding gold is a science and an art, and Fronteer is at the forefront," he says. "For the average investor, the gold exploration and mining business is a complicated area with conflicting images and outdated stereotypes. At one end of the spectrum is the image of the prospector, living alone for 40 years in the bush, looking for the motherlode with his mule. At the other end, there is the polished multinational mining company that actually makes the holes in the ground, digs up the gold and turns it into bullion. There is a whole universe between these two extremes that the public doesn't understand." This is the realm of the discovery stage, what O'Dea calls the 'sweet spot.'

"This is the magical area where new gold discoveries are made and massive value is created, seemingly overnight," he says. "This is where stocks go from 50 cents to 20 dollars, and it is where Fronteer's intelligent alchemy of science, education and experience are focussed. Fronteer uses intelligence and science deliberately and strategically to focus on this sweet spot, or discovery stage. We take properties that are prospective but which have no quantified resource. Through good science, we discover their untapped potential, quantify their resources and sell the asset to a mining company for a handsome multiple on our investment. Jonathan Swift once said that vision is the art of seeing things invisible. Fronteer is focussed on discovering and analyzing gold deposits that are still invisible. Just like an iceberg reveals only one-tenth of its mass above the water, most new discoveries require innovative ways of utilizing technology and expertise to optimize their potential. Fronteer's core business lies in the science of discovery. Fronteer's expertise, technical competency and use of science and technology will allow the company to find the gold that remains hidden."

Hailing from Newfoundland, Mark O'Dea grew up on the island province and attended Memorial University in St. John's, leaving both the city and the campus in his third year of studies to relocate to Ottawa, Ontario, where he graduated with an Honours B.Sc. in Geology from Carleton University. "I come from a family that did a lot of travelling while I was growing up," he says. "As time went on, I thought geology would be a great field to get into – partly because of the travel and adventure aspect, partly because it spoke to me."

Leaving Ottawa after graduation, O'Dea headed west and went to work in the mining industry, "ending up in the high mountains of the Stikine range in the Galore Creek area of northern British Columbia," he says. "In the off-season I'd go travelling, and in the summer season I'd go up in the mountains prospecting for gold for various junior exploration companies based in Vancouver. Then in 1991, there was a bit of a dip in the market. I thought about going back to university."

Invariably, the travelling bug bit him and O'Dea set off on the kind of holiday you don't find advertised in the travel brochures. "I went and mountain-biked around New Zealand and Australia for about six months," he says. "I just went out and clocked up the kilometres. I'd ridden through the Outback on my own and was rolling into Melbourne on my last legs – all lungs and legs and nothing else – and I had a free afternoon before catching a flight back home. I decided to pay a visit to Monash University and knock on the door of a professor named Gordon Lister, whose material I had read while researching my honours thesis. I'd liked what he'd written and thought it was pretty interesting, so I paid him an unexpected visit and asked if I could do a Ph.D. with him. He just kind of looked at me, in my emaciated state, and said, 'When can you start?'" O'Dea returned to Canada, duly applied for and received scholarships, and returned to Australia six months later in 1992.

"I loaded up my Land Cruiser with long-range fuel tanks and a car fridge and drove across Australia to my field area in NW Queensland," he says, where he focussed on the structural architecture of the Western Fold Belt of the Mount Isa Inlier. "It is a big base metal and copper-gold district in Northwest Queensland. I finished my Ph.D. in 1996 and was offered a professorship at Monash University. I contemplated it, but by that time felt I'd had enough of university, so I turned it down." Instead, he took a one-year Postdoctoral Research Fellowship, studying the evolution of the Mount Isa Inlier's Eastern Fold Belt. He returned to Canada in 1997 and set about looking for opportunities.

As fate would have it, "I got a call from an Australian contact named Mike Etheridge," says O'Dea, "who ran a consulting company at the time called Etheridge, Henley and Williams. They offered me a position – in Perth! I thought, 'Why not?' so I moved back to Australia and went to work for Peter Williams for six months. Shortly thereafter I was asked to move back to Vancouver to help establish their first North American office. After about 12 months, they were bought out by SRK, an international engineering firm from South Africa, with a big presence in Vancouver." O'Dea subsequently worked as a senior geologist with the mining and exploration division of SRK Consulting Canada from 1997 to 1999, where he worked for big clients such as Placer Dome and Goldcorp.

In 1999, he left SRK and founded his own company, Riftore Consulting Inc., a Vancouver-based firm providing structural geology services to the mining industry in Alaska, Canada and India. "Those were lean times," he says. "In between cold-calling people and looking for work, I had a lot of time on my hands. It was then that I took up the Goldcorp Challenge."

One of the most successful gold companies in the world, Goldcorp hosted the Goldcorp Challenge in 2000, a contest aimed at any individual, teams, organizations, academia or government agencies involved in the resource sector. The idea was to 'stimulate global brainstorming' on data from Ontario's Red Lake Mine, where past production, combined with proven and probable reserves, totalled more than 6 million ounces of gold. Declaring that, "We are exploring for the next 6 million ounces," Goldcorp opened their books – and the contest – to the world.

"I had worked for Goldcorp as a consultant, off-and-on, for about a year prior to the contest," says O'Dea. "I had done a lot of underground and surface mapping for them and had a good handle on the geology. When they launched the Goldcorp Challenge in 2000, they invited the world to participate in evaluating their data and to come up with targets indicating where to find the next 6 million ounces of gold on the property. They had requests for data from all over the world and they put together a panel of international judges to evaluate the submissions. They said, 'Here's our data – tell us where we should be looking, tell us what we missed in our data, and tell us where we should be drilling to find more high-grade gold.' At the time, I'd landed a six-month contract in India, of all places. As I was battling my second bout of dysentery in copper-rich mountains of Rajasthan, I got the email from Goldcorp saying that I'd won second place. I thought, 'Wow, great!'"

At the Prospectors & Developers Association of Canada (PDAC) convention in March 2001, O'Dea received his award – a US$80,000 prize, as well as, "a lot of notoriety and recognition," he says. It was during this event that he was approached by Hugh Snyder and Wayne Beech to run a junior mining company that they had founded called Fronteer. Hugh and Wayne had a successful track record of building mining companies and O'Dea jumped at the chance to work with them.

"When Wayne and Hugh invited me out for breakfast to offer me the position, they asked me if I had any ideas of where to start exploring for gold. I said, 'You bet I do. I know exactly where to go and look – Red Lake.' I knew the data, I knew the geology and I knew the geologists.

"Within about 12 months we had acquired a huge land position and managed to attract three partners to fund exploration. We were off to a great start and have continued to build momentum and assets internationally over the past three-and-one-half years."

One of Fronteer Development Group's key acquisitions in Red Lake was the property which helped FRG achieve an important milestone – a listing on Canada's senior stock exchange, the TSX. This listing added a lot of credibility to the company and increased the company's access to capital.

Throughout 2003, the company continued its focus on the Red Lake Belt, increasing its land holdings to 64,000 acres and advancing many of its properties through drill programs funded by joint venture partners. "Our exploration programs have led to the discovery of promising new gold zones," he says, "and ongoing exploration should lead to some new discoveries."

In an effort to diversify risk in terms of commodity and geography, Fronteer entered into a 50-50 joint venture partnership with Altius Minerals Corp. to explore and evaluate the central mineral belt of Labrador for uranium and associated gold and copper. Recognizing the inelastic supply-demand fundamentals of uranium and the impending energy crisis, they staked up an entire uranium district in eastern Canada that has a proven endowment of at least 20 million pounds of uranium, not to mention all the new targets that they are discovering. Many of those uranium targets have associated copper, gold and silver, so they form an attractive cocktail of metals. The world's largest uranium mine is mined mainly for its copper and gold. It is called Olympic Dam, and is in South Australia. Fronteer is one of the few companies actively looking for Olympic Dam-type deposits in Canada, and they have made an excellent start in Labrador and the Northwest Territories.

"Our uranium-copper projects in both Labrador and the Northwest Territories," says O'Dea, "represent an outstanding, early-stage opportunity for a major producer to secure the best possible land position in a rapidly emerging mineral belt located in a first-world country. Canada's stability – political and economically – is a big thing. People like to invest in companies exploring in Canada because, while the geological value might be higher in places like Ghana or the Congo, the political risk is also a lot higher."

Recently Fronteer took a huge step forward in the gold exploration front through the acquisition of two advanced-stage properties in Turkey. In a deal with Teck Cominco, they can acquire a 100 percent interest in a handful of substantial epithermal gold properties in the underexplored though highly potential and economically favourable region of the coun-try. Two of the properties in particular – the Agi Dagi Property and the Kirazli Property – have preliminary gold resources outlined with poten-tial for expansion into world-class systems, and boast large bulk tonnage-style footprints with potential for high-grade ounces. Both these proper-ties have regional-scale alteration systems large enough to host multi-mil-lion ounce gold deposits similar to the famous high-sulfidation epithermal systems of Yanacocha and Alto Chicama in the Peruvian Andes.

Though the area's mining history dates back thousands of years, the region remains mostly unexplored by modern mining techniques. In fact, over the past 20 years, the untapped potential of Turkey's mineral resources has attracted the attention of senior mining companies includ-ing RTZ, Inmet, Teck Cominco, BHP Billiton, Normandy (Newmont), and Eldorado Barrick, resulting in multi-million-ounce discoveries that include the Ovacik, K,A¸kdere, Kisladag and Copler deposits. Fronteer can earn 100 percent of all properties through defined expenditures over four years, and will manage exploration on the properties using staff from the Turkish subsidiary of Teck Cominco. The Agi Dagi and Kirazli prop-erties will remain the focus of Fronteer's exploration for the next 12 to 24 months to meet the objectives of defining several millions ounces of gold.

"Through our deal with Teck Cominco," says O'Dea, "we picked up solid assets in Western Turkey in a good, geopolitically stable area. It is very Europeanized and a good place to work and do business. This deal is a testament to the strategy and business model Fronteer has developed. Obviously, we're very excited about Turkey, and working with Teck Cominco as a partner is a huge endorsement. Plus, we're using their peo-ple, so we're not having to reinvent the wheel. Teck's people know Turkey, they know the language and they know the mining, political and land-management systems.

"One of the things that I'm proud of having built here at Fronteer," O'Dea continues, "is a company that both the majors and the investing public feel secure in owning. We've got big outside shareholders: Placer Dome, Goldcorp and now Teck Cominco – three majors. Not a bad con-stituency for a company of our size."

In short, Fronteer Development has covered a lot of ground – both lit-erally and allegorically – in the three years since O'Dea joined the team, diversifying not only its mineral portfolio but its roster of joint-venture partners. It specializes in the science of discovery and is focussed on an interesting mix of 'discovery stage' opportunities. It is also firmly grounded in the financial world with strong ties to the capital markets and opinion leaders. The company's stock trades well with enough liquidity to attract a healthy institutional base, and the company's portfolio is attractive to both gold and uranium investors. The management team at Fronteer are standing on the 'shoulders of giants.' The board and advisory Board are an experienced group of seasoned professionals who provide unique insights and guidance to the directors of the company.

O'Dea is quick to credit his colleagues at Fronteer for not only indulging his vision but supporting him every step of the way. "From the beginning," he stresses, "we were striking out at things that we had the technical expertise to deal with. We've got four Ph.D.s here with backgrounds in structural geology or geochemistry, and their strengths lie in delineating gold systems, like Red Lake, and in uranium-copper-gold systems, of the type we're looking for in Labrador and the Northwest Territories. The guys behind Fronteer have been involved in a number of very successful ventures. We have built a fantastic vehicle and have the right team behind it."

In particular, there is Dr. Rick Valenta, Fronteer's vice-president of exploration. "Rick is one of the world's gurus when it comes to evaluating and looking at these types of deposits," says O'Dea. "There are maybe half-a-dozen people in the world who can do what Rick does."

Valenta has worked in exploration and development on six continents and is recognized internationally for his extensive knowledge of gold-copper deposits. Over the past decade, he played a pivotal role in the Australian minerals industry by pioneering holistic approaches to mineral exploration that integrate geophysics and structural geology.

Then there is Wayne Beech. "Wayne is a key player behind Fronteer," says O'Dea. "He is a savvy businessman and property entrepreneur, who has an incredible track record. He creates companies and structures them, putting the right management team behind them."

Fronteer's current chairman, Oliver Lennox-King, has 29 years experience in the mining industry, including 11 years as a mining analyst with the brokerage community, as well as an additional 11 years in executive positions and directorships with junior mining companies. He is currently chairman of Southern Cross Resources, a uranium exploration and development company, and he serves on the boards of several Canadian resource companies, including Metallica Resources and Dumont Nickel. "Oliver was one of the founders and presidents of Pangea Goldfields," says O'Dea, "which had developed similar models to those which Fronteer is implementing." Lennox-King was likewise cofounder and president of Tiomin Resources.

Director George Bell has more than 36 years experience in the international natural resource industry. He is president and CEO of Hornby Bay Exploration Limited, a junior uranium and diamond exploration company, and a director of Southern Cross Resources Inc. Between 1967 and 1996, Bell held several senior executive positions with the Noranda Group of companies, and has held directorships and executive positions in the Americas, Asia and Europe.

Director Donald McInnes was project manager for Vancouver-based mineral exploration consultants Equity Engineering from 1987 to 1993. Since then, he has founded five public companies, three of them involved in mineral exploration and two in the technology sector, raising some $15 million in venture capital for these and other enterprises. Currently president of Western Keltic Mines Inc. and Blackstone Ventures Inc., McInnes is likewise a past president of the B.C. and Yukon Chamber of Mines and a director of the Pacific Mineral Museum, the Prospectors & Developers Association of Canada, and an advisory board member to the Mining School at the British Columbia Institute of Technology.

George Cross, special advisor to the board of directors, is "well-known around town and a great liaison," says O'Dea. From 1962 to 2000, Cross was publisher and owner of the George Cross Newsletter Limited, a 12-page daily newsletter primarily chronicling the activities of mineral and petroleum resource companies in western Canada. He has also served as a director of several public companies, and has been the author of numerous annual and quarterly reports, news releases and promotional brochures. He is presently a resource consultant with Canaccord Capital Corporation.

"It is all about quality and discovery," says O'Dea. "I want Fronteer to be a company that investors feel secure about. I want them to be able to sleep well at night and not worry about their investment in our company. If they've invested in us, they can be assured it's going to be for the long term. We hire the best people, build the best teams, do the best work and build the world's best portfolio of projects. Fronteer's share price has doubled over the last six months and it's going to double again. If you want a quick momentum play, we're not the company for you. We're serious about building real assets that have value. Why should anyone believe me? The only reason would be based on our track record – we've delivered on every promise we've made and, in doing so, we've garnered trust.

"Geology is my craft," he concludes. "I've spent a lot of time learning about it, and I'm fascinated by it. I am equally motivated by the business aspect of the company – keeping it financed and properly managed. But underlying all of this is the basic desire to do the best I can at everything I do – whether it's mountain-biking across Australia or running a mining company. Right now and in the future, the world needs more gold. Fronteer is the company that is going to find more gold."

GOLDCORP
INCORPORATED

Sometimes the measure of a company can best be determined by the measure of the person behind it. Such is the case with Goldcorp Inc. and Robert McEwen. With a treasury hitting close to US$400 million, a market cap of $3.2 billion and a portfolio boasting the richest gold mine in the world in Red Lake, it's certain Goldcorp is no ordinary company. That's because Rob McEwen is no ordinary man.

Once apprised of the company's wealth and inspiring success story, its top ranking in the Financial Post's annual list of the richest companies in Canada, the cutting-edge technology employed and multiple prestigious awards, one might expect Goldcorp's fearless leader to be intimidating at best, arrogant at worst or, at the very least, hurried and miserly with his time. This is not the case.

McEwen, who takes a break in mid-2004 to discuss Goldcorp's story, happens to be a delight – generous with his time and insights, engagingly provocative and thoughtful. His voice is measured and soft, and while he maintains a conversational tone, this chairman and CEO obviously thinks before he speaks. His relaxed demeanour aside, it's apparent McEwen is passionate about both business and the business of life in general. He doesn't spend this time spouting off geo-technical jargon, running down a checklist of accomplishments, interpreting dizzying facts and figures or, conversely, simplifying the story into key but broad words like focus and determination. He touches on all those points, but presents many of them in trademark McEwen parables.

McEwen speaks of things like being inspired by watching a stream when he was a boy – being amazed that no matter how firmly he tried to dam it with a big rock, eventually a trickle of water would find its way through. A new stream, a new sound, would be born. Out of an obstacle, an opportunity. Not a bad lesson to learn. He talks about travelling to Europe when he was a young adult and having his eyes opened for the first time as to Canada's place in the global scheme of things. He has absolutely no hesitation discussing politics and, in fact, can get quite emphatic about its perceived failings. He has a very definite world view, he questions everything and won't rest until he has found a better answer.

The bottom line is that McEwen thinks outside the box. He has never been and refuses to be a follower, is endlessly curious and unafraid, and is compelled to constantly re-frame problems in order to find alternate solutions. He sees no reason why he must settle for the status quo, and no reason why anyone else should either. He doesn't have to answer to anyone except his shareholders, and it's certain none of them have any complaints ... especially when they receive their nice fat dividends.

He could walk away from it all right now as a very rich man, but he won't. And why? To quote the man himself:

"There's more to find."

Yes, there's more gold to find, more money to be made, and more to give away – which he does on a regular basis. The beneficiaries of McEwen's generosity are organizations he deems worthy, with mandates that strike a personal chord, run by individuals or groups that share his vision for a better world. He is particularly struck by things going on in medicine, education and the arts and to that end, has donated millions of personal dollars to his chosen causes. In April 2004, he donated a million dollars to the Red Lake Margaret Cochenour Memorial Hospital for a much needed renovation project. Last year, he gifted the Toronto General & Western Hospital Foundation with $10 million to establish the McEwen Centre for Regenerative Medicine at University Health Network. A million and a half went to York University's Schulich School of Business where McEwen did his MBA, and within the last three years McEwen's donated over $14 million into various charities, including the Royal Ontario Museum and a museum up in Red Lake.

"I just thought that Mother Nature had been very kind to me and I should give some back. There are a lot of needs out there," he says simply.

Shrugging off any kind of Good Samaritan label, McEwen responds drily and pointedly: "The politicians don't seem to be doing it."

Point taken.

All these things that are an intrinsic part of McEwen's character and nature, have parlayed themselves into his business strategies and philosophies and Goldcorp's shareholders are the richer for it. A force to be reckoned with in the market, Goldcorp is a leader in hi-tech advances and is, in fact, the only company to hold back gold.

But where did it all begin?

For McEwen it began with his father, Don McEwen. A stockbroker by trade, the senior McEwen had Rob charting stocks at the young ages of 10 and 11 years. At age 12, Rob made his first investment.

"I made nine times on my money in about a year and a half and thought that's all there was to the stock market. I spent the next 30 years learning that wasn't the stock market," McEwen recalled.

In the mid-60s, McEwen's father took a keen interest in gold. When gold shot up to $850 an ounce in 1980, both he and his clients profited handsomely and 15-year-old Rob watched and learned.

"That's where I got the gold bug ... at the dining room table," he said.

During his late teens and twenties, Rob's home schooling continued as he observed his father grubstaking various people, putting money into their mining properties. This exposure gave Rob the view that 'gold is money', a credo he still embraces to this day. With such a background, a career in the mining industry would seem a given for the younger McEwen. Initially however, he resisted, believing his path lay in the investment industry and business school. Despite this conviction, and subsequent realization of an MBA from York University's Schulich School of Business, Rob's first summer job was at International Nickel (Inco) in Sudbury, working underground. He declined a scholarship when offered one by Inco.

"I don't think mining's going to be my life," he said at the time.

But while working on his BA in economic history, McEwen was also gaining an education underground, learning how to operate jackleg and jumbo drills and getting a hands-on look at the business of mining. After graduating with his BA, McEwen stuck to the original plan and worked for three years at his father's brokerage firm.

"I focussed on the market, but with a particular emphasis on the natural resource sector ... on gold mining worldwide," he said.

Following that stint, McEwen returned to school to pursue his MBA. Again, his father indirectly influenced that decision.

"My father had a Master's and I wanted to have a minimum of what he had. It was one of my goals," McEwen said.

With his newly granted MBA in hand, McEwen accepted a job at Merrill Lynch with the self-imposed condition he postpone his start date for six months in order to do some travelling. At 28 years of age, Rob McEwen wanted to see the world and that's exactly what he did.

"I ended up taking a trip that took me around the world, it was basically like walking into pictures of National Geographic ... throwing away my watch, and travelling in a converted army truck from London to Katmandu, then by bus, boat and plane through Asia. I also embarked on a tour of the Silk Road, following in Marco Polo's footsteps.

Grab a knapsack, throw it in the back of a truck, stop in the local markets and buy your food ... it was terrific. For a number of reasons, I figured I wouldn't be able to ever do it again"

This trip would have a profound influence on McEwen's world view. Combined with a keen interest in politics that was triggered in university where McEwen headed up a graduate student council, served on advisory boards to the deans and worked as a small business consultant, the overseas experience had a great impact.

"I still have very vivid memories of that trip ... it gave me a really different view of the world from a North American perspective," McEwen said. "Social issues, business issues, political issues ... we live a really privileged life over here, it doesn't matter where you are. North Americans better wake up because there's this huge labour pool over there that's going to come like a tidal wave across and they'll buy this place."

Back in North America, McEwen worked for Merrill Lynch for a couple of years after which he hooked up with his father again at the broker-age business.

"I came back and bought an interest in his firm, called McEwen Easson Ltd. at the time, and we created Goldcorp shortly thereafter, which was a closed-end investment company. We started work on it in 1980 and it finally went public in 1983," said McEwen.

At the time, the company was running two mutual funds – Goldfund and Goldtrust. After bandying about several names, they came up with Goldcorp. According to McEwen, they were creating a vehicle that allowed institutions to get around a requirement stating all their money be invested in Canadian companies.

"We created a company that would allow them to own gold bullion, which they couldn't own, and to invest in foreign securities through a Canadian company," McEwen explained.

"It was the first of its kind."

In retrospect, it's fitting that Goldcorp's beginnings were so innova-tive, catching the market by surprise and spawning immediate imitators. It's a pattern that continues to this day.

"As I was doing it, I observed various opportunities in the mining industry and I came up with some thoughts as to what a gold mining com-pany should look like," said McEwen.

But before Goldcorp's story took off in its current direction, there was a tragic setback in 1986 when Don McEwen suddenly and unexpectedly died. After six years of working shoulder to shoulder with his father, 'a great inspiration and innovator', Rob was on his own.

"The tests that are placed in front of you along the way are all about how you react to them. If you find you can get over them, as everyone should be able to, and you find yourself on the other side you can say: 'Wow, the next time something like this comes along, I have the confi-dence to keep doing it again. It's do-able.'"

Reflecting on his father's own struggles and determination, McEwen recalls how as a young man Don McEwen joined the British army's offi-cer training corps in India. While there, he contracted polio on three sep-arate occasions, the last attack felling him.

"He got sent home in an iron lung and the doctors said, 'Well, your legs are probably going to go gangrene, so we're going to cut them off and you're going to be in bed for the rest of your life and you'll be a vegetable.'

"That's probably not what you want to hear when you're 18 or 19. So he said, 'I'm not going to stay in bed for the rest of my life.'"

Ignoring the doctors' dire predictions, Don McEwen got up and got busy.

"From that point on, it was determination and the power of the mind. He got out of bed, worked himself until he was well developed in his upper body and he got around on crutches. There was nothing that would hold him back."

After leaving the hospital, Don McEwen pushed on with characteristic fortitude. Working for an insurance company during the day, he took his Masters of Commerce at night, became a serious student of the market and ended up having a successful career in the investment industry, becoming one of the pioneers in the gold investment arena.

"So for me, whenever I bump into an obstacle, and there have been a couple, I always think about what Dad had to overcome. Nothing is impossible," states McEwen.

It's all about that boulder in the stream, really. McEwen's sharp business acumen notwithstanding, there's something almost zen-like in the way he views life and, ultimately, business.

"There's always this energy flowing," he says. "To me, it's very much like life. You can have these obstacles dropped in front of you like a big rock, and it's taller than you are and you can't get around it, but it's the force of life that keeps going.

"There were a couple of interesting things that happened after the stream got around the boulder. One, the stream never stopped. And two, afterwards there was another sound ... this music in the stream as the water came over the rock and burbled along. It changed it, it didn't stop it. But that experience created some music, another aspect. So the stream was richer for that."

That's Rob McEwen talking. Profound, politic and, dare we say, a bit poetic. As Goldcorp's story unfolds, it becomes easy to see how all these experiences played a role in its ultimate and ongoing success.

Following Don McEwen's untimely death, the younger McEwen forged on in a manner that would no doubt make his father proud. He immediately brought in some partners at the brokerage firm to focus on building it, while he devoted more attention to gold mining investments. They hit the market in 1986.

"It was a key period and a lesson for me that the larger the number of people working for you, and if you hit the market at the right time, the more wealth you can create. We went from 20 people to 120 people in about a year and, until we moved to new quarters, we just kept adding bodies. You'd have to crawl over a desk or two to get to your own desk. It was really tight but really efficient. We didn't have a lot of overhead, it was very exciting, the market was hot, and we're putting money into everybody's pockets."

At this point, Goldcorp was still an investment fund investing in gold bullion and gold mining securities from around the world. Around this time, McEwen met a few different people who would have a great influence, Murray Pezim being one of them.

"I watched him make two fortunes, lose them both, and make a third. His actions demonstrated there is a cycle in the marketplace, times you want to buy, sit still, or sell. This flow is ever-present in the market and in mining, it's quite classic," said McEwen.

And we're back to flow. As much as McEwen understands the importance of getting around an obstacle that blocks the flow, conversely he also acknowledges the strategy of going against it. Following the pack is not in his nature.

"I enjoy buying distress," he says simply. "I like buying things that other people don't. I like to invest when others aren't buying. If you buy what's popular, you're never going to get a good return on it."

Aside from being inspired by Pezim, McEwen also credits his uncle Tim Beatty with playing a large role in his life after his father's death. A skilled investor, Beatty was head of Burns Fry, governor of the TSE, commissioner of the Ontario Securities Commission, and worked closely with McEwen. Also getting the nod from McEwen is Ian Delaney, who hired him at Merrill Lynch.

"Ian is a very skilled, very aggressive guy. He put in long hours and seemed to think harder than most of the competition. He showed that if you could do that, you could gain an advantage. And it's all about gaining an advantage."

Whether he's backpacking around Europe or discussing mining opportunities with Pezim, McEwen has learned to embrace the value in alternate perspectives.

"You look at a problem statement and re-frame it. When you re-frame it, you can often generate alternatives that haven't been considered and when you get there, you have other paths to follow," he says.

What you don't do, according to McEwen, is take the path most followed.

"I've learned that I won't stand in line," he says firmly. "If I do, I'm only going to get where I'm going as fast as the person in front of me. So I'll step out of line and see where I want to go. I've found that this path is never a straight line, but if you keep that vision, that target in mind, you will get there before many of the people you would've had to wait for."

In other words, step out of line and take control of your own destiny.

"A lot of people say they are fearful of the unknown and I don't understand that because the unknown, by definition, can be either good or bad.

"I would like to see more Canadians be proactive. I think as a country we have to take greater control because there is huge competition out there and if we don't recognize it and change, our lifestlye is in great jeopardy. It's a transitory stage in our life and the world is altering very rapidly."

So armed with his life lessons and philosophies, McEwen tackles the challenge of Goldcorp. In a typical McEwen move, he decided to re-frame the situation in an effort to create greater value. His decision was to convert the investment company into an operating company.

"In 1987, I asked the shareholders to change our investment restrictions to essentially free its latent economic strength. We'll be able to borrow, we won't be restricted in what we can buy and, in fact, we can concentrate our assets rather than make them diversified."

In 1989, McEwen jumped into a hostile takeover battle and bought control of two mining companies. Corona Corporation had made a hostile bid for two companies, Dickenson Mines and Kam Kotia Mines, one being controlled by the other. One of the companies also owned a controlling interest in another company called Wharf Resources. Corona essentially made a bid to acquire control of all three.

In the meantime, McEwen had been spinning his wheels for six months while waiting on another related deal that ultimately fell through, and he decided this was an opportune moment to take Goldcorp into its new incarnation as an operating company.

"I decided I'll jump into the takeover bid, make a higher bid and become what in the industry is known as a white knight, where you're supporting management. The other side didn't like that, they took us to court, they lost, and our bid was successful."

Within 45 days, Goldcorp was the controlling shareholder of two mining companies. McEwen let existing management run the companies, but he and another director took seats on both boards. It only took four months before McEwen began scratching his head and asking questions.

"I'm sitting there listening to a presentation of what we were going to do for the next year and because I like numbers, I started calculating what I thought the profitability would look like."

As the board began detailing its various working areas in one of the mines, McEwen sat back doing the math and came to the mystifying conclusion it didn't seem to add up.

"In the first area we were going to work, by my calculations we were going to lose money. I thought, 'Well, that's odd.'"

Intrigued, McEwen pressed on with his figuring and 'tuned out the board meeting'.

"I thought, 'We're losing there ... and there ... and wow, at current prices we're going to lose money in 50 percent of the areas we're going to work in. Why would we want to do that?'"

After confirming he had used the correct calculations for determining profitability, McEwen politely asked the obvious question – why are we approving a plan that will see us losing money in 50 percent of the areas we're about to work in? Nobody knew the answer to that question and when the president was ultimately queried, his response was unsatisfactory, to say the least.

His reply? "I'll get back to you."

Wrong answer. McEwen certainly wasn't going to sit still for that, as the board would quickly discover.

"I thought, 'I'm sitting around this table, everybody's 15 years my senior, they've all come from the mining industry and they're about to approve a plan that I don't think I'll make any money on.'"

A couple of meetings later, McEwen decided to exercise his right as CEO of the controlling shareholder and reconstitute the board.

"They didn't like that," he said, adding that at the time he was 36 years old and challenging professionals who were 50-plus.

Six months of behind the scenes maneuvering and intrigue ensued, with attempts to discredit McEwen or get rid of him entirely.

"They were saying, 'Here's this kid and he's controlling a pretty big company. But we're better known, we have more credibility, let's take it for ourselves.'"

A campaign was underway and McEwen realized he needed vigilance and canniness to determine who his 'enemies' were. Someone recommended he learn to play speed chess, 'so that your reaction time is faster'.

When the dust had settled a year later, McEwen was the one left standing at the annual meeting. He took out the board of directors and became chairman and CEO of both operating companies.

"I stepped out of the investment industry and into the mining industry."

It was a tumultuous but strong beginning and a personal victory for McEwen. Fortunately for Goldcorp's shareholders, McEwen's natural curiosity and relentless questioning would continue, as it does to this day. A year after replacing the initial boards, he found it necessary to replace the senior management team of the operating company. Obviously they hadn't learned the first time that McEwen wants creative answers to important questions. As it would turn out, the question he was asking this time concerned Red Lake Mine, now the richest gold mine in the world.

At the time, McEwen was told Red Lake Mine was on its last legs. It had a debt equity ratio of 1:1, about $50 million worth of debt, was extremely high cost, had a problem labour situation and outwardly, there didn't seem to be many incentives to invest in it. McEwen attacked the situation head on, asking the obvious question to head of operations – "How can we get our costs down?"

His reply? "Well, we can't."

Them's fightin' words when you're talking to someone like Rob McEwen.

"I said, 'Wait a minute. There's nothing you can do in a business that's 45 years old?' He said, 'No, either the price of gold goes up or we have to find more gold.'"

Wrong answer. That person found himself out of a job.

McEwen hired Rolly Francisco, formerly of Lac Minerals, to take over the duties of Senior VP and CFO. Together, he and Rolly rebuilt the management team and did a good job of improving the financial situation. Red Lake is now a major success story, recognized worldwide.

"We took an asset that was considered without a future and today it's the richest gold mine in the world, meaning it has the highest concentration of gold per tonne of any mine anywhere and it's one of the lowest cost gold producers in operation today," says McEwen.

"We went from being outside the top 25 gold mines by market cap to now being in the top 10. In profitability, we're right near the top. And certainly from a return on invested capital, we're the best."

That recognition is duly noted in last year's Financial Post annual survey of the 800 largest corporations in Canada, wherein Goldcorp was ranked third best by profit margin when gold was only $320 an ounce. Today its market cap is about CAD$3.2 billion, a far cry from its 1993 market cap of about $60 million.

For about two years after the board and management shakeup, McEwen found himself under attack from the same people he had previously ditched. It was becoming obvious to everyone that this young upstart not only had his own ideas, but they were good ones. According to McEwen, the campaigns being waged leading up to annual meetings were aggressive, vigorous and full of drama. The press was also constantly on alert.

"I could've sold theatre tickets," McEwen chuckles.

During those boisterous two years, the debt was eliminated and McEwen decided it was time to concentrate on exploration. In 1995, he handed $10 million to his exploration department and said: "Here. Go explore."

Six weeks later, they were back with something promising at Red Lake. Out of nine drill holes, the average grade or concentration of gold per hole, was 30 times what they'd been mining, at nine ounces per tonne. These new drill holes were well-removed from where they'd been previously mining and located in a completely different setting.

"That's when the rocket ride started. We just took off," McEwen recalled.

The next obvious question was size. How big is it? McEwen stepped up the exploration, despite being in the midst of ongoing labour strife at the unionized mine.

"So, we make this discovery but it's 2,000 feet away from where we're mining and it's not something you can bring onstream quickly. In fact, you can't even bring it on in a year. I want to work this mine better, I want to introduce new technologies and I'd like to see more training put in place."

In order to best determine what they had, McEwen knew changes needed to be made and he approached the union with his ideas.

The union's answer? "No."

True to form, McEwen wouldn't accept that and he dug his heels in.

"I said to our guys, 'Well, there's either going to be a short strike or a long strike because we have to change.'"

The strike lasted an unprecedented 46 months.

Although no gold was being produced from the mine during that time, McEwen and company weren't sitting idly on the sidelines. Exploration was stepped up by 25 percent and the deposit kept growing. But tension was building with each month the strike dragged on. The union wanted to go back to work, the shareholders were antsy, staff didn't enjoy being bussed in and out of the site, and the situation affected everyone in the small neighbouring towns of Red Lake and Balmertown. But McEwen knew if he agreed to the original terms, he'd be losing money. As well, the price of gold was plummeting. By 1999, it was $250 an ounce ... $110 lower than what it would cost to produce it. Exploration continued, but the union began picketing annual meetings demanding a return to work. McEwen could only point out the obvious – they can't control the gold price. Things took a nasty turn when he received a written death threat.

"It basically said, 'If you want blood, we'll give you blood. You've got 30 days. Remember Yellowknife.'"

The implication was ominous. The same union had been involved in a labour dispute at a Yellowknife mine and a union member was ultimately convicted of planting a bomb in the bottom of the mine that killed nine people. There was no way McEwen was going to cave in to that. He acted immediately.

First he reprinted the death threat in the local paper and offered a $35,000 bounty on the head of the person who wrote it. Next, he hired an investigative group of former drug squad detectives and metro police to check out the vulnerability of the mine site. He replaced all the windows in his own home with bulletproof glass and had a SWAT team visit the house twice. Fortunately nothing came of the threat, but its author was never discovered.

Time dragged on, the low gold price wasn't helping matters, and McEwen's offers kept dropping accordingly with each meeting he had with the union head. Strikers were steadily disheartened, but McEwen pushed ahead with other matters.

"We tore down the old mine, built a new mine, wired it with fibre-optics, beta testing with wireless, and we looked at automation underground. We're still doing that, we're working with M D Robotics, the people who make the Canadarm."

McEwen wasn't about to let a strike hinder progress and rebuilding a state-of-the-art plant was conducted through the picket line.

"We set up a camp. We weren't doing any production, all we were doing was exploring and then building the new mine, so we hadn't taken any jobs away that way. I said, 'Look, the faster we get this built, the sooner you can come back.'"

Just before starting up production at the new facility, McEwen made one last offer.

"You're either with us or you're not. The contractors who built the new mine are going to mine it and unfortunately we only need a third as many people."

Finally, the strike settled with McEwen offering a package that included stock options. Although there was some grumbling about that, Goldcorp's history proves it was an extremely profitable move if they'd held onto those stocks. But the intrigue wasn't quite over yet. After settling, the union decided to decertify and leave.

"I called my labour negotiator and labour lawyer to tell them and they said, 'Impossible. This has never happened in Canadian mining history.'"

But it did happen, another first.

"A vote was taken, they decertify, we're non-union and we go forward with the contractors. We remain to this day non-union, with a third-party contractor doing all of the hourly work," said McEwen.

With the tumult and drama now just a memory, a slice of Goldcorp's colourful history, the road ahead indeed seems paved with gold. McEwen continues to push boundaries, explore new avenues of possibility, and keep abreast of technology and new talent. At Red Lake, a virtual reality lab has just been built to help accelerate the exploration effort.

"I think it's the first of its kind on any mine site in the world," says McEwen, reflecting on how far they've come.

"I look down the lane and see back a number of years ago ... the shack, the fire and the picketers, the gated fence and the tired town. Now there's construction everywhere, about 30 companies exploring in the Red Lake District, making it one of the most actively explored areas for gold. There's real prosperity now, it's really upbeat. Houses are painted, lawns are cut, flowers are growing. What a change. It's so nice to see, and a lot of that came about from our discovery and our continuing fortunate discoveries."

Part of what drew interest to the area and stepped up understanding of Red Lake was yet another creative idea on the part of McEwen. In

2000, he decided to hold a contest, an internet challenge that would enable them to better determine the size of the Red Lake discovery. They took all their proprietary geological data dating back to 1948, all the drill holes and everything related to the ore body, combined it with 2-D and 3-D software, and pushed it all out over the web.

"We said to the world, 'This information is yours, free of charge. It's for competitors or anybody who wants it can have it with no strings attached.

"We want you to take a look at what is probably one of the most exciting gold discoveries in the world and tell us where we'll find the next six million ounces of gold. For those insights, we'll give you prizes totaling half a million dollars US.'"

The challenge was launched in March 2000 at the annual PDAC conference and, within the four-month registration period, 1,400 people from 50 countries received the data file. Five judges were chosen from all over the world – Australia, South Africa, the U.S. and Canada – and were comprised of geologists, discoverers and academics. McEwen wanted to see the most innovative thinking and the best geological logic.

"It was extraordinary. We saw everything we would expect, but then we saw people using applied math, advanced physics, intelligence systems, computer graphics like I'd never seen before in the industry – and it was coming from all over the world."

Recognition began pouring in. Business Week named Goldcorp one of the 50 most innovative companies worldwide on the web in September 2000, Forbes did a write-up on the company, Northern Miner awarded them with 2003 Mining Man of the Year and the PDAC bestowed a Developer of the Year award for 2002. And that's just to name a few.

"We received lots of industry awards and our shareholders have done really well," McEwen notes.

But the internet challenge did more than garner recognition. It also performed its purpose and, as a direct result, enabled Goldcorp to indeed find its next six million ounces of gold. The judges selected 25 semifinalists who submitted 110 exploration targets, 50 percent of which were brand new.

"We hadn't given them any of our targets so we had all sorts of third-party confirmation about how we were going about our hunt. It put Goldcorp on the map worldwide and it accelerated our exploration program. We found the six million ounces and now we're looking for the next six million ounces of gold."

Out of this hi-tech process, Goldcorp delved deeper into the virtual reality field, linking up with Mirarco Mining Innovation, a research arm of Laurentian University. Laurentian was adapting technology used in the oil and gas industry to the mining industry and Goldcorp was one of its early sponsors and supporters. Recently, Goldcorp built a stand-alone facility at its Red Lake mine that is wired to Sudbury.

"If we need to use their technicians they can just be on-line. It's got a 20-foot wide screen about 10 feet high. It's neat. You put special glasses on and it all comes in 3-D," McEwen explains.

"It's all about trying to find a competitive edge."

Red Lake has become a growing, bustling concern where the activity is nonstop. In McEwen's words, "there's construction all over the place", the site now boasts 160 people on staff and another 200-plus on contract. Currently, they're expanding the mine and sinking a new shaft that will go down about 7,200 feet, or the equivalent of four CN towers. This will dramatically increase capacity.

"In the first phase it will increase our gold production by 40 percent and lower our costs by 16 percent to below $70 an ounce."

As to how long he sees this continuing, McEwen says 11 years minimum.

"But we've been finding high-grade gold at an average cost of $11 an ounce over the last nine years and we can produce it for under $80 and we can sell it for more than $380."

The math and savvy management puts Goldcorp at the bottom of the cost curve, an attractive proposition no matter how you add it up.

"As a company, we don't have any debt, we haven't sold any of our gold forward, we have strong cash flows, strong earnings and we reported our best earnings last year ... US$99 million and $260 million in revenue."

The treasury currently breaks down as US$330 million cash, $30 million in gold bullion and $18 million in marketable securities, adding up to a grand total of just under US$380 million.

In 2001, believing the price of gold had reached a 20-year low and was going higher, Goldcorp began withholding gold production. In 2001, they held back five percent. In 2002, they held back 10 percent of production and also bought some gold, believing it was about to go higher. By the end of September 2003, they had 270,000 ounces of gold sitting in vaults in Toronto and New York.

How much gold is that?

"It was more gold than the Bank of Canada, more gold than what was held by 50 of the 114 central banks that own gold," says McEwen.

Late last year, McEwen sold the gold due to a new Ontario government that changed the tax rates and, by doing so, made $72 more an ounce than would have if sold when it was produced. Currently, they've started rebuilding that position and at the end of the first quarter 2004, are up to 72,000 ounces of gold.

"We're the only gold company in the world that holds back gold, that doesn't sell all the gold it produces," says McEwen.

The reason other companies don't hold back gold, he speculates, is that their costs are generally higher. Goldcorp's break-even is very low.

"And I had a very positive view on the price of gold. I think over the next six years it's going to test the old highs of $850 an ounce. I think in 2004, perhaps a bit longer, it has to consolidate and trade in the range of about $370 to $450 and, during that time, it will present some opportunities to us. That's one of the reasons I sold our gold because I thought gold was going to stall for awhile."

Another bonus for shareholders is that Goldcorp pays one of the highest dividends in the gold mining industry in North America, says McEwen. Since they started paying dividends in 2001, $97 million has gone out as of mid-2004.

"As the price of gold goes up, we'll continue to pay out more. I think it's a very good discipline for management to say that the money we're making isn't all going to be used on projects – we have to give some back to shareholders immediately while we're building assets. We just have to be more efficient with the assets we're being given."

And although Red Lake is the overwhelming story, shareholders have a stake in other projects, all managed with the same eye to excellence and innovative hand. There's another gold mine in South Dakota, the Wharf mine, which will be closing in three years and an industrial mineral operation in Saskatchewan that produces sodium sulphate, the principal ingredient in detergents. There's plenty of information on Goldcorp's website as to all its properties and projects, but Red Lake is 'the driver', according to McEwen.

"Red Lake is the central theme, but it's not the only one," he says.

Goldcorp is also continually looking for properties and has invested in about eight or nine promising junior companies. In many cases, Goldcorp holds a reasonably large equity position in addition to joint ventures where they're earning an interest in the property or have right of first refusal.

"We're extending our exploration reach in a number of corners of the world through relationships with these juniors. If they do find something, we're in a good position to help them take it further. We have the financial strength and operating strength and the desire to see their dream materialize."

It's difficult to peg Goldcorp precisely as to where it fits in the hierarchy of mining companies. By market cap ($3 billion), they're in the top 10 largest gold mines in the world, albeit at the bottom of that list with other majors up around $13 billion. By comparison, McEwen reckons a large junior company would be in the 2 to 3 hundred million dollar market cap.

"We're close to a major by valuation in the marketplace. By production, we're not in the top 10," explains McEwen.

"Our balance sheet is one of the best in the industry, we're the only company in the world that holds back its gold bullion production, we don't have any debt, we don't hedge, we pay a monthly dividend. And we're North American based, so there's low political risk. We're at the bottom of the cost curve for the industry, so there's low commodity price risk."

And of course, there's McEwen himself and what he consistently brings to the framework of the company. That's something you can't put a price on.

"We try to push the envelope and keep pushing it ... to see if we can be a little more innovative because following the herd just means you eat their dust and you get there after they do."

McEwen has a great desire to get more people interested in gold, and educated in investing, in watching the cycles and the market more closely. Part of the reason Goldcorp has such a presence in terms of name recognition is that its CEO understands not only the value in telling your story, but also the responsibility of doing so.

"You should tell your story and tell it well. Part of the goal is to get people to think about gold. One percent of the total equity investment dollars in the world goes into gold stocks ... one percent! That means there's 99 percent of the market that has no exposure to gold. To me, that's an untapped market. That's the market you're after, rather than fighting for a share of the one percent.

"It's a lot more work, but if people start thinking gold and they associate Goldcorp with gold and gold starts moving ... then our shareholders should be the beneficiaries. So it's all about growing the per share value of the company."

And does he have any advice for potential investors and shareholders? You bet he does. Buy gold and buy it now. If McEwen's predictions are correct and gold hits all-time highs in this new cycle, the time is right. Or, as McEwen would say:

"Gold is money. And Goldcorp is gold."

HIGH RIVER GOLD MINES LIMITED

On the cover of its 1999 annual report and in every report since, High River Gold has posed the same question – Why gold? The answer to that question has fallen to David Mosher, High River's amiable and approachable President and CEO.

"We felt that even though we were at a bottom in 1999, this was the most opportune time to buy gold and gold shares during the last 20 years. And it's turned out to be correct," says Mosher, who is relating High River's story from his Toronto office in mid-2004.

Certainly there was very little enthusiasm for buying shares of gold companies back in the late-1990s, but High River not only managed to survive the dark days, it's now a large, thriving, junior gold-producing company poised to emerge as a healthy mid-tier company with considerable assets in West Africa, Russia and Canada. Having successfully stayed the course through those bleak years speaks not only to faith, determination and savvy management, but also to investor confidence in the High River team. Mosher recalls those early days when the lustre of gold wasn't nearly as bright as it is today. "We really had to batten down the hatches and do everything we could to survive, so that when things turned around we still had a company we could finance and then move the assets we had into development mode."

He credits professionals like 'technical analyst' Ian Notley for correctly interpreting trends and cycles, and 'astute investor'Eric Sprott with not only accurately forecasting the gold market, but also putting his faith and money in High River back when nobody was interested in either gold or High River.

"Eric did very well with the funds he managed and heavily invested them in the gold market at bottom-basement prices. Fortunately for us, he liked High River and took a significant position in us at the time."

Sprott clearly knew the answer to 'Why gold?' and, although these days it's an easier question to answer, Mosher continues to ask and answer it every year.

"We felt if we couldn't convince people they should buy gold, there was very little reason for them to buy High River Gold. Each year we have updated the 'Why gold?' question." Although Mosher concedes it was 'very lonely'in the late-1990s, things began to look up in 2000 as the gold market improved immensely. High River was able to capitalize on this transition period to acquire a new gold-polymetallic project in Russia (Berezitovy) at a very reasonable cost and to take a project it held in West Africa (Taparko) off the shelf; bankable feasibility studies have now been completed on both of these projects. In addition to developing these two new mines in Russia and West Africa, High River also has interests in three operating gold mines – two in Russia and one in Canada. High River's attributable gold production from these operating mines was 118,000 ounces in 2003.

The operator of the Berezitovy Project during the development and production stages will be High River's Russian subsidiary, OJSC Buryatzoloto. "There, we have about one million ounces of reserves, it will be an open-pit project and produce about 100,000 ounces a year over about a 10-year mine life," Mosher says.

"We expect to be in production commencing just prior to the end of 2005." Over in West Africa where High River's mining camp has been active since 1996, the Company recently consolidated its interest in the Taparko project, located in Burkina Faso. In addition to three separate deposits on the Taparko property, High River recently acquired the reserves from the nearby Bouroum property of close to 110,000 ounces.

"Which gives us an approximate mine-life of about eight years,"

Mosher estimates. "We will produce 100,000 ounces a year for the first three years and then a little less for the remainder of its life."

High River's actual land position in Burkina Faso is immense, somewhere in the neighbourhood of 5,000 square kilometres. Mosher expects to be in production on the Taparko project by the last quarter of next year, 2005.

Both Russia and West Africa have become familiar landscapes to Mosher now, but they're a far cry from his roots in the Canadian Maritimes. Growing up in New Brunswick, Mosher then moved to Nova Scotia where he graduated from Acadia University with a BSc in geology. Throughout his university years, Mosher spent his summers with a geological consulting firm, traveling around Canada and working in various provinces. Following graduation he did a stint in Toronto and then, through the same consulting firm, got an opportunity to work in Australia where he stayed for nearly ten years from early-1970 to late-1979 before returning to Canada. Initially Mosher was project geologist for the consulting firm until it was taken over by Pancontinental Mining, one of the firm's clients.

"With Pancon, I became project manager of the Jabiluka uranium project in the northern territory," explains Mosher.

After finding one small deposit, things quickly began to move with the discovery of a huge deposit in the northern territory. In fact, the relatively high-grade deposit became the largest uranium deposit in the world and Mosher was there for the ride.

"I was Project Manager for four years during the discovery through to its really becoming a major deposit. Then I became Exploration Manager for Pancon Australia and ultimately came back to Canada for Pancontinental, as Coordinator of New Advanced Projects for the company."

Mosher ultimately left Pancon in mid-1982 and did some consulting on his own. Through his independent consulting work, Mosher played a support role in a number of public companies as a director, involving himself in both the technical and financial sides of the business. One such company was Nor-Acme Gold Mines, listed on the Toronto Stock Exchange since the 1940s.

Nor-Acme had a project that sparked Mosher's interest – a former gold mine in Snow Lake, Manitoba, that had been in production for about 10 years, from 1949, producing approximately 600,000 ounces of gold.

"My interest in this particular company was the fact that this project still had an orebody that was open at depth and the mine had really shut down as a result of a very depressed gold market and very low gold prices. We felt it had additional potential and deserved more work," said Mosher.

To that end, Nor-Acme ultimately did a joint venture with High River Resources out of Vancouver, whereby they could earn a 60 percent interest in the project for spending a certain amount of money in exploration, which they did.

"Then at that point in time, we felt we needed additional funding, it was a difficult market, and the best way to raise funding was to put the orebody back whole again. So it was decided to merge the two companies, Nor-Acme Gold Mines and High River Resources." The year was 1988 when High River Gold Mines was formed as a result of the merger and took a Toronto Stock Exchange listing. At the time, the company was still being operated from Vancouver while work progressed on the project. An initial feasibility study showed that under market conditions then, the project was marginal. Enter Inco Gold, which later became TVX, as a joint venture partner for the new merged company with an option to maintain the property for five years but with no requirement to put it into production. Five years later, with little improvement in the market, TVX let the option lapse. "So High River was really a one-project company that was not being well managed during that period because their best asset was really on hold," Mosher said. Things degenerated to the point where the TSE listing came up for review and the company's directors were put on notice that listing privileges could be cancelled. Mosher, who was still a director but worked in Toronto, was asked by the company's major Australian shareholder if he could step in and deal with the TSE, put a business plan together and try to maintain their listing privileges.

"They didn't want to see the listing privileges cancelled because if they had been, that might have been it for the company. Once a company loses its listing privilege, it's very hard to get these things up and running again. It usually falls into oblivion." While Mosher was considering various options, he was approached by Don Whalen, an interested High River shareholder. Whalen joined forces with Mosher to try and give High River a chance at the future they felt it deserved.

"He also became a director of the company. We approached the TSE, got a couple of weeks to put a business plan together, and essentially put our own money in to finance the company. We put a program in place and then moved the company forward." While Mosher and Whalen were busily trying to keep High River afloat, two positive things happened. For starters, the gold market began to show a slight improvement. "Secondly, we decided to take a risk and drill a deep hole on the New Britannia project," said Mosher.

The risk paid off, with the hole hitting a very good intersection.

"It created a bit of a catalyst for us in the marketplace, which was improving, and allowed us to fund the company and move on."

In the beginning, Mosher and Whalen weren't looking very far ahead as to what their roles in the company may be. They were still only directors and, as Mosher puts it, he and Whalen felt like they were acting more-or-less in a consulting capacity.

"We were trying to be a halfway house for this company until it got up and running and properly managed."

But as things evolved, both men found themselves becoming more interested in the company's progress and increasingly involved in its management. They decided since they were already doing all the work, they might as well make it official.

"We decided maybe we should just continue and put a more definitive long-term game plan in place for the company and move on. So that's essentially what we did." In June 1992, Mosher took on the duties and title of President and CEO and Whalen became Chairman. High River shifted operations from Vancouver to Toronto, and the entire board was restructured.

"We then decided we would focus on gold, with our major interest initially being to try to develop the Snow Lake, Manitoba project. Then we would focus on advanced development and production opportunities. We would do exploration, but really advanced exploration, not grassroots.

"And that's how the company essentially started."

As credibility began to build, Mosher and company were able to move beyond their own financing and secure funding from the brokerage community. Acquiring an interest in the Taparko project in Burkina Faso was in line with their objectives and vision, as was their subsequent involvement in Russia, initially as a significant minority shareholder in Buryatzoloto, a Russian company with two operating mines.

In Burkina Faso, West Africa, High River has an 80 percent interest in Taparko and a 90 percent interest in Bouroum, with the Burkina Government holding the remaining 20 percent and 10 percent interests. As an added bonus, the company holds a 10 percent equity interest in Jilbey Gold, a company with exploration permits adjacent to the Taparko property. Jilbey has initiated a drill program subsequent to receiving significant gold assays from surface exploration on the Bissa project.

In Russia, High River currently holds a 66 percent controlling interest in Buryatzoloto, which has become its Russian mine subsidiary.

With two advanced exploration/development projects in two different countries slated to go into production within a year's time, High River could conceivably triple its attributable production from just over 118,000 ounces in 2003 to approximately 350,000 ounces in 2006. This scale of production isn't often found at the junior company level, and High River is clearly on the brink of joining the intermediate ranks.

According to Mosher, High River is all about growth.

"We've become a very aggressive growth company with the objective of moving over the next few years to a 500,000 ounce per year gold producer. With just the existing projects we have right now, and the successful development of the two new mines, in a couple of years we'll be at about 350,000 ounces on a consolidated basis – Buryatzoloto and High River together.

"It's a very significant achievement I think, from a zero starting position." Very significant indeed. But those advanced projects aside, High River has also developed a worthy pipeline of future projects through strategic alliances with three TSX Venture-listed companies: Jilbey Gold Exploration Ltd., Pelangio Mines Inc. and Intrepid Minerals Corporation. High River holds an equity position in each of these companies, along with certain back-in rights, first rights of refusal and operatorship rights.

"We feel all three of these companies are doing very well and are already at a point where they're developing advanced projects that we believe will become candidates for development and further production in the near future," Mosher says. Since 2000, High River has also added some new talent to the company – of particular mention, Daniel Vanin, Executive VP and Chief Operating Officer. Mosher explained that Vanin has a long history in mining, particularly in mine development and operations, and credits him as being gifted with superb people skills, something that's extremely valuable when dealing with worldwide operations.

"Daniel will ultimately take over total responsibility for our mining activities worldwide, including the support function for Valery Dmitriev who heads our mining operations in Russia," Mosher explains, adding that Dmitriev's title is Director General of Buryatzoloto, a function comparable to that of President and CEO. "Valery is a dynamic individual and a born leader who deserves the credit for our success in Russia."

Aside from Dmitriev, High River has a substantial personnel base in Russia that is managing and operating the existing mines and greatly assisting in developing the new Berezitovy Mine. In fact, there are literally thousands of people working through High River and Buryatzoloto, the latter company doing all its own contract work.

"Russia historically has been very people-intensive on projects. We probably have in the order of 4,000 people working for us in Russia through High River and Buryatzoloto at this time."

By comparison, the New Britannia Mine in Manitoba had less than 400 people at full staff, now even less as the mine is nearing closure. Once Taparko is in production, the on-site permanent staff will likely number 350 to 400, mostly Burkina Faso locals. When Berezitovy is up and running, Mosher estimates it will have an on-site staff of approximately 700.

Interest and confidence in High River is quickly gaining momentum, and its current share price of around $1.70 clearly won't stay at that level for long. With the announcement of bankable feasibility studies on its two new projects, and steady successes on the company's strategic alliances with Jilbey, Pelangio and Intrepid, all of which have made significant announcements on their explorations projects, coverage is expected to widen dramatically. In 2003 for example, a financing was done through Sprott Securities and Dundee Securities, with Sprott placing 80 percent of the shares. Currently, High River is covered by six brokerage firms including Sprott, Dundee, CIBC, BMO Nesbitt Burns, Paradigm and Orion, with more expected to come on board. That exposure has parlayed itself into greater interest in High River with institutional investors.

"We're getting much better coverage now. We're considered a credible company with a good management team, both here in Toronto and also in Russia, and I think we're viewed in the market place as an emerging mid-tier gold producer."

Analysts currently have share price targets for High River's shares at between $2 and $3 on a 12-month time-frame.

"The conclusions of the analysts, generally speaking, is that we are undervalued with respect to our peers. We are a little bit unique and there aren't any really identifiable peers exactly comparable to us."

With such a growth profile and increasing scrutiny, Mosher realizes it's only a matter of time before another company might consider acquiring High River. Although he wouldn't dismiss that opportunity out-of-hand, for now he's content and pleased to be continuing to take the company forward in its strong growth mode.

"So far we've been able to maintain our independence and grow, and we're quite happy to do that. But I think you always have to be prepared for the possibility that at some point, a larger company might make an offer that you and your shareholders can't refuse."

Personally, Mosher considers himself a builder. It's a skill he's obviously mastered, having taken High River from its inception, in its current form, in 1992, through the difficult years of 1997 to 2000, and coming out the other side with such an impressive and diverse portfolio of mines and development projects and respected partners. He wants to continue to build, but now his energies are focussed on building alliances that will strengthen his company's position for the benefit of all High River shareholders.

"I think sometimes in order to ensure you get access to the best opportunities for the company, you have to build an alliance with a larger company. Russia is an area where we have attracted a lot of attention."

For a number of reasons, it's not as easy to work and do business in Russia as it is in other countries. Where many other companies have tried and failed in Russia, High River has succeeded and receives due credit for this accomplishment from its peers. "Most of the larger companies give us full marks for being successful there, for not getting into trouble, for not being the focus of any problems, and for building a credible operating and development base and being able to successfully do business in Russia. Therefore, we're an excellent partner for a large company wanting to get involved in Russia and expand its own horizons."

Mosher considers Russia to be one of the best frontier areas in the world for acquiring ready-to-develop projects. There are innumerable projects that have already received a lot of work, but need the expertise and capital to take them into development. As well, Russia is now becoming more involved in hard-rock mining, both open-pit and underground, as most of its previous placer mines have been exhausted.

As far as taxation and legal regulations are concerned, Russia is quickly moving forward and reforming its structures to be more in line with international laws and rules. Buryatzoloto, for example, has been audited by PricewaterhouseCoopers for eight years, and its financial statements and annual reports are comparable to those of any North American company. But Mosher cautions it's easy for a company to get into trouble in Russia, if it makes the mistake of trying to force a North American approach.

"Russia is an area where some western companies feel they've been burned ... there have been a few bad situations which receive most of the media attention. Unfortunately, the Russians usually get labeled with being the bad guys but quite often we think there's fault on both sides as to why something hasn't worked out," Mosher says, noting that western companies certainly need to do their homework from a legal and people context beforehand.

"You can be up for some big surprises if you don't understand what you're dealing with. Title is a bit different, and you must understand the requirements of your licence because they're different from North American. You have time constraints in Russia and you have to be able to meet those time constraints or you can be up for serious fines. You could even be in default to the extent you could lose your licence."

Fortunately, High River has never encountered a problem in Russia and in fact, is enjoying strong support from local governments. Mosher attributes much of their success to having chosen their partners well. Thanks to Buryatzoloto, the EBRD (European Bank of Reconstruction & Development) is involved by way of taking an equity interest in Buryatzoloto and being their primary debt provider. An international organization headquartered in London, the EBRD's shareholders consist of over fifty individual countries that participated in its funding. The bank's mandate, according to Mosher, is to go where other banks can't or won't go in order to assist good projects.

"They have a mandate for funding projects in Russia and therefore, are very much respected by the Russian governments, both federal and regional," Mosher says. Through its relationship with Buryatzoloto, High River also has the credibility and resources of the EBRD on its side, something Mosher likens to having 'political risk insurance'. Aside from its respected name alone, the EBRD relationship has proven to be valuable in countless other areas.

"Another advantage of the EBRD is that it's a great halfway house for meeting with our Russian partners and for directors' meetings in London ... which isn't a bad place to have meetings. We can use EBRD translators and use their offices. We can also bring in EBRD experts in different fields if we need them. It works extremely well." Recently, High River invited EBRD investment banker Mark Rachovides to become a member of the High River board.

"Mark is a very knowledgeable individual, especially in the Russian context, and we're very happy to have him as an independent director. I think we'll be using him on a number of different committees."

Also on the board is Alexandr Balabanov, who in the past worked for a bank owned in part by the EBRD.

"He has done such a tremendous job and worked so hard on behalf of Buryatzoloto, and High River indirectly, we've made him Chairman of Buryatzoloto every year. Alex is a very valuable asset for both Buryatzoloto and High River."

Mosher strives to ensure these Russian individuals get special mention, not only because of their expertise but because he wants all business with his Russian partners to be 'transparent'.

"In working together and building up trust between partners, it's good to have cross-directorships. We have three Russians on our board of directors and three High River directors on Buryatzoloto's board. It's a good situation and, as mentioned, we have one EBRD member on our board and two from the EBRD on the Buryatzoloto board."

High River's board is yet another aspect of the company that distinguishes it from other juniors, in that its makeup is as diverse as High River's projects.

"We've got three Russians, one Australian, three Canadians, a Malaysian and a Greek on our board," Mosher says with a grin. "That's about as international as you can get." It's obvious Mosher loves working in Russia and, business relationships aside, he says simply, "Some of my best friends are Russians now."

Unlike most North American companies that insist on joint ventures and having direct interests in projects, Mosher and company took an equity position and as such, he considers the relationship with Russia to be 'a family affair'.

"We took what might have been perceived as a bigger risk at the time, but in a way it was a much easier thing to do. When you have an equity position, you want what's good for all shareholders and therefore there was a common purpose with Buryatzoloto management that simplified our life in the early days and kept us out of confrontational positions."

Having conquered the formula for successfully doing business in Russia, High River will undoubtedly be considered an attractive alliance partner for other companies. Mosher is certainly amenable to such a prospect and acknowledges that alliances are a beneficial way of acquiring properties that may be considered too large for High River. "We're generally looking for million-ounce projects capable of producing 100,000 ounces of gold per year – the type of project we think we have a good capability of handling, developing and putting into production. If it's a 500,000 ounce per year producer, that's a significant deposit with larger capital requirements which we feel might best be handled with the assistance of a larger company as an alliance partner.

"We have had discussions and we are continuing discussions with companies in respect of putting an alliance together. That's not to say we may not be taken over tomorrow or the next day, but we're just going to move on and build value and see where we go." On the face of it, Russia may seem far removed from High River's other major development project in West Africa and not only by distance. Although the language, weather, governmental structure and regulations are completely different, one key ingredient is the same – local support for High River's plans in each host country. As they have in Russia, Mosher and company have also developed an excellent relationship with the Burkina Faso government and recently received the permit to move ahead and develop their Taparko project.

"We entered into an investment agreement which was ratified and became part of the law of the country, so it's the strongest title you can get in Burkina Faso," Mosher says.

"I can't say enough about the Burkina government. They've been so supportive, it's just been a pleasure to work in Burkina Faso."

High River's visible presence since 1996 on the Taparko property hasn't hurt Burkina's profile either. Until recently, any attraction Burkina may have held was overshadowed by its neighbours, Ghana and Mali, both of which have had major gold discoveries and deposits developed. Although Burkina historically had a gold mine in operation, it hasn't enjoyed anything other than artisanal mining recently. Mosher believes High River's project will be the first one up and running and will become a catalyst for attracting more development in Burkina.

"Burkina, although it has the same geology as Ghana and Mali, was always given a lower rating as to the chances of finding a major deposit," Mosher says, speculating this was only due to the lack of exploration activity.

But thanks in part to the work being done by High River and its partner Jilbey Gold, some extremely interesting discoveries are being made and other companies are now flocking to the area and setting up shop in the vicinity. Burkina, according to Mosher, is becoming a 'hot spot'. The influx of new companies notwithstanding, High River is already miles ahead of the game, well situated both geographically and in terms of loyal local support. Their team has gained the confidence and support of the government, having stayed the course in early years when things didn't look so promising. During a recent meeting with Burkina government officials, Mosher was gratified to hear that their loyalty to Burkina was recognized and appreciated.

"We worked there in good times and bad times and I was quite surprised and pleased when I met with them not long ago, that they said they were very appreciative that High River worked through the tough times when a lot of companies just up and left."

Now, with bankable feasibility and environmental studies completed, and a permit in hand, High River is looking forward to developing a successful mining operation at Taparko and further expansion throughout Burkina Faso and West Africa. The feasibility study evaluated construction of a mill and infrastructure on the Taparko property to process ore from three pits on Taparko and three pits on the nearby Bouroum property, 49 kilometres northwest of the planned Taparko mill. This combined operation would process approximately one million tonnes of ore per year and average more than 90,000 ounces of gold per year over an eight-year period – exceeding 100,000 ounces in each of the first three years. Based on a US$350 per ounce gold price, reserves exceeding 600,000 ounces of gold have been established for the three pits on the Taparko property with ore containing a minimum of 110,000 ounces of gold expected from Bouroum. A gold price of US$400 per ounce more than doubles the gold resource to 1.3 million ounces for the three Taparko pits alone. Added to that potential is High River's alliance with Jilbey Gold on a number of other exploration properties.

"We've had results that indicate we have a very good chance of outlining additional deposits that we could ultimately mine as satellite deposits and truck to the Taparko mill." Because there is excellent potential for satellite deposits, High River has designed the facility with a longer-term operation in mind. Previous exploration has defined 16 prospective gold targets within the Taparko property alone. The agreement with Jilbey provides High River with back-in and operatorship rights on Jilbey discoveries within trucking distance of the Taparko mill and a right of first refusal on discoveries outside trucking distance. High River now controls over 4,000 square kilometres of prospective property within trucking distance either directly or indirectly through Jilbey. "The mill is meant to handle over 100,000 ounces of production a year initially but we certainly will have the capability of going to 200,000 ounces a year if we are successful. Certainly, with more capital, we could go higher than that."

Such excitement brewing in both Russia and West Africa would seem more than enough for most companies. But High River also has a strong presence back on its home turf in Canada, specifically in Manitoba and Ontario. In 1995, High River and TVX Gold Inc. (now Kinross Gold Corp.) commenced production at the New Britannia mine in Snow Lake, Manitoba. A 50-50 joint venture, High River operates the exploration side, while Kinross operates production. The initial feasibility study indicated the mine would produce 725,000 ounces over a 7.5-year period, closing in early 2003.

The mine has exceeded those projections, producing in excess of 770,000 ounces of gold to the end of 2003 and is now expected to close in late-2004 or early-2005. High River and Kinross are currently in the process of deciding whether to continue exploration and extend the mine's life or commence an orderly shutdown of operations. For his part, Mosher would like to pursue further exploration while keeping the infrastructure on care maintenance and the equipment on standby.

"If we can do that, the mine might have another life. Snow Lake is considered the 'town with nine lives'because of the number of times it's almost become a ghost town and then an orebody was discovered nearby. I really don't think we did the area justice from an exploration sense and that's why I personally feel strongly motivated to try and make an exploration project out of it," Mosher says.

Back in Ontario, High River is hooked up with Pelangio Mines Inc., another strategic-alliance partner, having acquired 18 percent equity in Pelangio in September 2003. Pelangio owns 100 percent of an excellent property position covering most of the Detour Lake gold camp, including the former Detour Lake mine previously held by Placer Dome. Pelangio's property covers approximately 70 square miles of the well-known Abitibi Greenstone Belt, with resources on Pelangio's property totalling approximately 1.76 million ounces of gold – 520,000 ounces in the measured and indicated categories and 1,240,000 ounces in inferred. For its part, High River is acting as Pelangio's technical advisor, providing technical expertise and operations management. All of these projects, properties and alliances combined are what make High River a distinct and unique company, clearly larger and more diversified than most junior mining companies and poised to make the leap into mid-tier. Mosher is most proud of how his various teams have pulled together and made it through the difficult times, and he's not speaking only of the lean years.

A tragic accident on July 1, 1998 tested the will of everyone involved in High River and its Russian counterparts when a helicopter carrying Mosher and 12 other people from High River, Buryatzoloto and the EBRD, crashed in Russia. Three people were killed in that crash and several others severely injured and burned. The High River team lost a good friend and one of its directors, Colin Chapman, a well known and respected Metallurgical Engineer. Also killed in the crash was Ms. Randa Smine, a Doctor in Environmental Science with the EBRD and Evgueni Nefedov, a manager with Buryatzoloto. Mosher recalls that the tragedy couldn't have come at a more negative point in time for their industry in general.

"It would have been very easy for either company or both companies to throw in the towel and say, 'Enough is enough.' It was a huge amount of stress ... the normal stress of operating a company, trying to survive and pay the bills and payroll and keep your assets in a good state ... and on top of that, you get a tragic accident. I know our office was high-stress for quite some time and I'm sure the same situation existed in Russia." Mosher concedes it took some time for the survivors to recover from their injuries, both physical and emotional, but everyone struggled through those days with the same fortitude and strength of purpose that has come to define High River and its Russian friends and partners.

"Through all of that, our Russian management team, ourselves and the EBRD stood tall and said, 'Let's make sure we go forward and succeed, because if we don't, the lives of our friends will have been lost for nothing.' It was because of that strong mental attitude and refusal to give in to anything that we persevered in a very high stress environment for quite some time." A black stone memorial bearing the names of the three victims now stands at the Zun Holba mine site where the helicopter went down, and Mosher and the other survivors have frequently visited this lasting testament to their colleagues. He's proud of the way everyone struggled through the aftermath of the tragedy and came out on top.

"I would say the crowning achievement is having actually succeeded in surviving, in upgrading the mines and in growing the companies because it was tough enough operating in Russia during those days and paying the bills. Since High River got involved in Russia, Buryatzoloto's two operating mines have grown from 55,000 ounces per year to 155,000 ounces and the company is very profitable."

Mosher is also pleased to announce that Buryatzoloto will be paying a dividend this year, and he's equally heartened to see his company making a positive impact on people's lives, particularly in Russia and West Africa.

"It's one thing to make money in this business because everyone likes to make some money and do well; but, we only go through this life once and I really do believe if you do something positive, it makes you feel a lot better about the whole thing." Like anyone else who succeeds in this business, Mosher thrives on challenges and the thrill of building and exploring to find natural treasure – 'the gold at the end of the rainbow'. With two major development projects moving forward in Russia and West Africa, it's certain there's no lack of immediate challenges for Mosher to tackle head-on. "We're starting from scratch, if you like, in building them so there are greater challenges ahead. I'm sure everybody will be writing report cards on us as we move forward. But we're ready."

And finally, there's a curious side-note on High River's presence in Russia and West Africa. If one believes in fate or magical occurrences, it would seem to bode well for success in both countries. Having extracted the company's current name of High River Gold Mines from the merger of Nor-Acme Gold Mines and High River Resources, Mosher and company carried on with the name despite having no real connection to its origins, which Mosher speculates may have initially had something to do with High River, Alberta. Changing a company's moniker to something more fitting not only undermines the credibility built up through name recognition but can be a costly proposition. They decided to live with it, and forged ahead with business in Burkina Faso and Russia, neither country having any connection whatsoever with High River. Or so they thought.

After working in Burkina Faso for awhile, Mosher discovered a serendipitous connection. In local dialect, Burkina Faso means 'land of the honest man', a translation Mosher was aware of from the beginning.

"Burkina Faso, however, is the country's new name, it used to be called 'Upper Volta', which means *Haute Volta* in French – or 'High River'."

Obviously this was a pleasing revelation, lending some coincidental relevance to the High River company name. But, as Mosher would later discover, it wasn't to be the only one.

"We were having a walk with our Russian partners in Ulan Ude, the capital city of the Republic of Buryatia, where the headquarters of Buryatzoloto is located, when we came to an area where the rivers were flowing and it was quite picturesque. My wife Linda asked what the place was called."

The startling answer, after being translated from Russian, was 'High River'.

Mosher leans forward over his desk, and smiles with amusement as he recalls hearing the translation.

"It was interesting that in two areas where we had done business, there is a High River aspect to both of them," he says with almost a touch of awe.

Does he think it's a sign that High River is meant to be in Russia and West Africa? "I don't know what it is ... coincidence or fate or what," Mosher says philosophically. But there's a twinkle in his eye when he says it, and one gets the feeling it is a very good omen.

HUNTER DICKINSON INCORPORATED

"We make mines," Bob Dickinson says about what he and the team at Hunter Dickinson do. It's as simple – and as complicated – as that. And they know what they're doing. They've been doing it very successfully (in many cases, share price increases have provided returns to investors of more than 1000 percent) since 1985. And while the company has grown, steadily building each new success on the one before it, some things have remained constant. The company's first offices were in the tower at 800 West Pender Street in downtown Vancouver. Now, almost two decades later, the company still has its headquarters there, although now they're bigger, with more people occupying three floors and nine public companies under Hunter Dickinson's aegis.

"Right from the beginning, we wanted to set ourselves apart," Bob Dickinson says. "We wanted to be seen as professional mine-developers." This was back in the days when the Vancouver Stock Exchange was seen as a kind of unfettered, less tightly regulated version of the Toronto Stock Exchange. And the conduct of some of the so-called 'Howe Street Cowboys' cemented that view among nervous investors. Hunter Dickinson's founders, Robert Hunter and Robert Dickinson, and office manager Shirley Main, wanted to make sure nobody would think of their firm as being similar in any way to the Howe Street Cowboys.

They were the founding principals of North American Metals, which partnered up with Chevron Canada in its development of the Golden Bear mine complex near Dease Lake in northern British Columbia. Dickinson was the geologist and Hunter was the finance person.

"We had the opportunity to purchase a 50 percent interest in the Golden Bear project that Chevron Canada had discovered," Bob Dickinson remembers. He's well over six feet tall and trim but powerful, an impression tempered by his easy-going openness and obvious enthusiasm for work he still so clearly loves even after almost 20 years. "Two years later, by 1988, we had earned a 50 percent interest in the Golden Bear deposit. With superb technical execution by our Project Director, Jeff Franzen, we drove a tunnel into the mountain for over a mile, through the gold ore body and permitted a 110-kilometre road from Telegraph Creek into the northern British Columbia wilderness. Also at the same time we commenced one of the first B.C. mining industry-First Nations relationships. That was with the Tahltan First Nation and their construction arm, the Tahltan Development Corporation. Our group was at the vanguard of that kind of relationship between the First Nations and the mining industry. Working with our neighbours has become a very important part of the mining industry – we've all grown during the last few decades."

In many ways, that relationship with the local indigenous people in the Dease Lake area set the tone for everything Hunter Dickinson has accomplished since. Its many companies find the most advantageous ways to work with the people who live where their projects are, to make sure they – as well as Hunter Dickinson's companies and shareholders – benefit from each new project, and from each stage of that project: exploration and development through management and operation. That philosophy and its sensitivity to local concerns – 'social license' as the Hunter Dickinson people call it – is just as important now to the parent company's 60-member staff as it was to those involved with that first Golden Bear project.

Two years after North American Metals was formed, it was the target of a successful hostile takeover by Homestake Canada, a subsidiary of the historic company that was headquartered in the United States. Coming north across the 49th parallel, Homestake was targeting an established underground gold deposit with a lot of upside potential as their first effort in Canada. After many days of wrangling, North American Metals shareholders took Homestake Canada's increased offer and, Bob Dickinson says, "sold out just after the 1987 crash at five dollars a share. From zero to five dollars a share in two years was a huge liquidity event. And that set the stage for rapid growth by our group."

Indeed, that momentum repeated itself, albeit on a larger scale, with Hunter Dickinson's next effort, Continental Gold Corp., which was started in 1988. Continental Gold found, developed and engineered the Mount Milligan gold-copper porphyry deposit near Mackenzie, in the middle of British Columbia. Continental Gold shepherded the Mount Milligan project right up to the permitting stage, at which point another miner declared its interest in what had been developing. Placer Dome Inc. determined that the Mount Milligan project that Continental Gold had midwifed was a must-have. Offering Continental shareholders $20 a share, Placer Dome bought the project for $252 million in 1990.

Continental's Mount Milligan project was significant in other ways, too.

"We met Ron Thiessen – a highly-skilled financier and deal-maker – who is the current president and CEO of our group," Dickinson recalls. "Also Dave Copeland, a partner whose skill is project engineering; he continues to be the director of project development for Hunter Dickinson. Mark Rebagliati, who went on to become recognized as mining man of the year by the Prospectors and Developers Association, also came on during that period. He's the chief geoscientist here in our group. That's when we started to really grow. We had our first moderate-size success with North American Metals, five dollars a share; Continental Gold, twenty dollars a share. Things are starting to hum: two years for the North American Metals success, two years for the Continental Gold success, then more people, bigger ideas, more creativity – that's when the group started to launch."

Through its development and growth, Hunter Dickinson has acquired a reputation – or perhaps had one attributed to it by market observers – as a company that explores and develops mines, but not one that operates them. But that is not entirely accurate. If just starting mines or locating deposits were all that mattered, Bob Dickinson and his colleagues would be working on a greater number of smaller initiatives. That is not the case. Rather, to meet Hunter Dickinson's criteria, a prospective mining opportunity must offer high potential in large-scale wealth creation to justify

the group's interest. That same concern for and heed to the ideas of shareholders often determines the future and the development of many of the
companies'projects. The shareholders decide whether to accept takeover
bids or whether to seek other styles of transactions, and the Hunter
Dickinson executives follow shareholders' directions. As Bob Dickinson
says, Hunter Dickinson finds mines to create wealth. Once the mines have
been established, it's up to shareholders as to who should run them.

"Our targets are large-scale mines. They cover the precious metals.
We look for large platinum group metal mines. We look for significant
gold-silver mines. We look for large-scale open-pit gold-copper or copper-gold porphyries. We're not interested in the 'Ma and Pa' small-scale
mines. Not all of our targets have worked out, but we don't go into anything that hasn't got a high probability of being a successful discovery
that major mining companies around the world would be interested in.
That's one of our strategies. If someone comes in with a hundred, two
hundred, four hundred thousand-ounce gold target, we're not interested.
That's for somebody else. We're interested in millions of ounces of potential so that, when we are successful, there is huge wealth created. That's
what we like to do. It's almost the same amount of energy to go after a
small mine as to go after a big deposit. And we have the people here who
can do it, some of the best geologists in the world: Mark Rebagliati,
Jimmy Oliver, Dave Jennings, Bob Cluff, Dan Kilby, John Payne, Richard
Haslinger, Bruce Youngman, Darrel Johnson and Lena Brommeland to
name a few.

"And one shouldn't think that selling a mine is Hunter Dickinson's
default course of action. We go out, find and develop a major deposit that
creates substantial wealth, and quite often it's so enticing to the major
mining companies that they'll come along and make an offer. It's typical
in the industry that the majors will take over or buy or joint-venture all the
great discoveries that the junior mining industry has made. That's what's
happened to us, historically. We've found these large projects and the
majors have made offers to us. We've taken those offers to the shareholders and they've been accepted. That has been our track record. We've had
three huge financial transactions – takeovers, basically. We've had North
American Metals, we've had Continental Gold, and we've had El Condor
Resources."

That track record also means that in addition to becoming very good at finding and developing mines, Hunter Dickinson has become very adept at understanding all the financial options open to the company, an added set of skills and knowledge it wouldn't have acquired had it been content to focus exclusively on geology and strictly exploration-related matters. The company's business sense and its ability as a mine developer has meant an accrual of financial savvy, almost as though the mining knowledge proved to be magnetic, drawing other kinds of talent and intelligence.

And that accrued financial and business knowledge means new opportunities for a company that started as a mine finder and developer. Hunter Dickinson is now in a position to find opportunity in projects other companies have not been able to run feasibly, breathing new life into mines that once seemed to have been doomed because of the caprice and fluctuation of roiling commodities markets. That's a good part of what Hunter Dickinson's Taseko Mines concentrates on.

Taseko purchased the dormant Gibraltar Mine near Williams Lake in south central British Columbia in 1999. Its owner, Swedish mining giant Boliden, put the operation on stand-by when the price of copper dropped to about 61 cents a pound. At that price, it couldn't run the mine economically. Compounding that, Boliden had an an environmental incident in Spain, was trying to manage a difficult media storm and wanted to sell non-core assets, of which the Gibraltar operation was an example.

Seizing the opportunity, Hunter Dickinson's Taseko stepped in and bought the mine at the bottom of the market, and are re-starting it now that copper prices have rebounded. Dickinson predicts the Gibraltar Mine will produce 80 million pounds of copper annually, and employ 300 people.

And that's just phase one of Taseko's plans. Also near Williams Lake is the Prosperity gold and copper porphyry deposit, which is scheduled to be moved up into the permitting stage once Gibraltar is humming along. In addition, there is a three-million-ounce gold deposit that's on British Columbia's Queen Charlotte Islands called Harmony, that could move through the feasibility stage into production in a few years as well.

Then there's Amarc Resources – essentially a pool of cash and a focussed technical team assembled to explore and develop early stage projects in British Columbia.

"People will say, 'Why B.C.? Isn't that strange,'" Bob Dickinson says. But then he explains. "There's been about ten years of socialist government in B.C. when very little exploration and development happened. That left a huge void of new discoveries and no new exploration. Over the last ten years the mining industry and the way you go about finding mines on a scientific basis has changed so dramatically that few of these new techniques have really been utilized in British Columbia; it's just been a vacuum. Now, with a new government and the new interest in British Columbia, we saw this gap and re-established Amarc, raised substantial money and created a dedicated B.C. team to acquire and develop projects and use new ideas. We hope to find a major untapped mineral belt in B.C. We're acquiring very exciting prospects right now. The goal of Amarc is to make this province's next major mineral discovery, and we hope to make that within the next two years."

And those are just two of Hunter Dickinson's nine companies.

On a different continent, in a different hemisphere – in South Africa's Bushveld Complex, the world's premier geological environment for platinum group metals to be precise, is another pioneering effort that typifies the unique way the Hunter Dickinson Group approaches the challenges that mineral exploration and development offer. Anooraq Resources, which is focussed on platinum-group metals, is finding a way to work with a very different South Africa than existed even a few years ago.

"South African rules and regulations have been changing after apartheid, and they want to open up their country to foreign mineral exploration. And a company like us, where you have a lot of flexibility and creativity and the ability to move quickly, can acquire major mining assets which a year or two before would not have been available," Dickinson says. "Our first discovery is called the Drenthe deposit, a 4-million-ounce PGM deposit at which we now have a major drilling campaign underway."

The key to success for Anooraq has been forming strategic partnerships with major stakeholders with roots in the area. On the business side, that means a bond between Hunter Dickinson's Anooraq and Anglo American Platinum Corporation Limited, the largest platinum group metals company in the world. Ninety percent of its assets are in South Africa, so it has a great deal of knowledge, expertise and understanding that pertains immediately to the opportunity at hand. This is knowledge which can only give Anooraq an edge in getting the most out of its opportunities in South Africa.

For Anglo Platinum, the changing political climate in South Africa means finding a foreign investor, a partner with the mining know-how and moral pedigree it needs to keep doing business. Anooraq and Hunter Dickinson fulfill all those requirements. In return, Anooraq gets the opportunity for access to some of the richest mineral deposits in the planet, in which it now has a joint venture stake.

"The strategy for our PGM effort was to go into South Africa and basically take a look on the ground, see which was the best company to form a strategic alliance with," says Hunter Dickinson's Ron Thiessen. "All the producers there have good quality people, but there was one that stood out bigger than anybody else and that was Anglo Platinum. They weren't going to be able to keep all their ground for themselves because they literally couldn't afford to explore everything and develop all the things that they found. From an exploration strategy standpoint, doing business with us, where we would come in and take ground that had exploration potential, develop it and then work with it later on, was a good strategy. They saw the opportunity for that and we formed a strategic alliance."

The company is also poised to get South African government approval and shareholder approval to form what's called a Black Economic Empowerment Company. Ron Thiessen explains what that will mean: "Black economic empowerment involves the majority of the South African population who are black in some form of ownership. Legislation requires that for existing mining operations, initially, they get 15 percent ownership moving up to 26 percent ownership over ten years. Anglo was required to get some of the black economic empowerment companies in as partners. The problem in South Africa is that there's not a great deal of venture capital available for junior or intermediate-size companies. The challenge for Anglo became how to bring a black partner into the deals without a lot of venture capital. Anglo brought us into the mix. In one case, we arranged a transaction with a black economic empowerment company that has the right to 50 percent of one of Anglo's largest new mine construction projects; we are effectively merging our company with the black economic empowerment company. It gives North American investors the opportunity to invest in a company that trades on North American markets and yet is fully-qualified as a black economic empowerment company and entitled to participation in all these projects in South Africa. It is a great marriage of opportunity in South Africa and capital and expertise from North America on a very large project, in the heart of the Bushveld, where 85 percent of the platinum-group metals in the world are produced."

From a business vantage point, all of that is encouraging, and would be for any company. But in this particular case, meeting business objectives also means human and political gains as well – gains so significant that South Africa's Ministry of Mines has been issuing press releases in tandem with Anooraq, extolling the company's work in South Africa, and particularly its efforts on behalf of black economic empowerment.

One of the things that sets Hunter Dickinson's corporate structure apart is its scrupulous and careful separation of its companies according to the kind of work they do. Each is focussed on a particular metal or a particular part of the world, with an avoidance of conflict of interest or intention.

"Shareholders that want to buy copper or copper and gold and want to be in western Canada could buy Taseko. If you want to be in South Africa and want to be in platinum-group metals, you should consider buying Anooraq," Bob Dickinson says. "A lot of people like our group as a portfolio. We have so many different projects, it's like a diversified mining portfolio. Buying a chunk of all the companies as an investor gives you diversification by region and diversification by metal. Most of our companies are Canadian-listed and American-listed. We have very loyal retail investors as well as being followed by the big institutional investors. Thousands of people have grown with us, thousands of people have tracked us, followed us through success after success."

That ability – that insistence – on finding the best way to apply its intelligence, experience and knowledge to a territory, to a community by adapting to whatever the local people are most comfortable with is something of a Hunter Dickinson hallmark. It served the company well in one of its first projects, the Golden Bear mine in Canada, it's served the company well in South Africa with its Anooraq Resources initiative, and it's working with Hunter Dickinson's Great Basin Gold on deposits in the United States' Carlin Trend and in South Africa's Witswatersrand Basin.

At first glance, it seems odd that a company that makes mines would be interested in developing in these two locations. The South African and Nevada regions are some of the most heavily-mined places on earth, which ought to be anathema to Hunter Dickinson's efforts to be pioneering, to make forays into untried realms and to rely on their intelligence and ability to carry the company through. But Great Basin is pioneering, by finding opportunities in these mature gold trends because it's already so heavily mined, not in spite of that.

"In Nevada, we developed a 1-million-ounce, very high-grade gold resource in a district that is one of the most overcapitalized mining districts in the world," Ron Thiessen says. "Because there are so many mills and structures in the area, we're able to bring this into production by just developing the mine itself and handle all the processing using other people's excess milling capacity in the area. That saves us 75 percent of the capital expenditure of the typical mining operation. It also means very low impact; our footprint is very light. Everything that we will be doing at the site we'll be doing within a pre-existing open-pit, so from an environmental permitting standpoint, and by the native groups in the district, we are a very responsible company because of the way we conducted our exploration, but also because of the way we tried to stay within previously disturbed areas and not create any new disturbances. That gold project is like a very strong insurance policy. We know what we've got there. We know the local profitability."

Hunter Dickinson's sensitivity to local factors helped in Nevada in other ways, too. "You would think in the Carlin Trend you wouldn't run into aboriginal issues. But it is in the heart of north-central Nevada and a lot of Native Americans live there," Ron Thiessen says. "It was in an area where there'd been historical mining; there'd also been extensive drilling and there was distrust. The first thing our guys said was, 'Why don't we survey for the aboriginal sites so we can identify them on a map and we can stay away from them with the drill rigs,' which nobody else had bothered to do. Most other people went out and tried to minimize these quarry sites. When you look at them, they don't look like much. You wouldn't think anything of them. To them it meant something. Our guys said if we survey them and get them on a map, at least everybody knows where they are and we can stay away from them. Our permitting time went from 180 days down to 75 days. The other major mining companies in the area were going, 'How come you guys are getting preferential treatment? How come you're getting your drill permits in 75 days? It takes us six months.' A simple thing like that."

"Great Basin is operating in two of the most prolific gold camps in the world," Bob Dickinson says. "We have established a 1-million-ounce high-grade underground gold deposit in the Carlin Trend, which is now permitted for driving a tunnel down into the deposit. Once its developed, we can start shipping that ore to nearby mills with relatively little capital cost, there's no building construction, it will be a highly-profitable operation. That project will do about 200,000 ounces of gold annually, so even though it's a small project in a sense, it has big numbers.

"The other gold project is the Witswatersrand Basin in South Africa. It is even more significant in terms of gold production than the Carlin Trend, believe it or not. More than 1.4 billion ounces of gold have been produced from the Witwatersrand Basin, where Great Basin is drilling off a whole new goldfield called Burnstone. We expect it to be very substantial. We were able to bring an opportunity to North American investors where they have a certainty of Nevada and the opportunity of blue sky in South Africa."

Or, if they're more interested in Mexico, there's Farallon Resources, working to develop the massive base and precious metals opportunities at Campo Morado in Mexico's Guerrero state. Just a few hundred miles north of Acapulco, halfway between there and Mexico City, Campo Morado is famous. Mexico's revolutionary founding father Emilio Zapata came from the region, and some of his ideas – many years later – made it hard for mining companies to do business profitably in the area. 'Mexicanizing' the country's natural resources in the 1960s meant Mexican companies got preferential treatment. And while that may have made sense for political reasons, it meant there was often a shortage of mining finance, since many Mexican companies had been led to expect that from international mining outfits.

"We've drilled out roughly 30 million tonnes of this mineralization and it's polymetallic – it's zinc, copper, gold, silver, lead," Ron Thiessen says. "We think there's potential to increase that 30 million tons to 50 million and ultimately maybe even more. It's a district that is roughly a hundred kilometres in length. Our concept is to develop the project on a district scale, to bring the whole thing under one umbrella in a large-scale industrialized project. It's of the size that it can take a big investment in new technology. We can actually move the project ahead to the point where we can produce metal right at site and not have to ship concentrates off to Asian smelters. Although the technology was developed 20 years ago, it's now refined to the point that it's operating commercially. To bring these leading-edge hydometallurgical technologies into play on the Campo Morado project and develop this entire district would be to Mexico what the Sudbury Basin is to Canada."

As in South Africa, getting the local people and the nation's government on-side is part of the Hunter Dickinson strategy. "I met with the deputy secretary and the mines minister for the federal government and I also met with the governor of Guerrero. They are supportive," Thiessen continues. "Hunter Dickinson can bring North American venture capital money into a district or into one of these really exciting projects."

"We always go in, even in the earliest days of exploration, discuss the project and consult with the local people within the region," Bob Dickinson says. "That's key to our success as well, where we involve the people and the communities – social license." "Before we put a single geologist on the ground, put a single camp in place, we actually got some local people to take us around to the various villages because we knew this was a remote area. They may view us as people who are going to take something away from them," Ron Thiessen says. "We did enough research to realize that, in law, they're probably squatters. They know they don't have a piece of paper that gives them this piece of land. You have to be very careful when you go in and amongst those people because you are foreign to them and they view you with suspicion: 'Are you here to try to move us off this land?' We got a group of locals to establish a protocol that allowed us to come in very safely. We didn't have to run an armed camp. We had no guards. In fact we had a policy: no guns on site – and we never had a problem. We employed lots of local people. The expat population was 40 or 50 on rotation, probably 30 or 35 people at a time, plus probably 100 locals doing lots of different things. And it brings some wealth to the community. Not wealth in the sense of mansions, but money – these are subsistence-farming people who typically have no spare money for anything. It brought jobs and opportunity and, interestingly enough, it drove subversive elements out of the area. People would rather deal with a guy who is happy to provide a paycheck."

Mexico's deputy minister of mines was initially skeptical about Farallon's ability to bring a project as big as Campo Morado to fruition. He suggested that, as a junior mining company, Farallon might not be big enough, even going to far as to indicate that perhaps a bigger international mining company might be better equipped to make things happen at Campo Morado. Ron Thiessen's view persuaded the minister that there was a different way to look at the situation: "When you look at the sequence of events, at how these mines are developed, you really want a junior company to begin the exploration and development because their whole raison d'etre is that project. Farallon does not have a project anyplace else. Everything that Farallon does is focussed on Campo Morado. We will bring a district-scale approach to this, and that approach will require tens of millions of dollars for exploration. A major mining company will have many exploration and development projects worldwide. Campo Morado would have to compete with something in Indonesia, something in Australia, something in northern Canada and the worldwide exploration budget for that company will be $20 million or $25 million, and so you'll be competing with ten or twenty other projects and you may only get a budget of half a million dollars."

He then made good on that, mustering $40 million for Farallon's work at Campo Morado within 30 months in the late-1990's. Farallon recently raised $7 million to begin advanced exploration and development.

Thiessen continues, "That's why we have different companies for different metals or different assets. We can go to investors and say, 'What is it that you like?' Some investors say, 'Well, I'm in a gold fund. I don't invest in copper, I don't invest in silver, don't invest in lead or zinc.' If we had all of our assets under Hunter Dickinson as a single public company, we couldn't get that kind of money in the door."

The company has resurrected one of its old names, but in a different place and with a different challenge. Continental Gold Corp. was one of Hunter Dickinson's early successes. Continental Minerals rose from an opportunity Hunter Dickinson was offered.

"A group brought us a major gold-copper target in Tibet," Bob Dickinson says. "Tibet's a very mystical, exciting place, so it's a big adventure for us. There's a lot of interest within the mining industry about getting into China. What an adventure for investors – to be part of one of Tibet's first major mineral discoveries and all the aura that is wrapped around that. We were shown a fantastic gold-copper porphyry target, and the type of deposit that we've had a lot of success with. Now we're in Tibet with a new gold-copper porphyry to move up the development ladder. And it's very exciting because it has only two diamond drill holes – and I have never seen higher grade gold-copper mineralization for a porphyry deposit than what is in these two holes. Here you have two holes, 250 metres apart and each of those core holes has a 200-metre high-grade intersection. It looks like another major discovery."

That same ethos runs through everything Hunter Dickinson's companies do, whether they're in Mexico, the British Columbia interior, Tibet, Nevada, Alaska or South Africa.

The company is such a model enterprise, it could probably consult to less enlightened mining outfits about how to do business better. Both Dickinson and Thiessen laugh at this, pointing out that they're far too busy creating wealth for shareholders. Leading by example seems a better option for a lot of reasons.

"Hunter Dickinson is actually a private company. Hunter Dickinson Inc. has all the premises, employs all the people. But more than that, more than the tangible assets, are the intangible assets that it provides to the Hunter Dickinson family of companies through boards of directors," Ron Thiessen says. "Each one of these public companies gets access to this highly-sophisticated company on economies of scale that they couldn't get if they had to do all of this competitively. Hunter Dickinson Inc. actually runs its operation on a not-for-profit basis. Our whole modus operandi is really to charge our companies our cost of operations so they get a break on everything. Instead of having to go and hire geological consultants at market rates, they get the advantage of being part of a large group. We're also very strong on the financing. We're our own investment bankers. So in many instances we're raising capital at considerably more modest costs than other companies. Hunter Dickinson is like a big mining house that provides all these services to these groups of companies. We cover the full gamut. We have relationships with the major mining community around the world. We have a modern outlook to mining, teamed with all the various skills that, taken together, create this magic."

IMA EXPLORATION INCORPORATED

It's no great surprise that Joseph Grosso would succeed in the mining business. Whether you call it savvy, charm or just plain old business smarts – he has the talent, the insight and the experience to deliver success no matter what the venture. His beginnings in the mining industry were simple, with the founding of a junior exploration company, IMA Exploration. IMA grew to become the foundation of an entire family of companies now known as The Grosso Group. The concept behind The Grosso Group is to provide a pooling of expertise under a shared infrastructure, thus reducing overhead costs while sharing information. Management continuity is provided by a common core group of directors who oversee each company within the group as it develops its own portfolio of properties. With The Grosso Group's vast experience in South America, its experienced management team and an impressive property portfolio, The Grosso Group has transformed itself into one of the most successful mineral exploration concerns on the continent.

Exploring for gold was not part of Joe Grosso's original life plan, at least not originally. Born into an Italian clothing-manufacturing family with a long tradition of working in the textile business, Joe grew up with every expectation of following suit; he graduated with a degree in design from a technical school in the beautiful and stylish city of Rome, Italy. Driven by a hunger to achieve success and always willing to try something new, he left his home behind and relocated half-way round the world to another wonderful city – Victoria, British Columbia's capital.

Here, he quickly established a successful clothing manufacturing business to the retail market. He was soon able to take over one of his suppliers and expand the business, eventually relocating to Vancouver where he enjoyed the scope of the bigger city, achieving a North American network distribution. By the time he sold the company in 1985, he had reached a peak of 250 employees and a need to change. The sale of the company brought another challenge forward; a non-competition agreement, which meant he had to turn his attention to another kind of business.

Soon he came to realize that his experience and abilities could be put to work in any variety of businesses. He became an entrepreneur, and transferred his financial and marketing skills into different areas. He worked for several years on a variety of projects including turn-around situations and coordinated the formation of several start-up business plans. Some of the start-ups included Ambassador Consulting Corp., Amera Optical Corporation, Alters Technology, Al Jean Wear Manufacturing and Chemex Lab.

He teamed up with Ernst & Whitney, Cooper Lybrand, Price Waterhouse, Peat Marwick and others for financial modeling and projections. Joe's view of his role in this world reveals his own moment of revelation: "I became like an opportunity's storyteller. The story began with the reason why the product – any product – was designed. The product had to be commercially economical, with the market pioneered and accepted. Then, I'd focus on how to plan supply, distribution and after-sales services. All at once, it became very clear to me that what I had learned in a practical way – certainly not in a formal or academic way – was certainly very applicable to many other industries." His remarkable skill and business ability led to his role as the president of Oxbow International Marketing Group, which provides strategic counsel and assistance with financing to emerging private and public companies.

Helping other companies was satisfying work and yet Joe Grosso was still searching. Then one day, on a trip to visit relatives in Argentina, he had what he calls his 'appointment with Fate'. He struck up a conversation with his sister-in-law's next-door neighbour, Dr. Vicente Mendez, who, as luck would have it, was a former chief geologist of the Argentine – a division of Fabricaciones Militares. In the course of their conversation, Joe Grosso's future would move in a totally new direction: "I asked him about what's going on in mining in Argentina and he drew on the back of a serviette napkin an image of the Argentine border with Chile. On the Chilean side, there were approximately 1,500 mining companies of various types and size and on the Argentine side, there were almost none."

Joe Grosso was profoundly inspired by the image that Dr. Mendez had created for him: "Quickly I wondered if God hated the Argentines and stopped all that good geology at the border. The answer was a definite no – absolutely not! Dr. Mendez assured me that they do have the geology in Argentina conducive to world-class discoveries."

Within ten days, Joe Grosso and Dr. Vicente Mendez had reached an agreement to form a new company, which they called Minas Argentina S.A. or MASA. MASA is a wholly-owned subsidiary of IMA Exploration. Dr. Mendez became the president of that company. With this move, Joe Grosso had set a new course for his life. Using his years of experience and intimate knowledge of the Argentine landscape, Dr. Mendez was able to steer the new company toward the emerging areas of mining opportunity in the country. Dr. Mendez shared Joe Grosso's intuitive belief that the geology that had made mining such a successful business in Chile would most likely continue across the border into Argentina. With this idea firmly in mind, Minas Argentina purchased 350,000 hectares of property on the border between the two countries. And thus began a new challenge for Joe Grosso; to familiarize himself with the properties of the company, which was spread over 14 different regions, and to decide which might support further exploration.

Very quickly the company ran through its initial capitalization, including money Joe Grosso had contributed from mortgaging his own house, and so it was time to find a partner who could offer the fledgling company some financial support. In addition to the funding that they sought, they were also in need of critical technological support; they wanted to support the company's efforts with the most up-to-date methodology and equipment currently available. And so, in 1995, the two partners put together a compelling package and set up some meetings to take place at the old Terminal City Club. They invited 42 mining companies to review their materials and offered them the chance to bid on the partnership opportunity. Ultimately, the successful bidder for the project was Viceroy Resources Corp., a mid-tier production company with some producing operations in the United States, and the cash and technology to take Minas Argentina in the right direction. Viceroy earned 50 percent by spending approximately $9 million in the subsequent 3 years.

The partnership between Viceroy and MASA prospered. From 1995 to 1998, the company was able to explore and develop its most promising properties and evaluate and acquire some additional prospects. Ongoing drilling and reconnaissance exploration on the most advanced project, the Guandacol Area, confirmed previously-identified gold targets and identified new prospective target areas. A significant discovery was made during the latter part of 1997 when ground crews identified the Quebrada del Diablo gold target.

The Gualcamayo Area, containing more than 47,000 hectares, offered the promise of multiple targets for a new mining area. Drilling on the other two main projects, Las Flechas and La Coipita, was completed in 1997 and the results were encouraging. However, due to significant option payments required and the market conditions at the time, the La Coipita project was dropped at the end of 1997. But more challenges lay ahead. The year 1997 was a difficult time for mining companies. During that year, a number of events unfolded that could have not been foreseen: the Bre-X fraud, which had an disastrous affect on the market for mining stocks; the sharp reduction in the price of gold and the weakening of base metals prices. When the Quebrada Del Diablo gold target was discovered, substantial funding was necessary – approximately $10 million – to fully explore and develop it. As a partner, IMA was required to fund its 50 percent share of the exploration program and would have had to raise its funds through issuance of equity. But given the state of the financial markets, raising the money proved well-nigh impossible without risking considerable shareholder dilution.

Unwilling to go that route, in the early days of 1998 Joe Grosso came to a difficult but practical decision; in order for the company to survive, IMA's remaining 50 percent ownership in the company was sold to Viceroy in exchange for 2.2 million shares of Viceroy and a 1 percent net smelter-return royalty. Also, through this sale, approximately US$1 million of debt owing was extinguished. Viceroy obtained 100 per cent ownership. And as full owners, they could focus their financial resources and expertise on advancing the properties.

Joe Grosso's sale to Viceroy quickly proved to be a wise move. The undistributed Viceroy shares and the current cash reserves of approximately $500,000 created a solid base from which IMA could pursue 100 percent-owned projects. But before any new exploration or development could take place, Joe Grosso knew he had an obligation to his shareholders that he had to address. "We knew that we had tested the patience of our shareholders, and so we issued a dividend, which is very untraditional for a junior mining company in Vancouver, or anywhere else that I know of. So we got a dispensation from the tax department to distribute a tax-free bonus, a dividend – because we disposed of assets that they (the shareholders) owned."

In a complete reversal of its previous condition, IMA was now a cash-rich company, but property-poor. Utilizing their contacts and network, Joe Grosso and Dr. Vincente Mendez set about acquiring a new range of property. By late-1998, the company had acquired over 114,000 hectares of strategically located properties in some of the more prospective regions of Argentina. They got lucky. Some of the property was so full of promise that it attracted the attention of one of the world's biggest gold mining companies, Barrick Gold Corporation. Barrick's interest in doing business with IMA picked up when IMA acquired property adjacent to property in Barrick's portfolio. As Joe Grosso recounts the story of their negotiations, he smiles at the memory. Clearly, being prospected by one of the majors felt great, especially after enduring some difficult times. But Joe Grosso was in no hurry to repeat history. His experience with Viceroy had taught him a few lessons, as his story shows: "We made good use of the funds from our partnership with Viceroy, and of the knowledge that they brought to the company. When Viceroy left we were definitely depleted in terms of expertise and so on. And then, along came Barrick. The king is dead, long live the king! They said, 'let's make a blanket deal here, let's make another Viceroy/IMA type of agreement', and we said, 'Oh no, oh no. We'll give you one property – just one.' They wanted to make it two. And so we signed an agreement with them for an option on the two properties. In total, we received close to $4.75 million, which in those days was a lot of money for a junior company that couldn't raise a dollar in the regular market. They proceeded to do a private placement, paying three times the market-share price for the option. We were pretty pleased with ourselves, especially because this all happened at a very bad time for the industry and financial markets, when the number of exploration mining companies left in the market was a mere token of what it used to be, two or three years prior."

At this point in the conversation, Joe Grosso is smiling broadly, happy to be counted among the surviving companies. The deal with Barrick was signed in June of 1999 and granted the option to select one of two designated properties – Rio de las Taguas or Potrerillos – both of which are strategically located relative to Barrick's Pascua-Lama and Veladero gold discoveries in the Valle del Cura area. After extending the terms of their agreement until December of 2003, Barrick's ultimate decision was not to go forward with exercising the option. But the money that the deal brought into IMA was put to good use, as Joe Grosso points out: "We went forward with building an incredible property portfolio of thirty-seven, which still survives today. Seven of these properties we have developed to the point where they are drill-ready. And thirty of which are still at early stages."

Of the seven properties that are drill-ready, the one currently garnering the most excitement is a bonanza-grade silver discovery known as The Navidad Project. IMA owns 100 percent of this property, which is the result of almost three years of grassroots exploration in the remote Patagonia region of Argentina. The discovery of the silver deposits at Navidad is remarkable for several reasons – the grades of silver are extremely high, even comparable to the discovery of silver in Nevada in the 1800s. And the discovery is regionally significant. The closest geological analogs for Navidad are other precious-metal enriched VMS systems with epithermal characteristics such as the Eskay Creek Mine and the Green Creek Mine. The discovery is without precedent in the Jurassic stratigraphy of continental Patagonia.

The Phase I core drilling program at Navidad commenced in November of 2003. The initial results were announced in December of that year, and indicated a very large, intensely-altered and mineralized system. These results compared favourably in terms of size and grade with numerous bulk tonnage silver deposits worldwide, like Pan American Silver's Alamo Dorado deposit in Mexico. The early drilling results on Galena Hill confirmed that anomalous chargeability rates are attributable to silver-lead mineralizations over very long intersections in excess of 200 metres. These large widths have dramatic implications for the tonnage potential of this zone. By the time 2004 rolled in, the additional results from drill-holes four and five on Galena Hill were announced. At drill hole four, 137 metres, silver was grading at 117 grams per tonne and from hole five at 83 metres, grading 229 grams per tonne.

As Navidad and Galena Hill are only 1200 metres apart, the final work of Phase I included testing the ground between them. The first drill-holes between Navidad and Galena Hills were undertaken in March of 2004. Of the five drill-holes tested, three returned significant silver intercepts, suggesting a connection between the silver mineralization at Navidad Hill and the Galena Hill silver deposit. All of the holes within the Galena Hill deposit area contained significant intercepts of silver-lead mineralization and continue to show excellent continuity of mineralization and silver-lead grades. By April, the Phase I drill program on the Navidad project was completed. After the results were analyzed, plans for an 8,000 to 10,000 metre Phase II drill program were announced. This program will focus on testing known mineralization at Navidad Hill, Barite Hill, and Calcite Hill, all located within a 5.8 kilometre mineralized trend that includes Galena Hill. In addition, Phase II drilling will further test the 'Connector Zone' which has recently been indicated by drilling between Navidad and Galena hills and the Esperanza Trend. The Esperanza Trend is estimated to be five to six kilometres long and runs approximately parallel to the Navidad 5.8 kilometre mineralized trend.

While the drilling was underway, IMA commissioned a resource estimation on the Galena Hill target. The report, produced by Snowden Mining Industry Consultants, indicated a resource of 207 million ounces of silver and 1.1 million tonnes of lead at 50 grams per tonne silver equivalent 1 cut-off grade. It includes 117 million ounces of silver and 495,776 tonnes of lead at 50 grams per tonne silver equivalent 1 cut-off grade. Inferred resources are 36 million ounces of silver and 56,776 tonnes of lead at 50 gram per tonne silver equivalent 1 cut-off grade. This resource includes only the Galena Hill deposit and portions of the adjacent Connector zone, and does not include known and interpreted mineralization at Navidad Hill, Barite Hill, Calcite Hill, or along the Esperanza Trend.

Geologic mapping, rock and soil sampling has shown potential for additional discoveries similar in style to Navidad within an 8 kilometre by 3 kilometre area. Drill crews have now started an 8 – 10,000 metre Phase II drill program that will target new zones outside the Galena Hill deposit. All aspects of the current program at the Navidad project are overseen by Dr. Paul Lhotka, IMA's Qualified Person for the project.

Although Patagonia is a very remote area, the location of the Navidad project is almost perfect; it's close to a highway, making it accessible even during the Argentine winter, which takes place in what North Americans would consider the summer months. There is a source of both power and water that has proven to be sufficient. The prospect for creating a mine that can produce on an economically feasible basis is good; but it's unlikely that IMA will take on that role. Joe Grosso explains that IMA is a company that is currently solely dedicated to finding viable deposits that could be developed by the company, sold to producers, either 100 percent if the shareholders agree, or in an arrangement that would see IMA sharing ownership in a partnership with a major company. IMA's current stance on the Navidad project is what Joe Grosso calls 'a nice position to be in'.

Making business decisions is Joe Grosso's particular strength. His work in the mining business has become a springboard for him to create a new role, which combines his business expertise with his new-found interest in mineral exploration. After working for more than a decade to put a talented and professional management group together, Grosso did not want to see it dispersed amongst the competition. But the expense of this professional salary base was too much for a single junior mining company to bear. His understanding of the underlying economics of the situation led to the creation of the Grosso Group, which takes the cost associated with hiring top professionals and amortizes it across a number of different companies, without penalizing investors with a high fixed monthly cost. The Grosso Group works to find projects and people, to arrange capital and to deal effectively in the public markets. This way, the valuable skills of Joe Grosso and his team can be applied to a broader range of companies and projects. The first company to join IMA under the umbrella of the Grosso Group was Amera Resources Corporation (now trading on the TSE Venture Exchange as AMS). Joe Grosso serves as the director and chairman of Amera. The president of Amera, Nikolaos Cacos, is also a director of IMA; he explains the genesis of the company: "Amera was started because so many opportunities came through the Grosso Group's offices each year, mining projects not only in Argentina and Peru but other parts of South America and North America. IMA couldn't possibly undertake all these projects. IMA had it hands full with 37 properties in its portfolio. It can only focus on one of those at a time. We thought that because a lot of good projects are coming through, we could create a new vehicle to take advantage of some of these opportunities that are beyond IMA's focus, and take some of these projects forward. And that's how Amera came into creation."

Amera had its first day of trading on December 2, 2003, so it's a very young company, but already it's performing very well. One key project is the Mogote project, which was in IMA's portfolio. About a year a go, the directors of IMA realized that if they were going to focus their resources on the Navidad project it might be wise to leverage some value in another property by creating a joint venture with another company. And so this was done between Amera and IMA for the Mogote project. Currently, Amera has spent over a million dollars on Mogote and has just completed the first run drilling program. Some of the majors have shown interest, and visited the property.

Mogote is a copper-gold porphyry target in an area characterized by some of the world's largest copper-gold porphyry deposits, and is located 11 kilometres east of Noranda-Metallica's El Morro copper-gold discovery (inferred resources of 7.4 million ounces gold, 6.2 billion pounds copper). The surface work that's been done on this property has unveiled a huge 500-metre trench of continuous gold-and-copper mineralization. And the geophysics done on the property also indicate there is a large target lying underneath it. It's got all the right features and demonstrates the classic characteristics of a large copper-gold porphyry potential deposit. Amera is now finalizing the previously announced drill program on Mogote. They currently hold a total of 75 percent interest in the property.

Amera's directors plan to take Mogote forward to the point where they can sell their interest for a multiple of the investment they put into the project and, by doing so, maximize shareholder value. Not one to waste words, Nikolaos Cacos explains the company's position succinctly:

"We know where our niche is, and we stick to it. That's what we're good at." With Amera prospering under the auspices of The Grosso Group, Joe Grosso turned his attention to another business opportunity. In order to ensure that IMA's present share price reflects the true value of IMA's assets and attributes, the directors and managers of the company decided that a corporate reorganization was in order. Their proposal will be presented to shareholders at the Annual General and Special General Meeting this year. The concept for the proposal was based on the desire to unlock the value hidden in IMA's full range of assets. In addition to IMA's 100 percent owned Navidad silver discovery, the company controls 36 exploration projects all acquired on advantageous terms over the past 10 years; six of which are being explored by joint venture partners. Considerable funds have been spent to advance these projects that are now at various stages of development and located in some of the most prolific mining districts in South America – several in very close proximity to major discoveries. Despite the advancement of many of these projects through quality exploration work, they are currently receiving little or no market valuation due to being overshadowed in the marketplace by the high profile of the Navidad silver discovery.

To unlock IMA's fair market value for all shareholders, management proposed to undertake a corporate restructuring which would have the result of splitting its present mineral resource assets between two separate public companies. Upon implementation of the corporate restructuring, IMA will continue to hold a 100 percent interest in the Navidad project, while the newly created public company, called Golden Arrow, will hold the non-Navidad projects.

These two separate public companies would be owned by all the existing shareholders, but each would have a separate focus. Golden Arrow would be committed to grassroots exploration while IMA Exploration Inc. would retain the Navidad silver discovery and focus on significantly expanding the drill program on the numerous targets within Navidad, and moving the project to production. In addition, IMA would conduct a more detailed regional exploration for Navidad-style targets, pursue listings on major U.S. and Canadian stock exchanges and complete a pre-feasibility study on the Navidad project in a timely fashion.

The remaining projects, other than Navidad, would be put into

Golden Arrow, a brand-new company with the same board of directors as IMA and managed by the same team at Grosso Management Group. Golden Arrow will then be free to focus on grassroots exploration for new mineral discoveries. The stock markets will then have the opportunity to fairly value Golden Arrow's exploration assets.

Shareholders of IMA will receive the same percentage interest in Golden Arrow as they presently hold in IMA on a basis of one share of Golden Arrow for every 10 shares of IMA. Upon completion of the reorganization, holders of IMA warrants will, upon exercise of those warrants, receive 10 IMA shares and one Golden Arrow share for every 10 warrants exercised. All outstanding IMA stock options will remain unaffected by the reorganization. Joe Grosso's description of this new venture is as energized as the man himself: "We have a very clear-cut job ahead of us. Now that we have separated the properties, we've created clarity for shareholders by providing a better sense of the value of the properties. And now we can get a better value for the other properties. It's very exciting. As a shareholder of IMA it's very exciting. Two horses running in the same race – and two horses can both be winners."

The two existing companies will benefit from sharing the knowledge and skills of the Grosso Group but there are differences between them, especially in terms of territory: IMA will continue to explore in Argentina and throughout South America; Amera has a broader mandate to explore all of the Americas – North, South and Central – for new areas of opportunity.

The market has shown its support for Joe Grosso and his team at Grosso Group; the share value for IMA Exploration stock (listed on the TSX Venture Exchange as IMR) has ranged from $0.35 to $3.80. His company is looking good with a market capitalization at $120 million. And the future looks bright for exploration; the markets for gold and silver are strengthening based on emerging markets such as India and China, as well as new uses for these historically precious metals. Silver is put to increasing commercial use in different applications related to computers and digital cameras.

Perhaps the key element of success that Joe Grosso brings to his exploration work is simple respect; respect for the land and the environment he is working within, respect for the traditions and culture of another society and, fundamentally, respect for the people who are affected by the work he does – ranging from the shareholders in his company, to his employees, to the people in the area where his exploration takes place. And this approach serves him and his company well. He is able to navigate the complex political world of South America, to forge contacts and support within the political infrastructure of Argentina. Thanks to his encounter with 'fate' Joe Grosso was one of the very early pioneers in the Argentine mining industry, which was opened to foreigners in 1992 by the Argentine government. Joe Grosso's self-assured approach to international relations is an enormous asset; he is quick to identify the primary challenge of working in Argentina: "I know how to stickhandle the difference in culture between North America and South America – which at times can test the patience of North Americans. It doesn't happen quite as quickly as you might like it."

Joe Grosso's efforts to cultivate his key relationships have paid off; he knows the bureaucrats and politicos and he knows how to avoid the mistakes of other companies whose efforts to mine in Argentina weren't quite so successful. It's worth it – to him the opportunity is abundantly clear: "Argentina represents one of the last great bastions of mining opportunity in the world. Due to the depreciation of the peso it has also become one of the most affordable and congenial. The mining codes and its regents are not unreasonable – I think it has been proven that federally, provincially and locally they are wide open to the future of mining."

He is committed to a practice of mining that is done to the highest standards – not just drilling holes to please management – and done in a manner acceptable to the indigenous community. His challenge – that a North American exploration company might find a way to flourish in Argentina – has largely been accepted. He considers himself a guest in Argentina, one who must observe the highest standards of business practice. His reference to the Latin blood of his heritage is an effort to establish some commonality with his hosts. The challenge of finding new targets to explore continues to fascinate Joe Grosso. As an experienced businessman, he sees the value and opportunity inherent in selecting properties at a young stage and bringing them to a lucrative point-of-sale. As the properties rise in value, the profits for shareholders materialize. And that, at the end of the day, is what motivates Joe Grosso.

IMPERIAL METALS CORPORATION

Imperial Metals Corporation sometimes seems as though it could be better named. Of course, the name 'Imperial' has decades of solid, deep, respected brand equity and achievement as part of its history, and the company has been a Vancouver mining leader since the late-1950s. But the last couple of years have seen the company work through the challenges of credit protection and reorganization, emerging strong and solid and ready to resume building and developing mines. Given the dramatic 'back-from-the-brink' turnaround, it's almost surprising that the words 'resurrection', 'phoenix' or 'Lazarus' weren't worked into the name of either the reorganized company or one of its mining projects.

Company Chairman Pierre Lebel says the story of Imperial today is the story of rebirth: "It's a new beginning to a company that's had a long and important history of exploration and mining in B.C." Lebel says credit for what many are calling the discovery of the year in B.C. goes to Pat McAndless, Art Frye and Brian Kynoch. "It's the classic story of a new discovery right next to an old mine, of rethinking something and looking at it in a different way." Explains Lebel: "Brian had been doing a lot of work on oxide-ore recovery and the team recognized that the Northeast corner of the property could become important in light of this work."

Not a bad accomplishment for a team that has never advertised exploration as its strong suit.

Imperial is a company with a comparably long history for a junior. Lebel searches through some memorabilia in his office, coming up with a small item: "Here is a chalkboard marker from 1959 when it was Imperial Metals and Power. We were into everything in those days. Our first prospectus dated December 20, 1960 had Coal, Coke Limestone, Electricity, Iron, Copper, Gypsum Chemicals and Research on the front cover. It was 10 pages long and those were half-sized pages. The company was seeking to raise $100,000 to advance its coal and iron properties. That period in Imperial's history culminated in 1981 with the formation of Imperial with the amalgamation of Invex Resources, Western Rolling Hills and Risby Tungsten under the leadership of Alan Savage."

Lebel, who got into the mining business 'by dint of chance and circumstance', did not connect with Imperial until 1983. In 1978, just recently called to the bar and practicing law in Sudbury, Ontario, he got an invitation from Archie Nesbitt, a law school buddy, to go duck hunting in Alberta.

"I told Archie I couldn't afford to go duck hunting," Lebel recalls of the encounter. But Nesbitt explained that the trip would be paid for by E&B Explorations, a German drilling fund operator that was looking to hire a lawyer for their Calgary office. The company was casting a broad net, talking to both established lawyers and relatively newly-minted attorneys whose careers were just beginning. At the time – the late-1970s – Lebel was in the latter group.

"So I came out, interviewed and they offered me a job at $36,000 a year plus benefits. That was about double what I might earn in my first year in Sudbury," Lebel remembers. "Then I had to explain to my wife, who was working on a teaching career and expecting our first child, how this duck hunting trip had potentially turned into a change-your-life-and-move-to-Calgary event. She said, 'If we don't go we'll always wonder about it. Let's give it 18 months.' So I became a mining lawyer in Calgary. We fell in love with the West and never looked back."

By 1981, E&B's owners were looking for ways to monetize their investment, prompting management to look for suitable reverse-takeover candidates. Dr. Hugh Morris, E&B's President, led the initiative. Morris was soon focussed on the freshly reminted Imperial Metals. "We saw in Imperial a junior company with an excellent track record led by Alan Savage, a highly-regarded dealmaker and John McGorran, a geologist with a keen eye for good properties. Hugh and Alan skillfully rolled

E&B's assets into Imperial for shares, achieving the liquidity objectives of E&B's owners and launching E&B as an independent public mining company via Imperial."

There followed what Lebel describes as a long period of rationalization. "We were doing well financially through excellent returns on our oil and gas assets, management fees and the sale of some of our minority uranium interests, but were unclear about our mission. The $100 million or so of gross asset value in the twelve Geomex limited partnerships that we were managing, generated handsome management fees, but it was difficult to drive value into the stock from this activity because it was so difficult to explain and assess."

When Alan Savage quit the outfit in 1986 for something smaller and more manageable, the company's board offered Lebel the post of president. "I was wary about lawyers running mining companies and only agreed to do it on a temporary basis until a more suitable candidate could be found," Lebel says. In this case, 'temporary' ended up meaning a decade-and-a-half, until the early part of the 21st century, when Lebel took over as chairman. "It was a huge transition. The learning curve was steep. Fortunately, Dr. Morris, a recipient of the J. Willis Ambrose medal from the Geological Association of Canada for distinguished services to earth sciences in Canada, remained as co-chairman. He was a great mentor and was backed up by an excellent team of geologists and engineers." These included Peter Cain, Tony Clark, Rad Pesalj, Ruben Corvalan, Peter Delancey, Dennis Gork, Bill Morton and Steve Quinn. The exploration team was led by the very capable Zarko Nikic. "On the oil and gas side, our assets were non-operated and we had a very solid guy by the name of Robert Mills looking after them."

Highlights of the period 1986 to 1993, included the creation, financing and listing on the TSX of Cathedral Gold Corporation as a roll-in vehicle for Imperial's gold assets. Cathedral explored extensively during this period in British Columbia on projects such as Bronson Creek, Takla Rainbow, Porcher Island and Ato. It also owned a majority stake in the Sterling gold mine in Nevada under the leadership of Peter Cain.

It was also during this period that Imperial began focussing extensively on Mount Polley, commissioning a $2 million feasibility report from Wright Engineers in 1990. "Wright concluded that it would cost

$145 million and take 18 months to build a 5 million tonne/year plant," recalls Lebel. Imperial tried to move the project forward in terms of development financing but got caught in a metal price downdraft. Corona, which held a 38 percent interest in the project, lost interest and sold out to Imperial for a mix of cash and shares worth $6 million. Imperial continued to advance the project in other ways, obtaining a mine development certificate in 1992 and completing, in the same year, the acquisition of the twelve Geomex limited partnerships which gave it a 100 percent interest in Mount Polley.

After six years of profits, the company incurred operating losses in 1992 and 1993. "We lost a lot of good people in those years as we downsized to adjust to lower revenues. But Imperial's fortunes were soon to rise again with the acquisition of control in 1994 by Calgary entrepreneur Murray Edwards. "Within an hour of working with Murray it became clear why he is so highly regarded and why everybody wants him on their team."

That year the stock almost doubled to $1.15. Edwards wanted Imperial to move forward as quickly as possible with Mount Polley but the Company's downsizings had left it too lean. Lebel recalls: "When Murray said, 'recruit the people you need,' the first call I made was to Brian Kynoch who was President of Bethlehem, a company chaired by Henry Ewanchuck. Henry and Brian had impeccable credentials, a great track record in mine development and operations and an established relationship with Sumitomo Corporation. Although Brian was intrigued by the challenge, he could not bring himself to abandon his Bethlehem shareholders. We then started talking about a merger. I knew that on the face of it, the idea would not be immediately compelling. Bethlehem essentially had three exploration properties, one of which was in El Salvador, and a small underground copper mine in Revelstoke nearing the end of its mine life. At best it would be perceived as trading dollars; no value added. But the board recognized the value of the people and the relationship with Sumitomo and felt that if this team was not prepared to abandon Bethlehem, they wouldn't abandon Imperial. The board concluded that Imperial would get real value for these intangibles and approved the merger."

Henry Ewanchuk and Brian Kynoch immediately got to work on

Mount Polley. They added Red Briscoe, Bob MacDonald, Cliff Overton, Malcolm Swallow, Rad Pesalj and Bill Ruffo to the team. Additional support was provided by the late Geza Budai of CSFM Engineering and Mike Pazand of Prime Choice. Key operating personnel, essential players in the mine-building phase, were in early. They included Mount Polley's first mine manager, the late George Wight, Don Ingram, Mill Superintendent and Don Parsons, Mine Superintendent. Project development financing was provided by Sumitomo Corporation which acquired a 45 percent interest as part of the deal.

The mine building team broke ground in May 1996 and completed the project in less than 13 months, five months ahead of schedule and significantly under budget.

With Mount Polley in production, Imperial sought other opportunities for growth and in 1998 merged with Princeton Mining Corporation, which held a 60 percent interest in the Huckleberry copper molybdenum mine near Houston, B.C.

With two mines in production in British Columbia and one in the U.S.A., Imperial seemed poised for significant growth but low metals prices kept the mines from achieving their expected financial returns. Imperial entered a difficult period as it struggled to break even under adverse conditions. Project debt was restructured, costs were rolled back. The B.C. Government chipped in through the Job Protection Commission with a financial support package, which included cheaper power for both Mount Polley and Huckleberry. These measures enabled the Huckleberry Mine to remain in production but the outlook for Mount Polley, facing a $15 million pre strip for the Springer pit, was less hopeful. Sumitomo decided to exit the project, selling its entire debt and equity in Mount Polley to Imperial for $11 million. In September 2001, a few months after completion of that transaction, Mount Polley was placed on care and maintenance due to low metal prices. There followed in 2002 a complete reorganization of Imperial's operations into two businesses, one focussed on oil and gas, the other focussed on mining to be run by completely separate management teams.

When Imperial emerged from this reorganization, it took a hard look at its mining assets and decided to focus on those properties that were most likely to generate shareholder value in the near-term and shed its long-term assets. In short order, Goldstream, Similco and Silvertip were sold, allowing the company to concentrate all of its resources on Sterling and Mount Polley. It then called upon its shareholders for a cash injection by way of a rights offering to drill some targets at its Sterling property in Nevada's Walker Lane Trend.

Pat McAndless believed strongly that the company should be looking deeper at Sterling, near high angle faults. By then Sterling was on care and maintenance, having started production in 1980 at a rate of 200 tonnes per day but never progressing beyond a small high grade producer. After suspending operations in 2000, it was now or never to address the seven or eight exploration targets that needed testing. The seventh target was called the 144 Zone. Pat McAndless, Chris Rees and Joe Marr hit paydirt on the first hole at a depth of 700 feet below surface near the high angle Rudy fault. "After making this discovery we drilled extensively from surface to expand the zone. But drilling was tough, and our success in penetrating the zone was limited. We got to the point where we were generating more questions than we were answering. So we decided to give it a rest until we could raise the money to drive down a ramp and get right on top of the deposit."

In the interim, Brian Kynoch redirected the team to Mount Polley. His thinking was that with flow-through funds readily available for exploration in Canada, the company should be exploring at Mount Polley to add to resources already in place, making the project more robust when mine operations are eventually restarted.

Brian and Pat thought that the northeast end of the property might be prospective, so Pat and Art Frye started cruising the old logging roads in that area, eventually locating an area of high grade oxidized float lying on the road 400 metres south of the property boundary. Interesting, but where did it come from? The material could have been carried there from a long way off. As they worried about provenance, Pat found an outcrop that looked like the source deep within Mount Polley's PM8 claim. So far, so good, but like most mining properties, you can find a lot of high-grade outcrop; whether it has roots is a different story. And the data from past exploration in the area indicated weak geochemistry and geophysics.

Equipment from the mine was mobilized to the area and with the assistance of geologist Gary Roste, a trenching program was initiated. In a surprisingly short period of time, trenching exposed a large zone of high-grade copper, gold and silver mineralization. The first hole drilled into the zone intersected 57 metres grading 2.54 percent copper, 1.15 grams per tonne gold and some 17 grams per tonne silver. It was a significant discovery located 2 kilometres north of the mill. The stock would rise from a low of 31 cents in July to $7 by December. "After all the company had been through, it was great to see support coming back for Imperial," Lebel recalls.

As the Company continued expanding the Northeast zone and finding new high-grade ore beneath the Springer pit, it was able to hang on to most of these gains with the stock trading strongly between the $5 and $6 range.

While Mount Polley is Imperial's number one property, Huckleberry has turned into a strong performer of late. "Huckleberry is certainly doing well at these metal prices but it's got twice as much debt as it can pay back with a three-year mine life. Unless a discovery is made similar to Mount Polley's, Imperial's equity in Huckleberry will have nominal value only," Lebel says.

All this discovery, progress and wealth creation is more remarkable for its arrival so close on the heels of a complete restructuring for Imperial Metals, which entered CCAA protection in November of 2001, as Lebel reflects while riffling through a stack of old Imperial Metals prospectuses and annual reports. Lebel is generous and self-effacing as he describes the people and events that helped Imperial emerge as the dynamic junior mining company it is now. Imperial's wholly-owned Mount Polley open-pit copper-gold mine is located in central British Columbia, 56 kilometres northeast of Williams Lake. The property consists of a mineral lease and mineral claims encompassing approximately 9,000 hectares. Commissioned in 1997, Mount Polley was built at a capital cost of $115 million. With a capacity of 20,000 tonnes of ore per day, it produced 133 million pounds of copper and 370,000 ounces of gold from 27.7 million tonnes of ore mined from the Cariboo and Bell pits before being idled September 2001 due to low metal prices. At that time an estimated 31.9 million tonnes grading 0.36 percent copper and 0.34 grams per tonne gold remained in the Bell and, still, as yet, unmined Springer deposits.

Preliminary metallurgical test work conducted on the Northeast zone ore confirms that metal recoveries will be good. All previous exploration at Mount Polley was focussed on magnetic anomalies. But unlike the other deposits, the Northeast zone is not magnetic, a finding which has lead to an extensive and ongoing re-evaluation of the entire property with induced polarization (IP) survey technology. IP coverage over the Northeast zone and along the eastern flank of the property correlates well to the mineralization in the Northeast zone. Other IP anomalies have opened up the potential for similar mineralization as well as possible extensions to the mineralization in the Northeast zone. In March 2004, work began on an updated reserve estimate, mining plan, and an application for a permit amendment to include mining of the Northeast zone. The mining will provide the basis for the re-opening of the Mount Polley mine. Ongoing deep drilling at the Springer zone has confirmed the presence of a significant body of copper-gold mineralization beneath the reserve outlined by previous drilling. The Springer zone is fully permitted for mining and is expected to provide long-term millfeed upon completion of mining at the Bell and Northeast zones.

The Huckleberry open-pit copper-molybdenum mine, located approximately 123 kilometres southwest of Houston in west central British Columbia, consists of a mining lease covering approximately 1,911 hectares, and 9 mineral claims comprising a total of 73 units encompassing approximately 1,825 hectares. Ore is mined with standard open-pit truck and shovel equipment, and processed through a SAG/ball mill circuit producing a copper concentrate and molybdenum concentrate. The copper concentrate is trucked to Stewart for shipment to Japan, while the molybdenum concentrate is trucked to and sold in Vancouver. Mill throughput averaged 19,000 tonnes per day to the end of December 2003.

Copper mineralization was discovered at the Huckleberry project site in 1962. Princeton Mining Corporation acquired Huckleberry by way of a plan of arrangement with New Canamin in July 1995. In June 1996 the Japan Group (a consortium comprised of Mitsubishi Materials Corporation, Marubeni Corporation, Dowa Mining Co. Ltd. and Furukawa Co. Ltd.) purchased a 40 percent equity position in Huckleberry and entered into an agreement to provide project loan financing in the amount of US$60 million in addition to their initial equity contribution. The B.C. Government also provided financial assistance in the form of a loan to Huckleberry for $15 million for infrastructure relating to roads, power lines and port facilities. The mine started commission activities on September 22, 1997 and achieved commercial production in October 1997. One month later, Princeton and the Japan Group provided an additional $4.5 million in equity for the project, and Marubeni Corporation, one of the members of the Japan Group, provided an extra US$10 million loan to provide additional working capital. The total cost to construct, install and commission the facilities was approximately $142 million. In May 1998 Imperial completed the acquisition of a 60 percent interest in the Huckleberry Mine through a plan of arrangement with Princeton Mining Corporation. Imperial and the Japan Group now each own 50 percent. In 2000, $3.5 million was spent on an addition to the mill to increase throughput capacity to 21,000 tonnes per day.

"I don't want to figure too highly in this story because I've only been a small part of it," Lebel insists, putting his attention and admiration instead on people like Murray Edwards and his present and former colleagues. "Brian knows how to get things done. When he teamed up with Henry Ewanchuck to build Mount Polley the results were truly amazing. They built Mount Polley for $115 million in less than thirteen months, with a capacity of seven million tonnes a year – roughly 20 thousand tonnes a day, and that was in 1997. The mine met or exceeded all of its operating criteria achieving design capacity within 4 months of startup. The engineers' report that we had done on the property in the early '90s said it would cost $140 million to build five-million-ton-a-year capacity and take 18 months to do it. That still stands today as a shining example of efficient mine-building."

Running a lean operation is crucial to Imperial's continuing success. That holds true in Imperial's downtown Vancouver office. Just thirteen people work there with three in accounting and five engaged in various technical pursuits. Support staff fill out the complement along with management personnel. The same drive to run things as efficiently as possible is at work in the field too, with Huckleberry's 230 permanent people. Mount Polley, when it starts, will have the same number. Currently, 60 people are on site with three drills, most of them contract people working with a dozen permanent staff and a mine manager. At the Sterling mine, three full-time employees rotate through the site for care and maintenance.

There's one more component to the Imperial personnel mix: consultants and contractors. As Lebel tells it, they are crucial, especially because of Imperial's focus on efficiency and frugality. Keeping them on staff full time wouldn't make sense, especially if their particular expertise is only needed in one or two very specific situations. Better to have access to that information, insight and knowledge when it's needed, and for just as long as you need it, than to have to keep the intellectual capital on the payroll permanently.

"Good consultants and contractors are invaluable. They are essential to our ability to get things done. But you must be careful never to give up your core competencies. We've got strong in-house metallurgical expertise. But some of the work we're doing has never been done before. An example is recovery of copper from oxide minerals using naturally occurring bacteria that process elemental sulphur into sulphuric acid. We have been working on this project for three years with a team of outside consultants and researchers from B.C. Research. In fact it was this project that sparked the Northeast zone discovery. Once we figured out that we could recover copper from oxide minerals at Mount Polley, we decided to take another look at areas thought to host oxide mineralization as well. We knew there were green rocks there but thought it wasn't worth following up. We had better targets elsewhere. It was the technology we were perfecting for recovering our oxide minerals that motivated us to reassess the Northeast Zone. And it turns out the zone is hardly oxidized. Science and hard work set the stage for this find, Lebel explains."

Imperial's scrupulous reputation and smart management mean that, inevitably, there is interest from large players in the mining business. But part of Imperial's strategy is its size and concentrated efficiency, something that makes it work better on its own than as a unit of a larger company – although that's not to rule out the possibility of partnering with a larger entity, if everything about the deal makes sense.

"There are always a lot of discussions in this business," Lebel says. "You're talking to a major about a joint venture and their position is always, 'if it's small, we'll walk away and you guys can operate it, but if it's big, then of course we'll want to double up and become the operator.' Our thought is always that it would be a lot easier for the big boys to operate something small with all their depth of resources. Give Imperial something big and rich, we'll fly with it. We're used to eking out positive cash flow from marginal projects. You've got to be sharp every day and watch costs, if you hope to make any money."

Murray Edwards, a well-known and respected Calgary entrepreneur, has been a major shareholder of Imperial since 1994. He continues to influence the company in terms of culture and operating philosophy. The business philosophy that he brings to the table is to stay with things; be patient, keep working at them over the long term. "He backs that up with support and leads by example," says Lebel. "He's always the first guy to put up his money, participating through thick and through thin. One of the principles of doing business in an Edwards company is to remain independent, to try to keep your assets 100 percent. If the initiative turns out, you keep the whole thing. If not, you regroup and try again. Some people think Murray is all about winning. But he operates on a much higher level. He is driven by success and sees wins and losses as part of the process of building long-term successful companies."

Unlike a lot of other mining companies, Imperial is determined to follow through on assets it discovers and develops. Whereas numerous mine operators will gladly tell potential investors they're grooming a particular property for a takeout, Imperial is just as forthright about its desire to keep working on its assets and put them in production. Lebel states, "We understand that the sharp end of the business, the place where the most gains are made, is on the exploration side. That's where you get something out of nothing and that's where a huge amount of value is created. In this rebirth phase, we've been much more concentrated on exploration than we were in the past. There's been a shift, definitely. Imperial's new mission statement is 'Discover-Develop-Operate'. We skipped the word exploration because we wanted to stay focused only on what adds value."

Because its principal properties are in British Columbia and Nevada, Imperial hasn't had to concern themselves with resolving political issues as much as some other companies with a more international range of operations. There were, initially, some First Nations issues that arose during the Huckleberry mine's build-up and development. But these were resolved to everybody's satisfaction as they arose, and without any rancor. Mount Polley hasn't faced any First Nations issues because the area had been previously developed for logging and ranching. That meant precedents, understanding between the people who live there and the mining company, and little friction in developing the project. "It has not been contentious and we feel it can remain that way," Lebel says.

And while its minerals are being mined in North America, the opportunity driving the mining isn't so much on this continent as it is in the burgeoning market of China.

"We're seeing huge demand from China," Lebel says. "Everything about China is large scale in terms of consumption. It is only since 1998 that the Chinese have been allowed to purchase their own homes. The result has been a mass movement of a growing middle class to own better homes. And better homes need copper. On average, about 250 kilograms per home. And they don't want to pedal or walk to these new homes. Twenty years ago there were 60 privately owned automobiles in China. That number has just raced past 10 million, and people who were making bikes 5 years ago are now building cars, in part because the Government has begun banning bicycles from its main roads.

"They can buy a Cadillac from GM, one that was assembled at GM's new Chinese plant which was built to produce cars not for export, but to serve the demand from China's growing class of millionaires. Volkswagen sells more of its cars in China than in the U.S. and is investing $7 billion in the next few years to double its production capacity in China. In less than two years China will overtake Germany as the world's number-three car manufacturer. Cars need copper. On average, 25 kilograms each.

"The Chinese also have a space program and are prodigious cell phone users. China knows technology. Technology needs copper.

"China's GDP growth rate was over nine percent in 2003. They have been growing their GDP at this level for about the last 20 years. Projected GDP growth rates of over eight percent are predicted going forward. How long is that? Japan, Taiwan, South Korea maintained GDP growth rates between 7 and 8 percent for up to four decades. If the U.S. GDP continues to grow at two percent, and China averages six percent, China will equal one half of US GDP in 2040. Simply put, continued robust growth is ahead for China."

All this growth needs power. China is installing 42 gigawatts of electrical generating capacity this year – equal to the entire United Kingdom system. And it won't be enough. All that power will eventually find its way into copper wire.

Lebel continues, "Overnight it seems, China has become the planet's number one consumer of copper, zinc, platinum, stainless steel, coal and iron ore. It is the number two consumer of oil, primary aluminum and refined nickel. Six years ago China was a net exporter of oil.

"And we have not yet talked about India, another nation undergoing a middle class revolution involving more than a billion people. Call it the Chindia phenomenon, a term coined by economist Woody Brock. What is taking place in these countries is on a scale that has no real precedent. To quote Donald Coxe of Harris Management Investment, 'it is the most widely disseminated increase in personal wealth and freedom in the history of humanity. China is key to the surge in commodity prices we are now experiencing.'"

The other international consideration that affects Imperial's business is the American dollar. The price of gold is almost always in reverse synchronization with the U.S. greenback. When the U.S. dollar weakens, gold gets stronger. A strong U.S. dollar puts downward pressure on gold prices. But the "glamour factor" affecting investors' perceptions of gold's value often counterbalances some of its drop in price.

"Everybody in the gold business is making money right now at these prices," Lebel says.

It might seem that somebody who's been in the mining business and dealing with the international metals and commodities markets as long as Lebel has would almost constantly be educating investors. But Lebel says his knowledge and expertise stop short of being able to predict the future or divine where markets are heading or when. "I get the sense, always, when I talk to our investors, that they know a lot more about the gold and copper markets than I do. I just stick to making sure that we are taking care of the things that are in our control. What investors want is a good company to bet on. A company that gives them the best odds for success. It's their business to take risks on metal prices and, as a rule, they would prefer that we not hedge metal prices beyond what is prudent to ensure operations can be maintained in a sudden downturn. They rely on us for accuracy regarding tonnes, grade, production rates and costs. They want us to do our part well so that they can properly execute their various investment strategies."

But is there a typical Imperial investor, a particular kind of market watcher or mineral-savvy player who's more likely to be drawn to its mix of efficiency and intelligence, as well as its management experience. "I think the typical Imperial investor is a value investor, looking for a solid junior miner with a lot of leverage on the upside but with high margin resources for downside coverage" Lebel says. "Look at the kind of margin we're going to enjoy on the Northeast zone deposit: You've got material that is worth $25 or $26 a tonne at current prices that will cost you $8 a tonne to produce – maybe with smelting, $10 a ton. So your margin is north of $14 a tonne. That's a lot of money at a production rate of 20,000 tonnes per day."

Imperial's criteria for successfully operating day-to-day include owning their projects one hundred percent, being independent, focussing on discovery, development and operations. And that kind of down-to-earth, solid, literal, no-nonsense philosophy is what drives 55-year-old Pierre Lebel, too. "As a group we are driven by a need to achieve," he says. Imperial's operating philosophy is to strive for improvement on a daily basis, a mindset aptly expressed by former Mount Polley mill superintendent Don Ingram, who was fond of saying: "If we don't come to work to get better, we might as well stay home."

"What I really like about Imperial is the cohesion of its employees, the culture of making things happen, of learning, of self reliance and of genuinely caring and looking out for each other. When things click – that sense of achievement, accomplishment and having a team of people really proud of what they've done. That's all I need. That and a couple of good books,' says Lebel."

Much of that philosophy is shared by the company's investors and its major shareholder Murray Edwards, whose continuing support, loyalty and faith Lebel is grateful for.

"One of the most important aspects of Imperial is the support it's gotten from its major shareholders," he says. "It continues to be an extraordinary partnership. Not many junior companies can undertake significant mine development projects successfully. It could not happen without Murray's guidance and support. When it's needed you get the full impact of his time, talent and resources and also that of directors Larry Moeller and Peter Geib. Things get done in a hurry. It's the story of Imperial in this era."

MINERA ANDES INCORPORATED

In an age in which satellites pick out geological anomalies from outer space, the idea of staking virgin ground on planet Earth seems a bit far-fetched. Although underexplored regions are common – precious metals producers often apply new mining technology to old workings – few exploration companies can claim to be working in hitherto unexplored regions; that is to say, areas that are both accessible and highly prospective, yet untouched by the prospector's pick. Minera Andes Incorporated, on the other hand – a Spokane, Washington-based junior exploration company – can indeed make this claim.

With more than half-a-million acres of holdings in the sprawling South American country of Argentina, Minera Andes is focussed on aggressively exploring for gold, silver and copper deposits containing 1 million gold-equivalent ounces or more. The company's primary strength lies in its exploration expertise. President and director Allen V. Ambrose and vice-president, exploration Brian Gavin have each spent a quarter-century in the field, utilizing scientific knowledge and hard-won experience to identify potentially massive reserves in virtually uncharted territories.

Upon delineating such discoveries in painstaking detail – as is the case with the company's co-owned advanced-stage San José project, which contains the high-grade Huevos Verdes gold-and-silver vein – Minera Andes markets its projects to proven, well-capitalized mining companies to develop and operate under profit sharing agreements. If and

when a mine goes into production, Minera Andes reaps revenues which
are then used to fund further exploration projects, thus leading to more
new discoveries and increased value for both the company and its shareholders.

"Brian and I are both technical guys," says Ambrose, an affable and
instantly likeable fellow, who trades quips and humourous anecdotes with
his colleague Gavin as naturally as he discusses complex exploration
strategies. The pair had crossed paths numerous times in the international geological community prior to taking Minera Andes public in 1995
(TSX-V: MAI; NASD OTC: MNEAF). "We're geologists by profession
and training – exploration guys – and we saw Argentina as a ripe plum.
Due to past political and military situations, there hasn't been a lot of
modern exploration work done in the country. It hasn't been touched until
fairly recently because the country simply hasn't been conducive for
doing business. Then in 1992 and 1993, the government implemented a
whole new set of mining laws. Brian and I were in Argentina around that
time, working as consultants, and we just liked what we saw."

To be sure, Argentin – bordered by Chile to the west and the south
Atlantic ocean to the east, as it tapers into the continent's southernmost
tip – has endured a troubled past since gaining independence from Spain
in 1816. More than a century of internal political wrangling was finally
squelched in 1946, only to be replaced by Juan Peron's extended reign of
authoritarian rule. A military junta took power in 1976 before democracy
was instated in 1983. Since then, concerted efforts have been made to
maintain peace in the country, while promoting economic progress and
democratic consolidation.

"Argentina was operating under military dictatorships and what-have-
you until 1983," says Gavin, "when democracy was ushered in following
the Falklands War. By the late-1980s, the country had sorted itself out
politically and, by the early-1990s, it had begun to straighten itself out
economically, as well – which was no small feat. Between 1962 and 1991,
there were serious inflation problems. People were literally taking wheel-
barrows full of money to go and buy a loaf of bread. The currency was
perpetually unstable and, because Argentina was being run by a military
government throughout much of that time, you couldn't really do any
business there. The economy was similar to that of Russia under commu-

nism, though Argentina was never a communist country. In a sense, it had all the bad characteristics of a communist state without the ideology.

"There had been some exploration work carried out in the 1960s and 1970s, funded mostly by the United Nations," he continues. "A lot of money was being sent to Argentina, but rumour has it that not all of it made it to the field – it sort of got sidetracked. There was, however, a rudimentary database of geological information. In fact, one of the challenges we had was that most of the geological information was held by an outfit called 'the military factory,' meaning that the exploration data were being handled by a branch of the army."

Even these safeguarded documents turned out to be dodgy at best. "There was a serious lack of topographic maps," says Gavin. "Either detailed maps didn't exist of certain areas, or else they were wildly inaccurate. You would have things like a 7,000-metre-high mountain peak misplaced by five miles – which is quite a serious problem if you're flying around in a helicopter looking for it. As a result, we spent a lot of time gathering data from legitimate sources during the day, and then gathered a lot of maps and information from more 'informal' sources outside business hours. Though most of the areas we were looking at had air-photo coverage, often the photos had been taken home from where they were supposed to be." In addition, although some of the most interesting geology in Argentina straddles the country's border with Chile, a history of skirmishes between the two nations resulted in strict laws forbidding civilians from going within 20 miles of the Chilean border.

Nonetheless, by the early-1990s, a handful of foreign mining companies were conducting exploration work in the country, though little progress was being made. "Some of the bigger problems had been addressed by the time they started changing the mining laws," says Gavin. "Argentina finally got a stable democracy when Carlos Saul Menem came to power in 1989. The currency was fixed one-to-one with the American dollar, which stabilized inflation, effectively killing it overnight. As part of the package that allowed the country to do that, however, Argentina had to conform to certain World Bank agreements, including implementing new mining laws based on Chile and Peru's reformed mining laws, and provide mining investment incentives."

In 1992, the long-overdue process of amending Argentina's mining and investment laws commenced, thus transforming the country into a favourable destination for foreign explorationists. "That's when the flood-gates really opened," Gavin says. "I'd been doing consulting work in the country, as had Allen, so we were already there and got in on the ground floor. Then all of these foreign mining companies started pouring in. By 1995, there was something like 65 junior exploration companies in the country. All of them claimed to have offices in Argentina, but very few were serious about finding anything. They all wanted to get a little flag on the map, but they weren't really out in the field doing exploration work."

"Argentina is a country that really hasn't had a lot of modern exploration work done on it at all," says Ambrose, "even though it has incredibly favourable geology. Chile, for example, had been a big copper producer, but we felt Argentina had really been overlooked. Brian and I knew each other from the industry. He had been working in Argentina, finishing a countrywide analysis as a consultant for a major mining company, and had a lot of knowledge and expertise of the country. Around that same time, I was working independently in the country on projects for different companies. We got together while running an exploration program for another company called N.A. Degerstrom. We picked up properties in Degerstrom, a private engineering-contracting consulting company, and then formed the private company, Minera Andes, which the projects were vended into.

"We put together a company that is very persistent at exploring and now we have a project, the San José, that is going into development," Ambrose continues. "The analogy I like to use is that, going into Argentina is akin to what it must have been like going into Nevada 100 years ago. These properties are in a very primitive, early-days stage. There are gold- and silver-bearing ore veins sitting right on the surface. In many areas, there has been no previous prospecting and there are no old workings or anything like that. As far as we can tell, we're the first company to take a sample out of these properties. It's pretty impressive for a geologist to be able to go into these areas and make these kinds of finds."

Born and reared in Spokane, Washington, Allen Ambrose graduated with a Bachelor of Science degree in Geology from Eastern Washington University and immediately went to work in the sector. "Spokane used to be a bit of a mining centre in the United States," Ambrose explains. "A lot of major companies had offices there from which they would run their regional offices in Alaska. It even used to have its own stock exchange, a penny exchange with notorious promoters who sold stocks from the numerous small silver companies in the neighbouring Silver Valley near Coeur d'Alene, that became one of the largest silver districts in North America. At one point, it was a hotbed of entrepreneurial mining exploration with a lot of silver companies based there. Teck Cominco's U.S. headquarters are still in Spokane, but there are not many mining companies left there today."

In 1982 and 1983, Ambrose returned to university, intending to complete his graduate degree, "but I never finished because I got too busy working," he says with a laugh. Indeed, he has extensive experience in all phases of exploration, project evaluation and project management, having worked as a geologic consultant throughout North and South America for several major U.S. and Canadian mining companies. He was a co-discoverer of the Brisas del Cuyuni gold deposit in Venezuela (later acquired by Gold Reserve Corporation) and has worked as a geologist for Cyprus Minerals, Kidd Creek Mines, Molycorp, Boise Cascade and Dennison Mines. He likewise initiated an exploration program in Honduras that led to the acquisition of several exploration projects and their subsequent leasing to other companies. At least one of these projects is now an operating mine.

Prior to launching Minera Andes, Ambrose designed and assisted in conducting a generative gold exploration program covering the Argentine Andes, using Landsat imaging and ground-based geological data. He also conducted detailed geologic exploration of two copper oxide properties in Argentina and completed a Landsat program over selected regions of southern Argentina. "A lot of geologists tend to gravitate towards South America or places outside of North America," he explains. "Personally, I was attracted to Argentina because you can make things happen there a lot faster."

On the other side of the Atlantic, Brian Gavin was born in West Yorkshire, U.K. and completed his B.Sc. Honours degree in Geology at the University of London. Relocating to the United States in 1978, he garnered his Master of Science degree in Geology and Geophysics from the

University of Missouri-Rolla. "I did my thesis in Montana," he explains, "and, consequently, I ended up doing a great deal of work in Montana and the Pacific Northwest." He has worked in all phases of exploration, including project evaluation and project management in the search for precious and base metals, as well as industrial minerals. As a project manager and consultant, he has worked in the U.S., Mexico, Nigeria, Argentina and Romania.

From 1981 to 1993, he was a consultant with the geological mining-consulting firm of Ernest K. Lehman & Associates, after which he was employed by N.A. Degerstrom and served as vice-president, exploration for Minera Andes. He has managed a property portfolio of approximately 1.2 million acres and has overseen the evaluation of more than 100 properties. Since June 2001, he has served as an officer and director of Franconia Minerals Corporation, and is also a director of Minera Andes S.A., the Argentine subsidiary owned by Minera Andes and Minera Santa Cruz S.A., the operating company of the San José Project.

"Minera Andes's rationale from the beginning was to raise money in the mining markets," says Gavin. "We wanted to spend about a million dollars a year, and that's a pretty big chunk for a private individual with their own company. It made sense for us to get public money involved because that gave us access to more money. When we took the company public, we were able to expand from a working budget of between $800,000 and $1 million a year to a working budget of $3 million a year. For several years, we were, in Argentina, roughly the same size – in an exploration sense – as Rio Tinto Inc. That is to say, our exploration efforts in Argentina were on the same scale as the biggest mining company in the world, except that we didn't have as many committee meetings as they did."

Both Gavin and Ambrose credit the Canadian venture market with allowing them the leverage to make substantial strides in a relatively short period of time. "It's all part of the beauty of the Canadian system and why Canadian exploration companies are so successful," says Ambrose. "If you're out there acquiring quality projects and you are aggressive, a lot of money comes your way. Like Brian said, there were probably 65 companies in Argentina by 1995 and most of them were junior Canadian companies. Canadian juniors have become responsible for the majority of the world's discovery efforts. It's because of the way the system works – there is a significant pool of risk capital going into funding these companies. Over the years, we've raised quite a bit of money and looked at quite a number of properties. We increase our knowledge base on a geologic region, we become more and more focussed on the area, and we carry out our business plan, which is to get to the discovery stage."

That initial discovery came in March 1997 in the form of the Huevos Verdes high-grade gold and silver vein, part of the almost 100,000-acre San José project in southern Argentina. "From our previous work in the country," says Gavin, "we knew which areas we wanted to start with, and then we developed our expertise along with our knowledge of the country. We had an exploration philosophy of, 'Let's look at a lot of properties, and let's look at them in detail because they're hard to get to.' We started out with only a couple of people, but by 1997 we had 15 geologists and about 50 people altogether in the field. We probably looked at a total of about 150 properties during our first five years and, at one point, we had about a million acres of land.

"We would go and look at properties in the Cordillera and in the higher Andes that might take four or five days to get to on mule," Gavin continues. "These properties were located at elevations of over 10,000 feet and the helicopters available to us didn't fly that high. Consequently, it might take $25,000 to go and look at the property because you've got two geologists, a guide, the mules, a guy to look after the mules – that's four people right there. If you need another animal to carry the food and supplies, that means another animal and another guy to help look after the animals. It got to the point where we had 20 animals and 10 guys, with some of the animals carrying hay for the other animals."

As it turned out, Minera Andes was none too soon making the Huevos Verdes discovery on the San José project. "At the time, we were quite lucky and considered ourselves true geniuses," Ambrose says with a laugh, "because we did a major financing in December 1996, right before the crash happened. As it turned out, it was probably our biggest financing, so it was quite fortuitous. When the Bre-X mining scandal hit in April 1997 and caused the crash of the junior mining sector, all the equity funding went away. We ended up running the company off that financing for several years. We were able to just keep exploring, in addition to developing the Huevos Verdes project as far as we could.

"At that point," he continues, "we brought in a joint-venture partner because we knew the San José project was developing into something big and looked like it could be a mine." It proved to be a shrewd maneuver. By bringing in the Lima, Peru-based mining company, Mauricio Hochschild & Cia. Ltda., as property manager-operator and 51 percent owner, Minera Andes was able to move ahead while other junior exploration companies were closing up shop. Not that Minera Andes emerged unscathed. "We went from employing 15 geologists to virtually zero," says Gavin, "and our stock price went from the $2.50-$2.75 range to four cents."

"Even though we were developing and we had more assets and exploration properties than when the company was founded," says Ambrose, "nobody cared. Our share price was lower than it was when the company was founded. But the important thing is that we were able to carry on with our financing and keep our property base intact. Furthermore, we were able to enter into a joint venture that allowed us to keep the company going. Now, we're at the stage where we're doing a feasibility study on the San José project, and it is developing nicely through the joint venture.

"When we were looking for a partner," he continues, "we went around and talked to several companies that were experts in developing this particular type of vein system. You have to get the right people on a vein to effectively mine it, and Mauricio Hochschild & Cia. Ltda. ended up winning the beauty contest, so to speak. They came up with the right offer and proposal. Plus, they produce about 450,000 ounces of gold and 10 million ounces of silver annually in their various mining operations. They're a substantial, private, mid-sized mining company generating $200 million a year in revenue." Adds Gavin: "We found the mineralization was such high grade, that even with the market going south and the price of gold going down, it was still of a sufficiently high grade to get people interested. It's the kind of deposit from which you can still make money with gold at $250 an ounce."

Of course, this is no longer a concern. Mauricio Hochschild & Cia. Ltda. employs approximately 100 workers, miners and geologists at the San José project, where a 28-kilometre road to the work site has been completed and is in use. Surface facilities have been constructed and two

45-degree incline shafts have been sunk, allowing access to the main Huevos Verdes gold-silver vein, where work is underway to define the ore reserve. Four mineralized systems totaling more than 30 kilometres are currently known to exist at San José and, of this distance, only about 20 percent has been drill-tested for mineralization at depth.

Based on market prices of US$300 per ounce gold and $5.00 per ounce silver, the current resource, based on a cutoff grade of 100 grams-per-tonne of silver, is 700,000 ounces of gold equivalent. The Huevos Verdes vein has an indicated resource of 1,058,000 tonnes with a silver grade of 266.8 grams per tonne and a gold grade of 3.1 grams per tonne, totalling 9,075,300 ounces of silver and 106,000 ounces of gold. Meanwhile, the inferred resource is 1,541,000 tonnes with a silver grade of 318.7 grams per tonne and a gold grade of 3.5 grams per tonne for a total of 15,789,700 ounces of silver and 173,000 ounces of gold.

"One of the reasons we decided on a Peruvian partner," says Ambrose, "is because it is an underground mine and they have a lot more expertise working with this type of deposit. There really aren't very many North American companies with underground mining expertise these days. Plus, it's a very big area – almost 100,000 acres – so we had to part-ner with a company with that kind of experience. The thing about Argentina is that it is so underexplored and underdeveloped, we're pick-ing up huge districts where there are dozens of veins and targets on a property. If this same-sized tract of land was in Canada, for example, it would probably be owned by several different companies. As it is, we own one big area where they've already identified over 30 kilometres of the system, and we're just developing two kilometres of it.

"You have to stick to what is going to give you the best chance of suc-cess," Ambrose continues. "We gladly backed off on our general explo-ration so that we could focus on this one high-grade property – particu-larly when we realized, five years ago, that we had something that could become a mine. While Hochschild manages the development, there is also great exploration potential at San José and, as professional explo-rationists, we provide advice and feedback on the Hochschild program to maximize discovery potential."

In the meantime, Minera Andes is continuing its ongoing exploration programs and has made a series of new discoveries, already lining up the next project and the next partner they'll be bringing onboard to carry out their business plan and cycle. "We've got several new exploration properties," says Ambrose, "and we have a number of guys working in Argentina who are going out, following the same model and building a nice database that directs our exploration and tells us where we want to be, based on all the work we've done in Argentina. We've got guys who have expertise in looking at vein systems and finding new ones, we've announced a couple of new properties that look very promising, and we've been doing geophysics, as well as high-resolution satellite imaging, combining the latest technologies."

Notable among these properties are the Los Azules discovery, a copper system that has been drilled with extremely favourable results; the Cerro Mojon gold-silver vein in the Santa Cruz province; and two new properties, La Huella and El Trumai, which contain mineralized geologic structures remarkably similar to the San José project. "These properties illustrate how we emphasize our strengths in exploration," says Ambrose. "After we explore a good property, we bring in a proven operating partner that can use its strengths to develop and manage production on a profit-sharing basis. Some junior companies want to handle everything from exploration to production. My observation is that this usually doesn't work very well.

"With the San José project," he continues, "we had somewhat of an educational process going on, where you had companies like Goldcorp and Meridian coming out developing these high-grade veins that are incredibly successful. As a result, high-grade veins have become more accepted in the mindset of the exploration industry and the investment community. At the time we made our discovery, however, the mindset was that most people in Argentina were looking for disseminated projects, not high-grade veins. We kept focussing back to the vein systems because that's the way the mineralization occurs. Although companies were exploring for veins in Canada and the U.S., nobody was thinking in those terms when it came to Argentina."

As for the logistics of working in a country with such a colourful and sometimes volatile history, the Minera Andes team is more than pleased to be working where they are. "The great thing about the area of Argentina in which we work," says Gavin, "is that there is nothing there that will sting you, bite you or shoot at you. We're not working in the jungle and Argentina is socially quite stable. There has never been a major problem with kidnappings or violent crimes – it's a really peaceable place to work. Also, it's a lot more Europeanized than the rest of Latin America, a very European-style country. Of 39 million people who live there, approximately 60 percent are of Italian heritage, 30 percent are Spanish and the rest are a mixture of German and English. Essentially, it's a big empty country that was not really settled to any extent until the 19th century. In fact, there are places in Patagonia that look identical to Montana – mountains on one side, cattle on the other and trout streams running across the landscape."

What's more, it is economically feasible to do business in Argentina. "Prior to 2002," says Gavin, "there was a 10-percent premium cost over working in the United States – the way the currency was pegged against the dollar made it quite expensive to do business there. Since 2002, however, when the Argentine peso was devalued by a factor of three, it has been quite cheap to work there, much more reasonable. These days, now that we're in a situation where our joint-venture partner is actually developing a mine, we're going to be spending a lot more money than we have been over the past couple of years, but we'll also be getting a lot more value out of it now than we ever did before."

Indeed, with the San José project well into the development stage, Minera Andes Incorporated is poised to realize the outcome of their labour. "We have a resource that has been defined in the vein from a technical point of view," says Gavin, with more than a hint of optimism. "Drilling and underground sampling is what is being done right now in order to give us more confidence in what kind of mineralization we have. From there, we move in technical terms from having a resource to having a reserve. Workers are constructing two shafts on the vein, consisting of about 500 metres of underground workings. Eventually, they will work complete construction of a total of approximately 3.5 kilometres of underground workings, so we can better sample the area we've drilled.

"So far," he continues, "we've drilled 56 holes into the vein and each one is four-and-a-half-inches wide over a distance of about 2.5 kilometres long. That means there is a big gap between the drill holes, and we're trying to estimate what is going on between them. This is a type of deposit

that is notorious for being erratic, so we expect there to be wide varia-
tions. Having said that, however, I should note that the Peruvian miners,
who are our joint-venture partners – and who are the experts here – don't
particularly trust drill holes. They'll look at a drill hole that has a high
grade of gold mineralization in it and they'll say, 'That's good.' Then
they'll look at another one that has low grade of gold mineralization in it
and they'll say, 'That's good, too,' because it tells them the vein is there.
They don't expect it to be 100 percent high-grade mineralization.

"They are now preparing to go underground so they can actually tunnel along inside the vein and they can see how it functions," he says.
"They want to get a feel for the variation in grade. When they got underground, they expect to see small areas of very high-grade material –
which you wouldn't expect to see in a drill hole because you wouldn't
necessarily have the good luck to actually hit one. Those are the type of
things that add the gravy to the operation. You don't need very much volume of that type of material to add to your production."

"If the feasibility study comes back with positive results," Ambrose
adds, every bit as optimistic as his colleague, "we'll hopefully have revenue coming off a producing mine. We're looking at having the feasibility study done by the first quarter of 2005, which means Mauricio
Hochschild & Cia. Ltda. will have the whole underground mine developed by that point, with all the buildings and infrastructure in place. If we
get a positive feasibility, we should be able to go to the bank to get funding to build a mill to produce the ore into gold and silver."

Though that may sound easy enough, Minera Andes had gone
through some lean years and put in a considerable amount of time, energy, money and – perhaps most of all – expertise to get to this stage. "It
could have been much more difficult," Gavin says, "but we have quality
assets. I think maybe the biggest challenge was educating investors about
vein deposits, but once they discovered they can make an awful lot of
money from them, it didn't take too much convincing."

Having a strong team comprised of proven and experienced personnel certainly helped, as well. In particular, Ambrose and Gavin acknowledge their Argentine lawyer and accountant, and a team of outstanding
geologists, including U.S. geologist Thomas Borovicka, who was responsible for discovering the San José property in the first place. Meanwhile,

with four people in its Spokane office and eight in its Argentine office (including legal assistants), Minera Andes has been able to make optimum headway while keeping costs down, thanks to low overhead.

"As you get known in the industry," says Ambrose, "you garner a certain standing. At Minera Andes, we've become known for being solid technical guys. We're pretty much a no-frills company and we are not promotionally driven. We simply get the job done. We have a good reputation of doing exactly what we say we're going to do, and that carries a lot of weight.

"But we always like to distinguish ourselves, too," he adds. "There are a lot of junior companies out there trying to do what we're doing, but you really have to know what you're doing and stick to a very focussed business plan in order to get from point A to point B. You'll see a lot of companies honing in on certain areas and then five more companies will show up, but they will be in and out, too. Typically, junior companies have a hard time sticking to a plan – either because they don't really have the money, or else they're just promoters looking at land plays. Next month it will be somewhere else. Sure, we've looked outside of Argentina in the past and even seen a few opportunities, but it tends to confuse your investors. I believe that if you don't stay concentrated on a region, you can lose focus. We need to be in a place where we can use our skills, and right now that place is Argentina."

NORTHERN ORION RESOURCES INCORPORATED

The primary challenge for many people in the mining business is finding their quarry. Of course, development and financing and running a mine all present their share of difficulty and problems to be overcome. However, apparently, some miners thrive on greater rations of challenge than others. David Cohen and his North Orion team apparently thrive on the kinds of situations that might make lesser competitors waver – challenges like linking two gold refining and production facilities and extending the life of the mining complex they're part of by building a nine-kilometre tunnel through a mountain. And that kind of bold initiative is part of David Cohen's essential makeup. The drive is not part of a corporate philosophy or 'mission statement'.

"We don't have a mission statement," Cohen says bluntly. "And we're not going to have one either. You waste your time thinking about that kind of stuff." Northern Orion's lack of a mission statement is part of a gutsy, bold outlook that stares at the realities of the mining business – as brutal as they can be – without flinching. "It's legalized gambling," is the way Cohen puts it. Some may find romantic reasons or deep-seated historical motivations for getting into the mining business. Cohen's reasons are more focussed and immediate. And they're probably music to the ears of people who hold Northern Orion stock: "Increasing sustainable cash flow and shareholder value; building value however we can get it and the cash flow. It's great – we're probably going to do $50 million this year, which is a big number."

Not exactly a profile that fits poet Robert Service's ideas about 'men who toil for gold', but a pragmatic, smart approach, one honed, no doubt, by Cohen's career thus far.

Northern Orion is a partnership of Cohen and Bob Cross, an associate of long standing. Cohen was born in South Africa. That's where he grew up and where he got all of his initial knowledge about – and passion for – the mining business. He trained as a chemical engineer, then got an MBA. He went through operational training in South Africa at De Beers and Anglo American gold and diamond facilities. His next step took him into project management and the commercial side of mining projects with Fluor in South Africa. Eventually that landed him the position of Fluor's director of sales and marketing. From there, still with Fluor, he was transferred to the United States. There, he held executive positions in their mining and petroleum groups. In 1997 he moved to Canada to 'go back into the owner's side' of the resource business.

"I basically decided I wanted to work for myself, so here I am running a public company for everybody else," Cohen says. "I was in Colorado and running the mining business for two-thirds of the world, basically, on the commercial side and I got an offer that made sense: come to Canada, where it all happens, and give it a shot. I was offered a role at Miramar and Northern Orion – it was one company, effectively. So I came up in '97, just in time for the metals markets to crash."

Cohen's partner Bob Cross is also an engineer, also with an MBA. (Cross's is from Harvard.) He was the head of Gordon Capital's mining group. From there, it was on to Yorkton Securities, where he was chairman and CEO through the middle-1990s. In 1998, Cross moved back into private investing. He's been Cohen's partner in Northern Orion since 2001.

"Northern Orion has been a public company since 1987," Cohen says, picking up the story. "It is Toronto-listed and American-listed, so we're on both stock exchanges. It was effectively put together as a shell and then reengineered in the early nineties to become a South American exploration company. It was controlled by Miramar mining, which owned between 55 and finally 70-plus percent of the company – so very much a Miramar subsidiary. Focussed originally on finding gold in South

America, we found very quickly that we'd bought into a number of properties that were advanced exploration properties. The gold didn't pan out and we were left with a huge copper portfolio. We acquired a number of Argentine companies along the way; one of them was a large company, based in the U.S. with a lot of Argentine assets, called American Resources. They owned a 30 percent interest in a property called Agua Rica, which was an interesting copper-gold project in joint venture with BHP. From '94 to '97, Northern Orion and BHP put a lot of money into this project, drilled it, proved it up to be one of the world's largest and richest copper-gold deposits."

In total, about $55 million was spent on Agua Rica. Thirty percent of that total came from Northern Orion's bank account. In 1998, the result of all that spending and hard work meant a completely defined, well-drilled, metallurgically-tested mine.

Then the bottom fell out of the copper market.

"These projects typically take hundreds of millions of dollars; without the market in your favour you can't raise that kind of money," Cohen remembers. "Everything went quiet. Through that period of the mid-90s, Northern Orion went from a company with a market capital of $50 million to a company with a market capital of CAD$600 million, for 30 percent of that asset. The company's valuations went through the roof. And as the metal prices went down the valuations came down with it. From 1998 to 2002, nothing happened. It was dead. During that period Miramar, basically internally, decided it was going to focus on gold and outbase its copper asset, which was Northern Orion. In 2000, we worked with BHP to try to find a way to reduce the capital costs of Agua Rica, and to be able to put this project into production in a smarter, more efficient, more appropriate manner than putting $800 million or $900 million into the ground. And we were getting a fair way down the track and having some success when BHP decided they were going to sell Agua Rica. They made it a corporate mission: they're going to sell this thing, get rid of it, and that was in 2001."

As a result of that decision, 2002 saw one company after another kicking the tires, asking questions and considering Agua Rica as a possible acquisition. Finally, an Australian company called Mount Island Mines (MIM) bid for BHP. But Northern Orion, as part of its partnership with BHP had right of first refusal on any deals or overtures to buy. So when BHP got the MIM bid, Northern Orion decided the opportunity to buy BHP's share was too good to pass up.

"We bought the equivalent of 10 million ounces of gold and 18 billion pounds of copper, so $22 billion worth of metal in the ground – defined, drilled and there for $12.6 million. We paid them $3.6 million and owe them the other $9 million and a bit in a year's time," Cohen says.

Of course, buying metal in the ground is one thing. Getting it out of the ground, getting it refined and doing so at a reasonable cost are all important considerations, too. But once the BHP deal went through, the process had begun, and Northern Orion had the assets it wanted.

"Where it gets interesting is the company that made the offer, Mount Island Mines, is a 50 percent owner of a mine that's 34 kilometers away from us called Alumbrera," Cohen says. It was built in the mid-1990s and it cost $1.3 billion to put together – never made any money. Alumbrera itself was an ore body that was supposed to last for twenty years. It had some issues on their reserves in the late-1990s and it turns out that it will actually only operate for about 13 years."

A company called Rio Tinto, which also had a 25 percent interest in Alumbrera, decided to sell its stake at the end of 2002. A Canadian gold mining company called Wheaton River Resources bought that stake for $180 million. Copper prices at the time were 62 cents and gold was between $270 and $300 an ounce. As Wheaton River was considering whether to buy Alumbrera and how to structure the deal should it decide to buy, Northern Orion was buying its share of Agua Rica from BHP. As part of those discussions, the question of a stake in Alumbrera came up – Northern Orion eventually bid $19 million for a piece of Alumbrera.

"After a lot of back and forth, we recut the pie at Alumbrera: 50 percent to MIM, 37.5 percent to Wheaton River and 12.5 percent to Northern Orion. Last year we raised CAD$110 million and issued 910 million shares on the exchange. I think we hold the record for the most amount of shares issued. We started the year with a market cap of $10 million to $20 million, ended the year with a cap of $350 million. Today we have a market cap, on a fully diluted basis, of pretty close to $500 million. And we're earning fantastic money, we'll probably make US$50 million this year. We're going to pay for this asset in a year-and-a-half. We're absolute heroes because the market went in our favor – we were in the right place at the right time."

There's another key ingredient in this process, which Cohen remembers. "A lot of chutzpa, as they would say."

MIM changed its structure and its name to Xstrata. Alumbrera is in northwestern Argentina. It's an open-cut mine whose operations began in 1998. Production measured at the end of June, 2002 totaled 439 million pounds of copper and 759,000 ounces of gold. Five facilities in three Argentinean provinces make up the project: the open-cut mine and processing facilities at Alumbrera, Catamarca; a 316-kilometre concentrate slurry pipeline through Catamarca and Tucuman provinces; a 202-kilometre power line from El Bracho, Tucuman; the filter plant and rail loading facilities at Cruz del Norte, Tucuman; and port and handling facilities at San Martin near Rosario, Santa Fe. There are support offices in Tucuman, Catamarca and Buenos Aires.

Alumbrera's porphyries were created about eight million years ago in the roots of the Farallon Negro volcano. People have known about the rich mineral deposits in the region since the nineteenth century. As the twentieth century began, small-scale mining began in the region. It wasn't until mid-century – 1949, specifically – that the vastness of the Alumbrera deposit was gauged and understood.

The Alumbrera mine produces a copper-gold concentrate and a gold-silver rich ore on site. The concentrator can treat 100,000 tonnes of primary ore per day through a pair of identical grinding and flotation lines. Tailings are pumped to an engineered tailings storage facility for long-term containment. Copper and gold concentrates are pumped with added water through a 316 kilometre pipeline over the Nevados del Aconquija mountains to the province of Tucuman, where concentrates are dewatered to obtain an almost dry product (less than 8 percent moisture content). From Tucuman, concentrates are shipped by rail via the Nuevo Central Argentino railway by Minera Alumbrera Limited's privately-owned trains, to Puerto General San Martin, where vessels are loaded and shipped to international markets.

Some of the gold of Alumbrera deposit is what's called 'free gold,' not chemically dissolved in the other minerals, but freely liberated as discrete but very small gold particles – about 10 microns – but a significant fraction of the gold can be separated from the other material by gravity processes.

The high density of gold allows a centrifuge-type device (called a Knelson concentrator) to separate the gold from other particles of lower density. The Knelson concentrate, which contains about 500 grams per tonne of gold, is transferred to the gold room for further upgrading.

Xstrata is committed to conducting business responsibly and protecting its employees, the community's health and the environment. It developed an Environmental Policy and Standards in 1997 for all sites to follow to ensure minimal impact of their operations on the surrounding environment. The design, development and operation of the facilities are managed with a view to reducing the impact; ensuring efficient use of energy, water and other resources; minimizing waste generation and disposal; and where waste must be disposed of, doing so responsibly. Quarterly presentations to provincial government representatives provide information on the mine's acid rock drainage prediction program.

From the early stages of Alumbrera's development, local communities were kept informed regarding the progress of the operation. Since commissioning, Alumbrera has had considerable impact as a direct and indirect employer and provider of infrastructure. The project has helped fund roads, including heavy vehicle by-passes around the towns of Aimogasta, Santa Maria, Londres and Belen, so that the movement of trucks transporting supplies to the mine does not compromise people's safety and quality of life. Minera Alumbrera Limited (MAA) works closely with Argentina's government at the national, provincial and municipal levels to resolve the inevitable problems arising as a consequence of the development of a large scale mining industry in its infancy in Argentina. MAA has concentrated community assistance in the Alumbrera neighbourhood on training, education and health, and buying supplies locally where available, to encourage regional business development.

"We have two programs to support the local community around Alumbrera," Cohen explains. "One is a community relations program that Alumbrera runs in the towns and the villages. The other one is an Agua Rica program. Primarily in Ander Berlau, which is the small town that will be most affected by Agua Rica, we do things like training teachers;

we've trained about 700 teachers in various things. We participate in a number of community events, we are active in the environmental side, we have an environmental program that's running with a number of community participants. So it's a broad-based community relations program. In the community Alumbrera employs almost 1,700 people. The multiplier effect is almost 15-to-1, so you're talking about 30,000 people that will in some way, fashion or form benefit from Alumbrera. If you get a salary, you take it home and there are four or five people at home – each of them is benefitting indirectly from your salary and if you're buying goods and services from somebody else, they're participating too.

The government of Argentina has been very supportive of the Northern Orion operations. There are two fiscal stability agreements – one at Alumbrera, one at Agua Rica, which outline the firm's tax regime and duties: how everything is paid for, who's liable for which expenses, who reimburses whom. That's been scrutinized repeatedly, and it's withstood some of the most intense examination and thorough vetting.

"They've opened up their mining considerably," Cohen says. "They've had to. This thing produces, at the moment, 96 percent of the province's income. And for the first time ever last year mining produced more foreign exchange than beef exported out of Argentina, so suddenly everybody is saying, 'Jeez, this is actually a real business; it employs 1,700 people, with the multiplier effect, about 20,000 people earn some sort of income out of this mine.' They're not going to allow it to dissipate. So there's been a lot of support."

Alumbrera generated cash flow for the company, as well as giving them ownership of 12.5 percent of one of the cheapest copper producers in the world. And then there's the gold: Alumbrera is the second largest gold mine in South America. In focussing on the copper deposits there, Cohen contends, people forget about the gold and the magnitude of the gold deposit.

"We've got this built-in hedge against our two metals, which has worked very well for us. Low cash costs, great operating team from Xstrata doing a great job. The mine is one of the most spectacular mines you'll see anywhere."

As good as Alumbrera is, it has one serious limitation: there is relatively little left in terms of its resources. Estimates of how much is left vary. Some say six years, others eight, with two years of much lower grade stockpile sitting on the surface. "We've got six years of blue skies and sunny days," Cohen says. "And then what happens?"

Agua Rica is what happens next. Sitting 34 kilometres away from Alumbrera, it's entirely owned by Northern Orion, not just partly owned, as with Alumbrera. And Agua Rica holds 18 billion pounds of copper and 10 million ounces of gold. There's one more measurement that matters with Agua Rica. In terms of its elevation, it's 400 metres higher than Alumbrera.

Northern Orion could build a new plant at Agua Rica, with its estimated cost running somewhere between $600 million and $800 million, and with an estimated time to get into production of about five years. Conversely, Cohen says the "right way to do it," is to get more of the company's money's worth out of the $1.3 billion that's already been spent on Alumbrera by sending Agua Rica's ore there for processing and production. Because the properties are on either side of the same mountain, Northern Orion plans to build a nine-kilometre tunnel through the rock between the two mines.

"We've now taken Alumbrera and added thirty years of life to it," Cohen says. "An Argentine company called Yacimientos Mineros de Agua de Dionisio (YMAD) sold us this property in the early-1990s. The terms of that deal were a 20 percent royalty, 20 percent NPR and, at the end of the life of deposit, all of the infrastructure goes back to YMAD at zero costs. So in six, seven or eight years' time, there's a plant sitting in the middle of the desert in Argentina with no ore deposit that belongs to the government. And we're sitting 34 kilometres away with an ore deposit that might need a plant. Today the rock comes from here, tomorrow the rock comes from there – it doesn't make any difference. The first ten years on this thing run about 1.5 or 1.6 porphyry in terms of grade. At today's prices that rock is worth about $35 a tonne – that's years one through ten. Years ten through 30 it's going to be worth somewhere in the region of $18 a tonne – that's the rock value. The operating costs on this side are $5 a ton and we're going to move 70,000 tonnes a day down this hill. So in the first ten years we're going to make somewhere between a million to a million and a half a day in operating profit. It pays for this thing in a year or two."

Some people might look at that prospect and see nothing but a collection of headaches, monumental challenges and daunting degrees of difficulty. Needless to say, David Cohen is not one those people. From his perspective, this is an elegant solution to a series of thorny issues, and one which is relatively straightforward to accomplish. "One, the capital costs are substantially lower. All you're building is the conveyor belt system. You're not opening up a mine. It's a rock quarry operation, not a mine. Second issue is environmental; there's a tailings dam that has a capacity for a billion tonnes of rock. By the time Alumbrera is finished, they'll have put 450 million tonnes of rock in it. We can put a huge amount of our debris into an existing tailings dam. We'll just keep operating into the same dam. They've got water well fields that pump water into this thing; you're in a fairly arid area, so permitting a new well field, we've got water for Agua Rica but it'd be a lot easier to keep running this thing – so there's reason three. Reason number four: there's an operating team of guys that have been running this plant very, very well since 1997. And they are way up the experience curve. If you look at any of the mines that are running anywhere in the world, it takes two to four years to get your operating team up to speed and really optimize that operation. And that's worth a lot of money. We would take over the operating team, because it's an all-Argentine team. It's not an Xstrata one or a Wheaton River one; it's an Alumbrera operating team. We'd take over the existing group, dropping ore at the plant and just keep running. That gets paid back in 18 months and Northern Orion is going to make $50 million a year. That's from our 12.5 percent interest in this thing. Agua Rica at 70 or 80 percent is going to give us somewhere in the range of $130 million to $200 million. That would be a bit of fun."

Currently, Northern Orion is working out all the engineering challenges to build and operate such a massive tunnel. After that, it must integrate the various mines and facilities in order for the plan to be profitable. The company is trying to make YMAD understand that there are other joint venture partners eager to find a way to work with Northern Orion. The company would need $150 million – three years' worth of cash flow. Although money could easily be raised through standard channels – the markets, principally – Cohen says that's not Northern Orion's game.

In June of 2004, Northern Orion announced an increase in the ore reserves at Alumbrera, extending the mining operations at Alumbrera by two and a half years. This extension increases contained metal reserves by more than 20 percent, equaling 350,000 more tonnes of copper and 1.2 million ounces of gold over the life of the mine.

New geological information, improved metal prices and operational cost improvements mean Alumbrera has added more than 80 million tonnes of ore reserves to its previous reserve base at new metal price assumptions of US$0.90 per pound of copper and US$350 per ounce of gold. The metal grade and cash cost profiles of the additional ore are in line with the previous life-of-mine plan. The supplemental ore was found predominantly in the northwestern and northern domains of the pit.

"Extremely good news for Northern Orion," says Cohen. "As one of the lowest cost copper producers in the world, every additional day that Alumbrera extends its life is positive for us. As a result, we should see an approximately 30 percent extension to our already substantial expected future cash flow stream from Alumbrera and an immediate increase in the valuation of our ownership in the mine."

It might seem as though running, in effect, two mines, as well as an audacious means of leveraging existing production facilities to run both even more efficiently would be more than enough for several companies. For Northern Orion and David Cohen, that's a good start. Although there's nothing specific in the company's plans for immediate expansion, such considerations are never far from Cohen's or Cross's agendas.

"As part of rounding out the company you have to be looking at other things," Cohen says. "We are looking at acquisitions to see which ones may or may not make sense. We're also looking at some grassroots explorations in Argentina. We've been there for ten years, so that's probably the best place for us to look. And so far in that search we're having reasonable success – nothing that's been made public yet, but reasonable success. We have guys that are well-experienced and have gone back to look at prospects they may have been interested in five or six years ago. That proved to be very successful."

The company is less worried than similar outfits might be about global politics and economics. "We've got two hedges," Cohen explains. "We've got the gold-copper hedge, which is precious metals versus base metals; instability versus stability and growth. And then we've got the

Argentine peso hedge against the U.S. dollar. As the dollar continues to fall, the Argentine peso has continued to track the dollar, so we're basically operating a lot cheaper than we were. Even if metal prices stay the same, we're making more money. On the global political side, uncertainty is good for us anyway; as long as there's uncertainty, gold prices will continue to be strong. Add to that the Chinese and Indian growth factors with copper – they're just going ballistic. I think we're going to see strong gold and strong copper, which for us is great."

NOVAGOLD RESOURCES INCORPORATED

The corner office suite hovers some 350 feet above street level in Vancouver's dynamic financial district. Two of the four walls are fitted with rectangular slabs of thermal-glass windows, offering unimpeded northwesterly vistas of the North Shore mountains, Burrard Inlet, Stanley Park and the University of British Columbia Endowment Lands. Sailboats, trawlers, commercial barges and oceangoing freighters speckle the deep blue palette of undulating salt chuck that vanishes into the horizon. Far off on the Strait of Georgia, a ferry chugs toward Vancouver Island, a mist-shrouded mirage on a sun-splashed day. It is what real estate hawkers call 'a million-dollar view'. More accurately, for those ensconced inside the upscale offices of NovaGold Resources Inc., it is a multi-million-dollar view.

"We started in 1998 with a company that had no money, no assets and a $2 million market cap," says founder, president and CEO Rick Van Nieuwenhuyse, whose nickname since high school has been 'Alphabet'. "Today, we've got $60 million in the bank with 17 million ounces of gold resource, 93 million ounces of silver, and 7.8 billion pounds of copper on the books. It's been like going from zero to 60 in a nano-second."

Indeed, over the course of a few scant years – years that included the very public collapse of the metals market – NovaGold (TSX: NG; AMEX: NG) has gone from a basement operation in Van Nieuwenhuyse's San Francisco home to one of British Columbia's top money-earning companies, occupying the 34th floor of one of Vancouver's most prestigious high-rise office towers. "It's been a real success story," says the affable, engaging and easygoing Van Nieuwenhuyse, perhaps a bit surprised but certainly not overwhelmed by his company's astonishing achievements. "To make something out of nothing, you have to have a vision of what you want to create and you have to stay the course."

Rick Van Nieuwenhuyse certainly has. Born in Ghent, Belgium in 1955, he immigrated with his family to Toronto at the age of four, where his father succumbed to cancer. Left at loose ends, his mother moved the clan to Southern California for a brief period in the early-1960s. "We muddled around for a while," he says. "My mother's wanderlust took us to California, but she decided pretty quickly that it was not a very good place to raise kids. So we jumped in the '67 Mustang and drove north." They kept on driving until they hit Anchorage, Alaska. The family loved the location and put down roots when Van Nieuwenhuyse was 11 years old.

"It was great for me," he says. "That's where I really connected with the outdoors and mining. In fact, when people ask me where I'm from, I always say Alaska." Through a friend of the family, Van Nieuwenhuyse got his first taste of the resource industry at the age of 13 when he took a summer job working at a small family-owned-and-operated alluvial and hard-rock mining operation. "I learned a lot of really fundamental things about what mining is all about," he says.

Returning to Belgium after high-school graduation (he holds dual U.S./Belgian citizenship), Van Nieuwenhuyse attended the Université de Louvain, taking a three-year program and graduating with a Candidature degree in Geology. "I love Belgium to visit but it is too congested for me to live there permanently," he says. "The truth is, you couldn't think of two more diverse places than Belgium and Alaska. Belgium is very socialistic, very established and traditional. It is structured, almost like a caste system – you're born there, you stay there, and you pretty much know what you're going to be doing for the rest of your life. In the United States you have much more free will, and Alaska is at the extreme end of the curve of the United States in that regard. There is a real frontier mentality there. The attitude is still kind of like, 'You can have this gun when you pry it from my cold, dead fingers.' It is an extremely entrepreneurial place. But I really like having a foothold in both places, I like the combination. Belgium gives me an appreciation for history and for the past and for tradition. With Alaska, you have the opposite side of the coin. It's a work-hard, play-hard, diehard, spirited frontier – the yin and the yang of life."

Van Nieuwenhuyse went on to earn his Master of Science degree in geology from the University of Arizona, returning home each summer between semesters to his adopted home. "I'd always come back and work in Alaska – though not in the mining industry because the mining industry didn't pay worth a damn," he says with a good-natured laugh. "I used to work in the fishing and timber industries because they paid you well. It was hard work and you worked long hours with overtime but, at the end of the day, you came home with a pretty big paycheck. I'd make $2,500 a month or more doing fishing and timber jobs. When I got my first summer job working as a geologist in Alaska, I was making $800 a month. Welcome to having an undergraduate degree and making a fourth of what I'd been making as a labourer."

He continued working in Alaska throughout the early-1980s after receiving his Masters, then headed south to Nevada for 10 years, honing his professional skills with a variety of established mining companies. Confident in his abilities, Van Nieuwenhuyse decided to strike out on his own as a geological exploration consultant with Nautilus Exploration, named after Captain Nemo's fabled undersea-exploration vessel. He was subsequently hired by many of the same companies that had already employed him as a full-time staff member during the previous decade. "At that point," he says, "I started doing a lot of work overseas in South and Central America. Eventually I ran into the folks from Placer Dome and they asked if I would be interested in going back to Alaska and re-establishing an office for them in Anchorage. That's when I left my consulting business and went back to work for a big company."

Placer Dome Inc. was most assuredly a big company. In fact, it remains one of the world's largest gold mining companies with substantial worldwide assets bolstered by considerable copper and silver resources. Headquartered in Vancouver, Placer Dome has interests in 18 mines in seven countries and a global workforce exceeding 13,000 people. With a reported market capitalization of US$7.3 billion at the end of 2003, Placer Dome is traded on the New York, Toronto and Australian

Stock Exchanges, as well as Euronext-Paris. In 2004 alone, the company expected to produce approximately 3.6 million ounces of gold and 400 million pounds of copper.

"Placer is a very good operating company," Van Nieuwenhuyse says. "In fact, I think they're one of the best operating companies out there. I learned a lot about project management, feasibility studies and what makes a good mining operation while I was with them. What I learned at Placer Dome went a long way toward setting up NovaGold." Among other things, Van Nieuwenhuyse gleaned an understanding of the inner workings of the international resource community and discovered firsthand the insidious behaviour junior exploration companies are capable of during a booming bull market. "While I was working for Placer," he says, "trying to make deals with the juniors was impossible because, at that time, they had more money than they needed. Why would they go into business with Placer? That is, unless they had something Placer was interested in buying. Consequently, it became not so much a game of exploration but a game of acquisition. There were these companies in far-flung places like Mongolia with 300 square kilometres of yak pasture and a market cap of $80 million. It made no sense!"

It is not difficult to draw a straight line between what was going on in certain quarters of the junior mining sector during the early-1990s and what ultimately happened when the Bre-X scandal broke in April 1997. "Bre-X was a major catalyst in driving the junior investment market down in 1997," says Van Nieuwenhuyse. "At times, there is a lot of truth to the old Mark Twain adage that a mine is a hole in the ground with a liar in front of it. But every story has two sides, and one positive result was that the fly-by-nighters got out of the sector. There was no reason for them to be in it because there was no money in it; thus, opportunities once again became available and cheap. The problem was that the public considered junior resource companies a bunch of swindlers. On top of the loss of investor confidence in junior mining stocks that resulted from Bre-X, we had a real pullback in metal prices across the board – gold, copper, zinc – all at 20-year lows. It was a tough time to start a junior exploration company – but that's exactly what we did.

"If a sector is hot," Van Nieuwenhuyse continues, "whether it is the resource sector or whatever, the fast-talking stock promoters will be there

– they follow the money. It's just human nature. I think we got rid of a lot of them in the mining and exploration sector since Bre-X, but I also have no doubt that they'll be back. There has, however, been a complete reversal in the industry since then. Gold is up over $400 an ounce, copper and zinc prices have doubled – in fact, nearly all the metals have doubled in price over the past two years. Commodities and metals are once again the place to invest.

"Exploration is a great business: you get to spend money – there are not many job descriptions like that. But in order to be successful at it, you have to create wealth and add value to the properties you're spending money on. Our corporate motto is, 'Creating wealth through discovery.' We truly believe that is what we, as exploration geologists, do: create wealth by making mineral discoveries – and NovaGold has certainly been successful at that."

Yet in 1998, when Van Nieuwenhuyse decided to leave his high-ranking post as vice-president of exploration for Placer Dome Inc., the market had not yet reversed – in fact, it had bottomed out. "At Placer," he says, "I was responsible for Alaska, then went to work overseas and was responsible for Asia and Africa. At the end of 1997, I had an opportunity to join another junior company that offered me a much better salary and the chance to run the show, so I spent a year completing a feasibility study on a project in Niger, West Africa. I was away from home over 70 percent of the time. Previously, I'd done a lot of work in Russia and Central Asia and all over Africa – Tanzania, Mali, Burkina Faso, Ghana, Niger and South Africa – I'd been on the road a number of years. It was tough on my family. In 1997, I knew that we were going to have a baby and so my family made a conscious decision that I not to travel so much and so far. That's when I re-formed NovaGold from an existing shell company that had no assets and no money. We set up an office in our basement with my wife Janna as the financial manager for the first three years. Because Alaska was a place I knew well, and because I knew there were existing opportunities to get started there, we went north to Alaska to buy a company called Alaska Gold."

There were still, however, some wrinkles that needed to be ironed out. For starters, the metals market had tanked and no one was interested in financing a junior gold company. In addition, even though Van

Nieuwenhuyse considers Vancouver to be 'the West Coast centre of the mining exploration business', he and his family were living in San Francisco. "The only reason we were in California was because Placer Dome had moved us there – someone had the bright idea to move the exploration headquarters to the Bay Area," he explains. "I never quite understood the logic behind that one."

Then, against all odds and in spite of a floundering market, Van Nieuwenhuyse convinced his old friends and business colleagues Greg Johnson, Phil St. George and Joe Piekenbrock to quit their jobs, as well. "Those were tough times in the gold business," Van Nieuwenhuyse admits, "but some excellent opportunities were presenting themselves. Sometimes the best time to get into something is when everyone else wants to get out of it."

Greg S. Johnson, NovaGold's vice-president of corporate development and communications, had been part of the Placer Dome's International Exploration Group (overseeing exploration and acquisition activities in Africa and Eurasia). Johnson had previously worked alongside Van Nieuwenhuyse with Placer's Alaska Exploration Group in the late-1980s and early-1990s. With experience ranging from grassroots discoveries to mine feasibility studies in the United States, Canada, Australia, Russia and Africa, Johnson – a graduate of Western Washington University with a Bachelor of Science with Honors degree in geology – played a key role in the 1995 discovery of NovaGold's flagship property, the 25-million-ounce Donlin Creek gold project in Alaska.

Phil St. George was in charge of exploration when NovaGold started up and played a key role in the success at Donlin. Having worked for Cominco in Alaska for several years, St. George is credited with, among other successes, the discovery of the huge Pebble copper-gold project in Southwest Alaska. He left NovaGold in 2003 and formed his own company, Holitna Energy, to explore for coal-bed methane gas in the Holitna Basin with the idea of supplying low-cost power for the huge Donlin Creek Project that he helped discover. "We still have very close contact with Phil," says Van Nieuwenhuyse, "and we wish him success in his new venture."

Joe Piekenbrock, NovaGold's vice-president of exploration, has more than 25 years experience in the minerals exploration and development sector. Having most recently managed exploration projects from discovery to advanced acquisition stages in South America for Placer Dome and Brett Resources, Piekenbrock likewise brings a wealth of northern experience to NovaGold thanks to years of conducting exploration for both Cominco and Placer Dome in Alaska. A key member of the Donlin Creek Project Team in 2002 and 2003, he holds a Bachelor of Arts Degree in Geology from the University of Colorado, and a Master of Science degree in geology from the University of Arizona.

"When I started with NovaGold," says Van Nieuwenhuyse, "it had 110 million shares outstanding. The first business was to re-structure the company and find some new investors. So we rolled it back 10-to-one, found a few new investors – enough to get a fresh start and put the right people into place. The initial team included Greg, Phil, Joe and my wife Janna – it's always good to have someone you trust with the money, especially when you have so little! As for the exploration team, Greg, Phil and Joe and I go back a long way – the three of us have worked together a lot over a long period of time. One of the more recent members of the group is Doug Brown, our vice-president of business development. He and I worked together at Placer on quite a few different projects, mostly overseas. In fact, we've all worked together at one time or another for many years and we know each other's good and bad points. It's important to have a good camaraderie with your colleagues – after all, if it's not fun, it's not worth doing."

Meanwhile, Don MacDonald, NovaGold's senior vice-president and chief financial officer, joined the company in 2003. "When the company grew, it grew pretty fast," says Van Nieuwenhuyse, "and it got to the point where it was inappropriate to have a CEO and CFO husband and wife. Janna did an excellent job with very little support. Those early years were tough, and she made sure we got the bills paid and all of the firm's documents filed on time. With very little money in the treasury, she had to juggle a number of things to keep the wolves at bay. When Janna stepped aside, Don came onboard. It's been a great transition – he's a real professional on the accounting and financial side, and he knows the mining business very well."

Van Nieuwenhuyse returns to a lingering question. "Was it hard to leave Placer?" he asks rhetorically. "By some accounts, I was a real fool leaving. In hindsight, my only regret is that I didn't do it earlier. I was originally thinking of leaving in 1992 when Placer shut down the Alaska office and wanted me to move to Coral Gables, Florida – yuk! What self-respecting geologist would move to Coral Gables? My good friend Curt Freeman of Avalon Development and I seriously discussed forming our own company, but in the end I stuck it out with Placer and went to Coral Gables – no respect!" Van Nieuwenhuyse shakes his head and laughs. "If I had left in '92, Curt and I would probably both be multi-millionaires by now. At that time you could raise $20 million without any trouble what-soever. The market was insane."

Raising money in 1998, however, was not so easy. "Initially, there wasn't any money to be raised," he says matter-of-factly. "There was no interest in gold from any of the traditional mining investment houses – the door wasn't even open to us. Greg and I would go and talk to financial houses – Canaccord, Haywood, Salman Partners – and they would tell us they had fired their mining analyst and hired a dot.com specialist – they had absolutely no interest in mining. Our survival was contingent on buying Alaska Gold so we could generate money ourselves. In hindsight, it was the turning point for the company. But at the time it was more like, 'Where are we going to get money to do this?'

"When I first started up NovaGold, it was just after the metals market got a little soft. Everybody was thinking, 'Well, it's still okay – the price of gold is just going to go down a little bit but then it is going to come back up.' Then what happened was the price of gold went from $350 an ounce to something like $250 an ounce. The problem was that there was no interest from investors in raising capital for the gold business. It was tough. We saw the opportunities there but with no money, we couldn't go after them.

"What got us over the threshold," Van Nieuwenhuyse continues, "was an arrangement I made to buy Alaska Gold, which was a company that has been in existence since the 1920s. It is an interesting company in its own right, set up by the Morgans, the Guggengheims and the Cabots, some pretty smart and wealthy people in their time. They obviously saw some things going on in the market back then and wanted to get their assets out of stocks and put them into gold which, as we now know, was a very smart move at the time.

"Alaska Gold later went through a number of reorganizations, including a stint as a subsidiary of Sharon Steel Corp., a company famous for going bankrupt at the hands of junk-bond mastermind Victor Posner, who ended up doing jail time. Sharon Steel was reorganized into a company called Mueller Industries and their core business was no longer gold. So here was an opportunity to buy Alaska Gold, but we didn't have any money and the market was of no help. So I had to arrange independent, private financing to buy the company, essentially taking out a big loan. Yet the opportunities we saw with Alaska Gold were twofold – on the one hand, it had gold assets that we liked and thought we could explore and define a mineable reserve to develop ourselves. More importantly at the time, however, we saw the ability to generate immediate cash flow from its huge sand and gravel resources, byproducts of 80 years of historic alluvial dredge mining, as well as from selling its non-core real estate assets. Though these were outside of our normal sphere of interest and skill set – that is to say, mineral exploration – it was on the back of this business model that NovaGold got its start to become what it is today."

It would take some creative entrepreneurial maneuvering, however, before the company scored. To begin with, Mueller Industries wanted US$8.5 million for Alaska Gold and NovaGold had no money. "In fact," says Van Nieuwenhuyse, "we were having trouble paying our bills at the time. I managed to round up CAD$4 million from Ron Netolitzky and Clynt Nauman at Viceroy Exploration Ltd., a public mining company that liked the idea of buying Alaska Gold for its collateral, but that still left us well short of US$8.5 million. Undaunted, I made arrangements with Kinross to buy US$1.8 million worth of land Alaska Gold owned near Fairbanks – land Kinross needed for a tailings expansion project at its Fort Knox Mine, and land that we did not own...yet. This helped, but we were still shy of the $8.5 million mark. So I went back to the owner and said, 'We've done our due diligence and there is US$3 million on the books for the mining equipment'– trucks, Cats, loaders and whatnot that were part of the operating fleet of Alaska Gold. I said, 'We don't see any more value in the rolling stock than US$500,000,' and we weren't lying. They came back to us and said, 'Well, we think it's worth US$3 million – our accountants have it on the books at $3 million and they don't want any further write-downs this year, so we need $3 million.' So I said, 'Well then, why don't you keep it?' And they did. We made an arrangement so that they could keep their equipment and store it on what was going to become our land at Alaska Gold, and we gave Mueller Industries two years to store it for free. That brought the price down to US$5.5 million and, with a little further finagling, we were able to get the balance as a royalty payment to be paid off over two years. They eventually sold the rolling stock at auction for $500,000, minus the cost to haul it to Seattle on the barge. We made a good call and did a great deal.

"It took a lot of quick-handed negotiations, but we were able to acquire Alaska Gold with no money. Within a year of that purchase, with sand and gravel aggregate sales and real estate sales, we paid back Viceroy Exploration Ltd. the $4 million they'd loaned us, plus we'd paid off the royalties to Mueller and still had about $1.5 million left over with which to conduct exploration." The shrewd maneuverings did not end there. The following year, NovaGold made enough money with Alaska Gold's sand and gravel businesses to leverage the amount of money available for exploration and acquire the Donlin Creek asset located in southwestern Alaska,150 miles northeast of Bethel.

"That was an asset both Greg Johnson and I knew very well. In fact, Greg was part of the original discovery team," says Van Nieuwenhuyse. "In 2000, the price of gold was hovering around $250 to $260 an ounce. All of the majors were tightening their belts and not spending any money on exploration. We'd heard that Placer Dome wanted to get out of Donlin Creek, even though they'd already spent $30 million on it. They knew it wasn't going to fly at $250 an ounce – not many mines are economical at the $250 gold level. I made one phone call to Rob Pease at Placer and he said, 'We like the property, but senior management will only let us spend exploration budgets on projects near our operating mines – we have no budget for plays like Donlin.' So I said, 'Let us have a crack at it.' We structured the deal to spend $10 million over 10 years to earn 70 percent interest; plus we gave them a back-in if we were successful. That deal cost one phone call and a plane ticket."

The next step was to convince the property owners, the Calista Native Corporation, that NovaGold could manage the property. "After all," says Van Nieuwenhuyse, "we were not Placer Dome. Rob Pease really went to bat for us and helped us convince Calista that we could advance the project properly."

Upon solidifying the deal, NovaGold began a wildly successful self-financed exploration in 2001. In a happy coincidence, the gold market turned around at about the same time and the company was able to raise money. "Finally," says Van Nieuwenhuyse, rolling his eyes in mock exasperation, "interest in junior mining stocks improved. We spent $10 million, earned our interest inside of 18 months, doubled the size of the resource at Donlin Creek, and improved the average grade by half-a-gram. All of that happened over a very short period of time and in a rising gold market. As a result, the company went from a $2 million market cap company to $150 million market cap company in no time and we haven't looked back – we just keep going."

Indeed, the company is presently advancing five separate million-plus-ounce gold deposits in Alaska and Western Canada, including three of the largest undeveloped deposits in North America: Donlin Creek (with Placer Dome), the Ambler Project (with Rio Tinto) and the Galore Creek Project.

The Donlin Creek Project, consisting of a 25.5 million ounce reserve, is one of the largest undeveloped gold resources in the world. With NovaGold holding a 70 percent interest and Placer Dome a 30 percent interest. Placer Dome is presently earning an additional 40 percent by spending over US$32 million toward development of the project by completing a feasibility study and obtaining final permits in order to make a decision to construct a mine capable of producing not less than 600,000 ounces of gold a year by November 2007. The project is currently envisioned to produce over 1 million ounces of gold per year.

At the Ambler Project in Alaska, NovaGold holds an option for a 51 percent interest in a joint venture with Rio Tinto. The property consists of 35,000 acres covering a metal-rich, volcanogenic mass sulfide district. The Arctic Deposit is thus far the most advanced target with an inferred resource of 36.3 million tonnes of precious metals grading 0.7 grams-per-tonne gold, 54.9 grams-per-tonne silver and base metals grading 4 percent copper, 5.5 percent zinc and 0.8 percent lead. It is one of the best and highest grade massive sulfide projects in the world. The equivalent of a 16 million ounce gold deposit, a minimum US$1 million is budgeted for exploration and development work on Ambler this year.

Another world-class asset is the Galore Creek Project, a multi-million ounce gold-copper-silver deposit in northwestern British Columbia. The company has an option to acquire a 100 percent interest in the project which hosts 5 million ounces of gold, 60 million ounces of silver and 5 billion pounds of copper. The equivalent of an 18 million ounce gold deposit, a pre-feasibility study is anticipated for spring 2005.

Back where it all started in Nome, Alaska, NovaGold's 100-percent-owned Rock Creek and Nome Gold deposits host a total of more than 3 million ounces of gold. The deposits are open-pittable and demonstrate excellent metallurgical characteristics. A preliminary economic analysis indicates that the project will cost US$40 million in initial start-up capital and produce gold for US$200 per ounce total cash cost.

"We started out focussed on gold," says Van Nieuwenhuyse, "but decided to branch out into silver and base metals. It was a proactive move. The philosophy is buy low, sell high – we don't want to be buying platinum when it's going for $900 an ounce, but when copper is at a 10-year low, that's the time to buy a good copper prospect.

"Although Rock Creek is the one that is closest to production," he continues, "Donlin Creek remains our flagship property and is by far the largest property in terms of resources. Placer has now exercised their back-in right to earn their additional 40 percent interest, and they now manage the property. They are completing a pre-feasibility study this fall with plans to make a mine production decision after obtaining permits in 2007. At Rock Creek, there are currently two dozen people working on site and we hope to have it in production by the fall of 2006. Once in operation, it will create about 100 well-paying jobs in Nome. Right now, however, we are most excited about Galore Creek – it is another extraordinary asset. Since we have an option to purchase a 100 percent interest, we are in the driver's seat to advance it to production – no large company partner to slow us down. Galore Creek is at the pre-feasibility study stage and we currently have about 80 people working there this field season."

"Generally speaking," he continues, "when people get nervous, they tend to migrate towards gold. And there is plenty to be nervous about these days: terrorism, soaring debt, inflation, deflation, stagflation, several wars in the Middle East, and very expensive oil, to name a few. However, I think we're seeing something way beyond that in this cycle-it's not just gold, it is all the metals: silver, zinc, copper, uranium – you name it. These metals are increasing significantly in value, driven largely by demand coming from China and India. You have two huge population bases that are just starting to industrialize in a big way, and they're not just industrializing for export, which is what they were doing 20 or 30 years ago. Now they're industrializing internally and they're buying cars, air conditioners, refrigerators – every one of those things requires a lot of metal to build. And that's not just a blip on the screen – there are 1.2 billion Chinese and almost a billion people in India, and they all want to improve their standards of living. I believe we are entering a 20-year phenomenon that will see unbelievable growth first in China, then in India."

All of which bodes exceptionally well for NovaGold Resources Inc. "When you're first starting out in this business," Van Nieuwenhuyse reflects, "you have no credibility. Nobody knows who the hell you are. Even if they think you're recognized as technically competent, you have to be successful at running a company in order to gain credibility and prove to the market that you know what you're doing. You may be the world's best geologist, but if you don't know how to run a company, how to raise money, how to promote – who cares? Now we have that credibility – not only technically but financially. We have demonstrated that we can raise money and we have demonstrated that we know how to run a business and, of course, we have a demonstrated track record as successful explorers. The next big step is to actually mine these resources. We're now on a track of transitioning from a junior exploration company to a quality mid-tier producer, a transition few companies have mastered. It will be a fun challenge."

Having made quantum leaps over the past seven years, NovaGold continues its growth story as the mining market gets progressively hotter. "Despite the fact that we've had such success in a really short time frame," says Van Nieuwenhuyse, "there are still skeptics out there. But that only makes us work harder.

"You have to be entrepreneurial," Van Nieuwenhuyse concludes. "If Plan A doesn't work, either have a Plan B or be prepared to come up with a Plan B and jump on it, work hard, believe in what you're doing, and believe what you're doing is right – despite what analysts say or even what specific shareholders might have to say at any given time. They all have different agendas and perspectives than you do as the person responsible for the vision of the company. Be a good listener, but in the end you really have to understand where you want to be and make sure you've got all the right people behind you. A successful company has to have a good working team spirit. You have to keep people motivated. You have to keep yourself motivated." Rick Van Nieuwenhuyse has never had any trouble doing that.

OREZONE RESOURCES INCORPORATED

In mining parlance, you're either in the ore zone or you're in the waste. Since there's no question where a miner would rather be, Ron Little staked his claim to the optimistic name when he started up Orezone Resources in 1995.

"It was a term I was very familiar with as a mining geologist and a mining engineer. It's a real true mining name," says Little, his voice betraying his roots with a slight Ottawa Valley twang.

On this occasion, Little happens to be in Toronto on company business and has taken a break to speak about Orezone's story and successes. Although the story has its beginnings in Canada, its current successes are being mined much further away, in the colourful environs of West Africa, specifically Burkina Faso. Little is not only excited about Orezone's three promising projects on the Bondi, Sega and Essakan properties, he lights up when talking about working in West Africa itself. He can't say enough about the people, their customs and the government, all of which get the same respectful nod from this president and CEO.

"You make such an impact on lives over there, as compared to what you would do here in Canada. This is the thrill of working in Burkina," he says earnestly. "A typical mine here in Canada may affect three or four hundred people. Over there, one mine producing more than 50,000 ounces a year – which is a pretty small mine here – is actually going to be the number one contribution to the GDP in the country. So, there's 12 million people over there, just in Burkina Faso, and we're basically going to have an impact on everybody by putting a mine into production."

Undoubtedly, Orezone will have no problem creating an impact now, but in the early days, they were pretty much under the radar. According to Little, even the local government wondered what they were doing there.

Little explains, "The Burkina government used to laugh at us because they'd visit our campsite while we were working and say, 'Where's your trailers? Where is everything?' And we'd be in a mud hut or moved into the local little school made of mud bricks. The government never took us seriously at the beginning because we weren't spending enough money in their eyes. All of our money was going into the ground-drilling.

"That mode was from 1997 to the end of 2001. But at the end of the day, we end up controlling most of the big assets. And just within the end of 2001, the gold market starts to come back. So it was all very good timing and great positioning."

But it was also faith on the part of the Orezone team, and a $2 million financing from First Marathon in 1999 that helped sustain their position in Burkina. Even though other companies were walking away from Burkina around that time, Orezone stuck it out.

"There's lots of mining around Burkina Faso, but Burkina was still uncharted waters and there were a lot of nonbelievers," says Little. "So still during the bad market, we were out there flying the Burkina flag and we started to pick up some of the better projects."

And pick them up, they did. In early 2002, Orezone took over a company called Coronation Mining, which held title to Essakan, a million-and-a-half-ounce resource and the biggest deposit in Burkina. In 2001, they had snatched up the Sega project from Repadre, now Iamgold, to the tune of about 300,000 ounces. And if that weren't enough, they took over Bombore from Channel Resources, with about a million ounces.

"We were just gobbling it up and it was cheap. Very cheap," says Little. "So we put together about 3.5 million ounces, mostly through acquisitions over a one-year period. And they're all within Burkina."

The market is most excited about Essakan, not only because of its known 1.5 million ounce resource, but because it's been joint ventured with well-known major mining company Goldfields Limited, in what Little describes as 'a monumental deal'.

"We'd be putting that into production right now, but Goldfields wants to see three million ounces, plus. And that's why the market is excited, because they know Goldfields wouldn't be there if they didn't see potential for more than three million ounces."

On a more personal level, Little is thrilled about Bondi, which along with Sega, is 100-percent-owned by Orezone and both of which are catalysts for a potential takeover.

"To play the game of takeover, Bondi is our wild card and we don't let Bondi go anywhere. It is a 100 percent, come hell or high water, and if you want it, you're going to have to take us over," says Little with assurance.

"And all of our other projects, like Sega, and anything that is potentially a two million ounce-plus deposit, we keep for ourselves and advance them. Because it's either going to make us a bigger company or it's going to make somebody pay a big premium to take us over. That's our philosophy on that."

Either way, it's good news for shareholders.

"Probably half of our shareholders want to see a takeover, but I think a lot of them want to see us continue to build this thing into a big company," says Little, conceding he's definitely partial to the latter course of action. "That's my personal desire. Yeah, I'd like to be the next Barrick, right?"

He laughs, but there's no doubt he means it. With his noticeably red hair and blue eyes, Ron Little sometimes looks more like a mischievous freckle-faced kid than a serious 41-year-old businessman. But make no mistake – underlying his easygoing manner is a very astute man who gets the job done. And although the bulk of his job now consists more of corporate concerns than fieldwork, he learned his business from the ground up, literally. And he started gleaning this valuable experience right out of the gate. During his first year out of geological engineering at Queen's University, Little got involved with St. Joe Minerals, a company that subsequently made a gold discovery in 1985 near Pickle Lake, in northern Ontario. Within two years, it evolved into a production decision with a high-grade narrow vein that Little describes as similar to, but smaller than, Goldcorp's mine in Red Lake.

"So I was fresh out of school, my first year out, and totally isolated. We're living in tents in the middle of winter, in there staking claims because they wanted to keep it top secret, and our daily routine for the first few months was riding around on skidoos and snowshoes for the first few months as it evolved," recalls Little.

In what became an eight-year stint with the Golden Patricia Mine, Little was steadily promoted up the ranks to chief geologist within the first two years, then to assistant mine superintendent after the mine was built, and finally to assistant mine manager. It was a fortuitous and supremely valuable start that would certainly stand him in good stead later on. Little acknowledges the importance of such a beginning.

"The great thing about that is very rarely does somebody get to discover and build and produce in that kind of short time frame, just out of school. And it gave me a look at every facet of the business. By the time I came out of there, I knew how to run a mill, how to run the underground, and build an operation. Out of all of that, I liked building the best. To me, it's not a discovery unless you actually build and produce something," Little says.

During these years, the company changed hands with majors four times. From St. Joe's to Bond Gold, to Lac Minerals, and then to Barrick. Little left the company just as Barrick was taking over, and headed down to South America to build an operation in Uruguay with some of the Lac Minerals people.

Within a year, he was starting a family and decided to return to his roots in Ottawa, Canada, after hearing a story that diamonds were being discovered just north of Ottawa. Getting involved with Garde Resources as vice-president of exploration didn't net any diamonds, but it did give Little some firsthand business experience and his vehicle to create Orezone.

"We certainly did not find any diamonds once I started operating – it came to a tragic end and the shareholders asked me to take over. Since there were no diamonds, the shareholders lost interest and essentially because of the debt, the company became insolvent.

"When I took over, I had to halt the stock, change the board of directors, solve the debts of the company...it was basically a crash course MBA. And I had to go find money to do it all," says Little, who ended up changing the company's name to Orezone, while running it out of his parents'basement for the first six months or so.

However, the real starting point for Orezone was when the stock market started getting bullish on gold stories and Little began putting together some gold properties in Quebec. Working with Andre Gaumond of Virginia Gold Mines, who Little describes as 'a very passionate guy', they discovered Virginia's La Grande property in northern Quebec.

"We (Orezone) had to step back and let Andre run with La Grande Sud and he did very well with it. We took a royalty on the best block and kept an interest in the bigger blocks around it," said Little.

"We raised money on those properties and we also had a joint venture with Eastmain which was not far away in Quebec. So we started building a Quebec gold story."

But it wasn't long before West Africa would beckon. Within the first year, Little made it known that he was looking to get an operation going somewhere, preferably an oxide-gold deposit that would require minimal start-up time and little capital. Through an introduction by one of Little's directors and old school colleagues, he met Chris Gleeson, a well-known geochemist who was working in Burkina Faso for two different companies.

"Chris told us he knew a target and the ground was available. He said a Burkina resident holds the ground but is looking for a partner," says Little. Before you could say Ouagadougou, that's precisely where Little found himself landing to meet his potential new partners.

"Locally, they just call it *Ouaga. Dougou* means village in the local tongue," explains Little. "It was exciting times. Burkina is 'Africa for beginners' because it's a very friendly place. I'm certainly more English than Francophone, but I could get by with my high school French because they were nice people and certainly there was interest to do a deal." Within three months, they had a done deal and had a drill on the ground that Chris Gleeson had identified.

"As it turned out, it was a bit of a treasure hunt because the target wasn't exactly where this old photocopied map said it was. But we found it about half a kilometre away. On hole 72, we hit our first well-mineralized hole, right near the end of the program in December of 1996," says Little.

Thanks to Little's previous experiences and track record, particularly with Golden Patricia, he was able to raise some money in the meantime. "So now we've got some money, we're drilling in Burkina, we make a discovery and things start to evolve. We find out very quickly that our target is not a deep oxide system, so a quick production decision is now not there. But we hit rock that looks like classic Canadian mining rock with the potential for a big system so we started acquiring all the ground around it. Within a year, we had built a big package of land (1,500 square kilometres) around our discovery and it started to grow into a new story on the market."

And it's a story that keeps expanding. Even in the beginning, Orezone's stock was trading quite well, in the $1.00 to $1.50 range. Little admits he should have been raising more money before the market went bad again, but fortunately Orezone kept getting good results and acquiring other properties in Burkina Faso. By the time the market slumped, they had financial backing and faith from some big names including the Royal Bank, TD Asset Management, Dundee Securities and Goldcorp.

When the market surged briefly in May, 1999, Orezone did its $2 million financing through First Marathon, which helped carry the company through a couple more years of a bad market in what Little describes as 'the darkest days of mining'.

"By 2001, we were just hanging on by our fingernails, still running with $100,000 or $150,000 in the bank and paying ourselves very little." But to their credit, they hung on. While many other mining companies were out converting to dot-coms, Little and company kept their eyes on the golden prize.

"We were always joked about as being the cheapest guys in mining and I think that's part of the flavour of the company...when times were tough, we toed the line. We were fortunate to be surrounded by a loyal group of directors and we also started an advisory committee," Little said, adding that he was inspired to form an advisory committee after reading that Barrick had done the same thing.

"I thought, 'Hey, what a good idea! Maybe I can get Rob McEwen (Goldcorp) or some real well-known mining people on a committee.' Fortunately, Rob says 'Yeah, great idea, I'll do the committee.' And that was a huge component, I think, in being able to finance the company. Rob took a real interest in what we were doing and he always had great advice. When most of us said black, he'd say white, and he was always very astute. So he was critical in a lot of key decisions, particularly in financings.

"So half the credit, I guess, goes to us doing the roll-up-your-sleeves work, but a lot of guys were in there giving us great free advice."

Not long thereafter, the hard work and faith would take a great leap forward with Orezone's takeover of Coronation. That's when Goldfields, a major South African mining company and number four producer in the world, showed an interest in Essakan and suggested a joint venture. The deal was sealed in 2002 at the annual Prospectors & Developers Association (PDA) convention, just two weeks after they had announced the takeover.

"It's a huge deal for us because they can only earn to 60 percent by taking it to a bankable feasibility. Normally they demand 75 to 80 percent," Little explains.

"Goldfields first earns to 50 percent by spending US$8 million, and by way of comparison, Orezone bought it for about CAD$7 million.

"So they have to spend $8 million just to get to fifty. Then they have to go to a bankable feasibility to earn sixty, and that may cost them another $10–15 million. It makes our deal look pretty good with Coronation," says Little with satisfaction.

It probably didn't hurt matters that Little had worked for Goldfield's vice-president of exploration, Craig Nelson, back in the Lac Minerals days. "Part of the deal was that Orezone operates the work and, because I had worked with Craig, he knew we could do a reasonable job. So I think this is why we came to a pretty quick deal." And as far as deals go, Little can't help smiling about this one.

"It's right at the back of the Goldfields Annual Report where they list their properties, which means they like the terms the least. We would put it at the front, but they put it at the back." With the deal in place, the market starts to sit up and take notice, and the stock begins to climb by July 2002 from 20 cents to 50 cents.

"By getting Goldfields in on that kind of a deal, it's like the Good Housekeeping seal of approval," says Little.

Just when the market begins to go flat in the fall of 2002 and Orezone's stock slips back down to 25 cents, an analyst at Canaccord picks up on the story.

"Graham Currie likes what he sees and starts saying it's one of the better stories out there and it's undervalued," says Little.

From that point, things begin to move. In 2003, Orezone starts to see drill results from several projects and a rise in its stock from 25 cents back up to 55 cents. In the process, they do a financing with Canaccord, in what is termed a 'bought deal'.

Little smiles and says, "They basically came to the table and said, 'Here's a cheque for five million dollars. Would you like it?'"

Eight months later they have more good results, and Orezone does another financing for $10 million with Canaccord and the Bank of Montreal, the latter of which introduced them to institutions in New York and Boston. Following that, the stock rises again, from about 60 cents up to a dollar between August and October of 2003.

Currently, Little is excited about Orezone's new American listing, which occurred on March 18, 2004. "So we're on Toronto (TSX) and New York (AMEX). We moved from the Montreal exchange in 1999 to the Toronto exchange because of our discovery in Burkina Faso. And then we went after the AMEX listing because we're getting more and more shareholders in the U.S. and it's a bigger market. The whole idea is to attract more retail shareholders."

In fact, more than 50 percent of Orezone's shareholders are large institutions, something that Little characterizes as 'pretty rare for a company at this stage'.

"We still think the gold market is going to be bullish for the next couple of years at the very least and having a listing down there enables all the U.S. citizens to easily buy the stock. The institutions know how to buy stock in Canada, but it's very difficult for your average U.S. citizen to just go to a broker and buy it here. So if you really want to attract a big retail market in the U.S., you need a listing there."

Although there is much to be optimistic about, Little characterizes his team as underpromoters rather than overpromoters. As such, Orezone's stock is undoubtedly undervalued. "We're very cautious about trying to talk up too many ounces and talk about a lot of hype – which is your typical stereotype for a mining promotion – to basically bullshit what you have," says Little.

"We've always taken the astute approach of saying, 'Here's our blue sky and we may not find it, but if it's there, we will find it.' And as a result, the stock hasn't taken off to a huge degree but it's been a nice, slow building story without any blood on the table. Everybody who has come in early or come in late is still making money and is still happy. And we'd rather build a company that way, than hype a stock to five dollars and see it come falling back down again."

Of Orezone's top three projects – Essakan, Bondi and Sega – the market likes Essakan due to the Goldfields' connection and Little is eagerly awaiting Bondi's potential.

"At Bondi, it's all Orezone's and, odds are, if there's a lot, somebody's going to come in and buy out Orezone. Bondi is the great discovery. It's come from recognizing the first target we drilled to saying, 'Hey, this is a better belt, let's grab the whole belt.' And because our discovery at Bondi is actually 25 kilometres away from our first drill hole, we made the proper call deciding to get a big piece of the belt."

As far as a time frame for production is concerned, Little estimates it will take approximately two-and-a-half years to get Bondi up and running. Because of the Goldfields' timeline, Essakan would likely take the same amount of time. Three years is the estimation for Sega, mainly because it's not getting enough drilling right now.

"A problem worldwide in exploration, is getting enough drills to do the work," Little notes. "If the market were to go bad again, Bondi and Sega are still easily projects we could joint venture to any other major. But you don't do this when the market is good. You keep them for yourself. For us and for Burkina."

There are currently no big mines in Burkina, at least none in the four or five million ounce range. There are plenty in Mali and Ghana however, and Burkina sits right in the middle. "It stands to reason," says Little, "that Burkina should be just as rich as its neighbours.

"We said, 'Look, there's no reason why there aren't any mines between A and B. It just hasn't seen the work that Mali and Ghana have had.' We think we've got some of the better ground in Burkina, based on geological merit."

If geological merit wasn't enough to convince anyone there was gold, the local villagers had their own unique and colourful way of proving it. With a couple of analysts in attendance, the Orezone team was treated to a sacrifice, or as Little describes it 'a bit of a voodoo trick'.

"They bring a chicken out and cut its throat and put the blood on the ground. Then the guy jumps around with the chicken spraying more blood and throws the chicken down about four or five feet away. Everyone goes quiet and watches, and all of a sudden the chicken con-vulses, flies up into the air, and lands right in the blood. Everyone says, 'Whoaa! This is a really good sign!' There's gold in them thar hills!"

Next up, a goat.

"Which of course, we had to buy," Little says grinning. After the goat was sacrificed, it was cooked and eaten.

"We quickly realized that after the goat, they wanted to go onto some-thing even bigger and we said, 'Okay, we believe you. It's blessed ground and we'll go on.'"

When asked what the next sacrifice would have been, Little shrugs. "Well, we didn't want to stick around and find out."

But they did stick around Burkina, confident in the area's potential and committed to maintaining a presence in Africa. Orezone also recent-ly acquired a big block of ground in Niger, next to Burkina, which Little believes is an extension of the Essakan property.

"It's basically double the size of the Essekan property and we've got that whole belt. Goldfields has no right to it, even though it's up against the Essakan property," Little explains.

For now, they're simply calling it the Niger property because it's so big. But once they find the best of several gold showings, it will custom-arily be named after the nearest local village. And that will be yet anoth-er chapter in the ongoing Orezone story.

"Orezone has been showing a lot of good drill results, but it has to start upgrading its total resources," says Little, alluding again to his pref-erence for building rather than being taken out. Our goal is to take the 3.5

million ounces to 6 million ounces within a year-and-a-half, double effectively what we have and by doing that, the market should value us higher. We're also looking at other smaller companies that have ounces that are not valued in the market. So we would still do an acquisition or another merger if we thought the value was there.

"If we don't want to be taken over, we've got to keep looking aggressively at other acquisitions. Otherwise we're going to keep finding, and likely our price won't go up as much as we're finding, and somebody will come in and post an offer and take us out. That's one of our bigger worries."

But with $14 million in their treasury and only $1.4 million in non-interest bearing debt that is tied to Essakan and can be converted into stock at any time, there's not a lot of worry for shareholders. In fact, Orezone has all the right ingredients for shareholder confidence and Ron Little is proud and pleased to list them, since he and his team worked hard to get where they are.

"We've got money in the bank, we've got two big sponsors – Canaccord and Bank of Montreal – we've got the endorsement and relationship with Goldfields, one of the best mining companies in the world, and we've got probably one of the biggest institutional shareholder lists for a company of our size. So all of that is a huge pillar of support to take this whole story to the next level."

Also, it should be noted, no shareholder owns more than 10 percent. "Nobody can backdoor us on a takeover," Little points out.

When asked what his forte is, Little responds in typical fashion. One of his better abilities, he says, is finding and surrounding himself with good people who, in turn, make him better.

"Everybody says we're a great team, he smiles, "but there are truly some great individuals here that either bring out the best in me, or have helped me pick other really good people."

Pascal Marquis is one such individual who gets kudos from Little. "Pascal is our exploration manager for Burkina and he's almost single-handedly put together all the old data on Essakan, come up with new techniques and has been finding ore bodies. We really give him credit for what he's doing at Essakan. He's a real rare geologist who is both academic and practical and can track costs. That's a really rare person.

"Some of the other key people we have are Jeff Achert, Mike Halvorson and Bob Mason. Jeff has worked with me for years, right back to Golden Patricia, and stood his ground with me at Orezone during the 'dark' years."

Mike and Bob are directors who also deserve credit for propping up Little when the market was quiet. "Both of these guys have given me the facts of life...it's nice to have several fathers," says little.

Armed with good people and properties, Little says he strives for balance.

"It's important to have something that's coherent. Investors always want to hear the same story and it provides consistency to getting to the next level."

That said, stock prices, financings and discoveries aside, it's good to know something of the human element that also makes up the Orezone package. Like most mining companies, they try to give something back to the local communities in which they are working and living. At Essakan, for instance, the Orezone team has brought water into the local school, fixed its roof, and hired many Burkina professionals.

"All of our geologists and technicians are local Burkina guys," says Little, "so they speak the local dialect as well as French. Pascal is our only ex-pat. Our philosophy is to train and promote the local people because this is how you build a mining industry and an operation economically."

Knowing it's standard for mineral exploration companies to contribute in some way to the local villages, Little was amazed when he heard about a 12-year-old boy living near Ottawa who was not only doing the same thing in Africa, he was also making Orezone's efforts look almost insignificant by comparison.

Ryan Hreljec had been raising money for water wells in Africa since he was six years old, a task he took up after a teacher told him children were dying because of a lack of good drinking water. During that time, he has managed to raise $800,000 and get 75 water wells drilled, recently being honoured with the Order of Ontario for his work.

"I heard him on CBC radio and I thought, 'Gee, this kid should be a junior mining guy!'," says Little with a grin, adding, "Again, I'm always looking for good talent."

But all joking aside, Ryan's determination and commitment made Little realize his own company could be doing a lot more than drilling four wells without pumps per year in Burkina.

"The market's good. We could be drilling 8 or 10 wells a year. It doesn't cost us that much because we've got the drill rigs there, we've got the people to pick the hole, all we have to do is buy the pump and the cement to finish it."

Inspired by Ryan's efforts, Little fired off a note to his website and proposed a water challenge to all the mining companies. If Orezone would commit to drilling 10 holes, then surely the larger mining companies could double or quadruple that amount. Barring that, they could send money to Ryan's foundation and he could ensure the holes are drilled.

"To sum it up, we announced this at the PDAC recently and got huge response. Newmont, Barrick and Goldfields all said it was a great idea. We all put money aside and will either drill the holes or give the money to the foundation," said Little.

"The goal is to raise a million dollars and drill 150 wells by this time next year. Each well usually affects about 300 lives. Water is the number one common denominator – before you can educate people in Africa, they've gotta be healthy."

Along with Little's admiration for Ryan, he also has huge respect for Ryan's parents, who have been running the foundation out of their basement – a spartan operation with big dreams and goals, much like how many a junior mining company starts out.

"Here we are, small-time mining guys...we really hit it off with Ryan and his parents because we could instantly relate to running something out of our basements. Here's mom and dad, working all-nighters on the foundation...they're not making any money, and they don't have stock options like I've got. It's just such an effort for them to support Ryan and his challenge, and with the amount of lives they're affecting, we said: 'Look, we can help you get to the next level.' I think they can turn this into a large foundation, but they just need that little kickstart. If mining can kick in several million dollars, then you'll get other companies and other sectors saying, 'Yes, you have to start with good drinking water.'

"We're honoured just to have the chance to give them that little push up. They can even run out of our office here, and we can help them get to the next level frugally, much as we climbed out of our humble beginnings."

This newest facet to Orezone is just one more thing Little can feel good about. And there's no question, he's satisfied with the journey thus far.

"I feel like I'm extremely fortunate to be here today with this package of projects, with this group of people and this market. There's an opportunity here and it's fun to do this," he says.

"Now that we've had some exploration success, life is going to be easier and I'm not going to be down on my knees anymore, looking for money to build a mining company.

"We can do it with our heads held high."

RUBICON MINERALS CORPORATION

A lot of mining companies get started because of a lucky break or a hunch. Rubicon began when three determined entrepreneurs realized that the machinations of two much larger mining companies had presented them with an opportunity that would allow them to vindicate some of their beliefs about how the mining business could be done.

"Rubicon Minerals came out of the takeover of Lac Minerals by Barrick Gold," explains David Adamson. "Three of us were principals with Lac Minerals' western Canadian office, a Canadian gold producer — about twelfth in the world in terms of gold production. Along came Barrick, took over the company, and that gave us the opportunity to decide whether we wanted to stay with this, or perhaps go to other parts of the world – because Barrick wasn't really a North-American-focussed exploration company – or do something for ourselves. We decided to do something for ourselves. So back in 1996, the three of us – Garfield MacVeigh and Michael Gray and myself – decided to pool our resources. We didn't think about building a public company. What we thought about was pooling some of our collective exploration expertise that we'd gained over the course of our careers – mostly in Canada, but some international and some in the United States. So between us we had well over 50 years of exploration experience."

Adamson is from the United Kingdom, where he got his undergraduate degree in geology. After arriving in Canada, he earned two more degrees in exploration geology, including an Ph.D. and went to work for

Lac Minerals for the next decade. He looked for gold, concentrating his search in Ontario and Quebec: Kirkland Lake, the Hemlo Camp and Timmins. Adamson's colleague, Garfield McVeigh, started his mining career in Kidd Creek in base metals. He worked for a series of companies across the country, finding major deposits for each of his employers, such as Hoyle Pond in Timmins and Myra Falls in British Columbia. Michael Gray, had worked for Cominco, Falconbridge and Noranda, including experience in major pre-feasibility projects.

"Between us, we thought we'd seen lots of projects come and go, some of them better than others," Adamson says. "Every year with a major company, you go cap-in-hand to senior management looking for money, just as you do in a junior mining company, where you're always looking for money from the markets. Some projects never got funded, even though we felt that they had a lot of merit from an exploration point of view. In 1996, we felt the best thing we could do would be to sit down and write a list of our top ten or twenty exploration projects, things we would like to acquire, notwithstanding the fact we didn't have a lot of capital. For a year we were out staking claims or consulting. The three of us working out of our basements, thanks to forgiving spouses, basically with a bit of a plan to build something, but not really a public plan. And one of the things that was near the top of our list then, which continues to be a point of focus for us, was a place called Red Lake, which is in north-west Ontario. It's a major gold-producing district, but it's about 50 years behind the other major districts in terms of production and development history. In other words, its main production didn't come on stream until about 1950, whereas Timmins and Kirkland Lake were already producing at the turn of the twentieth century. We felt from an exploration and geological analysis, it was a camp that still had a lot of upside potential. So we put that down as one of the main targets on our list."

A prospector named David Meunier had approached the new company at the beginning of 1996. Adamson says that in addition to the accumulated exploration and geological intelligence the three Rubicon founders shared, they also enjoyed excellent relationships with prospectors, a key component of the mining food chain. As a smaller company, Rubicon was – and is – happy to be one of the first stops for prospectors. If they'd been ninth or tenth, that would've subtly marked them as not as astute as their competitors, in addition to meaning that the prospectors approaching them had already been turned down by bigger outfits. But David Meunier, one of the top prospectors in Timmins, came first to Rubicon with a property in Red Lake he was eager to get Rubicon's views on.

"We took a look at it, and the information and the location of the project were excellent, plus the technical attributes we felt were there. There were signs in a previous company's work that perhaps Meunier's claims were in exactly the right setting geologically, as the major deposits in the camp," Adamson remembers. If this was true, the published maps at the time were in error and the implications for exploration would be important. "We felt that this was an excellent opportunity."

The group of three was eager to move ahead. But personal fiscal resources were reaching their minimum, and greater capital was going be needed. The president of Haywood Securities, John Tognetti, had just approached Garfield MacVeigh. MacVeigh told Haywood he appreciated the offer, but explained his position with Rubicon and his ambitions for it precluded his taking the position. Haywood president, John Tognetti, asked all three Rubicon principals to a meeting at his office, "to see if there's anything we can do," Adamson recalls. "We outlined our plan. If you think back, the flavour of the month (unfortunately, as things would turn out) was Indonesia, it was South America and, to a certain extent, it was Voisey's Bay in Labrador. We were doing none of those. We were kind of contrarian in a sense. We felt that North America had a lot of opportunity; low political risk, high geological potential...we also felt that this was a good time to be looking for assets that would make money at $250-an-ounce gold, not to bank on there being a strong gold market, although we felt there was going to be one. We also felt that diversification was a smart thing to do; in other words, make sure you've got some base metal assets, not just gold and make sure you're not just Red Lake. Most of those things were kind of unfashionable, but I think we managed to hit a nerve with John Tognetti. I think he felt that the people had credibility and had a clear sense of vision of where they could take this company."

The three met with other brokerage firms, most of whom initially seemed interested, but who were more interested in having Rubicon take over management of another project or company with assets anywhere but North America. Adamson remembers those encounters as marked by an attitude that came across as, "'We love your story, we've got this thing in Brazil for you,' or, 'Fantastic, why don't you go run this thing?' Once we got over the initial flattery that they loved our story, we realized they didn't really; they wanted a management group to go and run something in which they had already invested and had assets in."

John Tognetti was one of the few people in the investment community willing to consider Rubicon's plan on its own merits, and the three principals' vision on their own terms. He left it to Adamson, MacVeigh and Gray to determine what kind of an equity-for-underwriting arrangement made the most sense to them. After conferring with some other colleagues and getting a few more opinions, they returned to Tognetti with a proposal that saw giving up half the company in return for a particular amount, which Adamson will not disclose.

The plans moved ahead. Rubicon launched its Initial Public Offering in November 1997, just six months after the collapse. "We were, in a sense, taking advantage of a strong wave when we started the path of going public, Adamson says. "By the time we went public, the sky was falling all around us. But to their credit, Haywood and Tognetti believed in us and took us public."

Now, the three Rubicon principals work out of an office in Vancouver as part of a team of seven or eight people. Five geologists across the nation work as full-time consultants. Everybody else who works for the company is hired on a consultancy or contract basis. The company's field staff varies – anywhere from 10 to 40 people, depending on how much activity is going on at its various projects. This year, Rubicon is spending $5.4 million on exploration, split equally between Rubicon and its joint-venture partners. Its peak seasons for exploration are summer and winter. Spring and fall are breaks: ice is either forming or it's breaking up in northern Ontario, or there's mud. Either way, those transitional seasons mean unstable conditions that are tougher to plan for and deal with. Market capitalization is CAD$75 million right now, with 53 million shares issued and outstanding.

While the IPO was incubating, Rubicon put together what Adamson calls a portfolio of projects, the first one of which saw the partners returning to Ontario's Red Lake. Building on the option they'd gotten from David Meunier and re-examining the Red Lake region, Rubicon's leaders realized there was still a lot of available ground they could stake.

"And that's the cheapest way to acquire ground," Adamson explains. "You just go out and put pieces of wood in the ground, file with the government and the claims are yours. It's unusual for major mining camps to have major pieces of ground open for staking, but, in the case of Red Lake, this was just one of those cyclical events. I don't know exactly why it was, but it was. So in five different corporate guises, we acquired the ground, along with the Meunier option so that competition couldn't put two-and-two together and figure out that it was one entity doing this. Eventually we consolidated that into what is now one of the largest land packages in Red Lake. We control about 40 percent of the exploration real estate in Red Lake. That was – and continues to be – our main focus for investors; for a junior mining company to have a big piece of a producing camp is unusual."

With exquisite timing, a small gold-producing company called Goldcorp Inc. made a major discovery at its mine near Red Lake just after Rubicon had staked much of the remaining available ground. It's now one of the highest-grade gold deposits in the world. That boosted Goldcorp's stock price more than 1000 percent. "They were able to put Red Lake firmly and squarely right in the middle of investor interest," Adamson recalls. "We just happened to be sitting there with a big chunk of ground when all that was going on. In a way, Goldcorp's discovery meant that we had a lead agent out there promoting Red Lake, so when we went out to see brokerage firms in Toronto and Vancouver, we found it was easier to convince them that our assets in Red Lake had some real potential."

In what seemed contrarian when they first started working on it, Rubicon's strategy was predicated on a diversified North American approach to discovery and mining. "Red Lake is our key focus, and just as we had done a few years earlier with Red Lake, we felt that there was significant potential being indicated in Newfoundland," Adamson says. "Garfield MacVeigh was working with some base-metal projects there and said, 'There's something going on in terms of gold potential in this province, on the island itself, specifically.' So we put together a plan – we're not very shy, so we basically took out five major districts." That's part of the Rubicon plan. The principals learned early in their mining careers that trying to add ground to a comparatively small land position was difficult; when you tried to claim more ground, you found it was staked. It's much easier to stake a lot of ground in the area where you're confident of finding something worth mining and reducing that stake as the size and exact location of the mineral deposit becomes clearer. That strategy was especially useful in Newfoundland, where, as Adamson tells it, "the deals were available and the ground was available."

Red Lake continues to be the company's focus, as it was from the beginning. Rubicon has an asset and is drilling on it. The Newfoundland effort is a couple of years behind Red Lake, Adamson says. "We're bringing it along; we're doing the necessary exploration work to demonstrate potential, and advancing it."

That North American focus also helped the company during the fallout from the Bre-X scandal. Continuing support from the underwriters, Haywood Securities and later others helped Rubicon weather the storm, too. Without that, Adamson is frank, the company might not exist.

"If we'd been looking in November of 1997 for fresh funding," he says. "I think it would have been difficult, and I think we would have had a lot of pressure. But it's about integrity, it's about track record and all of us came from blue-chip, major company backgrounds, so it was very transparent. Investors could see they were dealing with people who have no history in the junior markets, which I think was an advantage. We didn't have pieces of ground to get rid of or to hide in that part of the world. It was because we were keyed on North American, we felt that there was great potential there. Really, the political harvest was ours to reap because we were focussed in North America we found that doors would be opened, because we were in North America. Part of it was fortuitous; part of it was because of good planning on our part."

The weak market also thinned the ranks, removing some less-than-stellar competitors from the race. But it also cut sources of funding and investment – particularly from institutions, who were suddenly more cautious and wary, even about companies they had no reason to doubt. "The institutions, who are now back in the market, totally left the market. The gold funds which would dabble in junior stock, with maybe two to five percent of their portfolios in juniors, completely walked and, for at least a year, did not want to know anything about junior company exploration. We had to be careful with our dollars. We had to look at partnerships with other companies as a way of spreading risk. It allowed some of the more risk-tolerant entrepreneurs to step up; people that were prepared to take the risk came into the market at that time. But they were few and far between, so there were grim times," explains Adamson.

And while institutional investors sat on the sidelines or cut back, exploration companies vanished. Those that didn't vanish tried to transform themselves. "A lot of them disappeared," Adamson says. "Some of them decided to become dot-coms overnight, which should have sent a message to investors. All of a sudden, clarity was everything." And if there was one thing Rubicon prided itself on, it was clarity: clarity of vision, of intention, of its message to individual investors and institutional shareholders, and clarity about which regions and projects were feasible and which were not. And it was that clarity they made sure to bring to the mineral conferences and gold shows throughout North America.

Adamson states, "In the first 18 months post-Bre-X, I think it was obvious which companies were able to survive a severe body blow and whose business plans were robust enough to ensure that kind of survival. I think we were one of them. And we're still around."

Adamson attributes Rubicon's staying power to its founders' strong technical skills, as well as "an ability to see ahead of the pack. Exploration's all about reducing risk. It's very difficult to find a mineral deposit. Investors need to do everything they can to identify companies that take as much risk out of the equation as possible. One is geological risk, the other is management and technical expertise. We've been able to demonstrate that we haven't put all our eggs in one basket. We have multiple chances at discovery. We are proud of our achievements so far. Recently, one of Canada's top analysts, Barry Allen of Research Capital, called Rubicon 'Canada's premier exploration company'. This is a great accolade. Our job is to translate this into tomorrow's mines."

Finding partners is another key element of cutting risk and reassuring current and potential investors. Adamson estimates that over the life of his company, fifty cents of every exploration dollar has come from partners. Placer Dome and IAM Gold are both partners in its Newfoundland efforts. Goldcorp is a partner in Red Lake. But partnership has its limits;

much of the challenge is applying it judiciously, figuring out when it makes sense to apply and where it would be better to go it alone. Adamson: "The skill is not to partner everything, otherwise you have no potential for 100-percent-owned investments. It's about keeping control and maximizing leverage of core assets as well as adding value through partnerships. Historically, practically all the company-making firsts involving junior companies involved those that maximized ownership of their key asset – Voisey's Bay, Arequipa, Hemlo, to name a few."

Adamson, Gray and MacVeigh started Rubicon as the best way to put their exploration and mining technical expertise to work. But they've also done a lot of learning as Rubicon has grown: they've had to learn how to manage a company and run it as efficiently and profitably as possible. In order to make sure they can do that, the three Rubicon principals have added considerable talent to the company's board. "We have people on our board like Philip Martin, who was in the capital markets in Toronto for thirty years," Adamson says. "Doug Forster, who's been very successful in the Vancouver markets, and David Reid, one of Vancouver's top mining lawyers. We saw our challenge as making sure we understood how to run the company. We've also hired specific talent to publicize the company – Bill Cavalluzzo, in Toronto, is vice president, investor relations. He was with Pangea and Goldfields, who were taken over by Barrick Gold. We used to work together at Lac. Identifying key people is every bit as important as finding key projects. Rubicon has been able to attract a top-notch group of employees as a result. Recently we have hired Peter Wong as chief financial officer. He has extensive experience in managing the finances of public companies."

That attention to the details of running the business means Rubicon is one of five exploration companies whose listing moved to the TSX last year from the TSX Venture exchange. Adamson says he finds he spends about 70 percent of his time attending to the business of running the company, rather than the geological and exploration or mining concerns he honed at Lac Minerals. Even with considerable learning and range of knowledge, experience and depth of knowledge, there are some things Adamson and his Rubicon partners need help on. There are also the securities regulations that prohibit internal parties of the company or those who have shares in the company to write reports about some aspects of

the company's business. That's when they call in the consultants. One of
the consultants was Roman Friedrich of Friedrich & Company, who once
worked as the president of Chase Manhattan Bank in Canada. He helps
with financial analysis of opportunities. "For instance, if we had an acquisition in mind, we'd ask Roman to run the numbers on its value and its
potential value to the company," Adamson says. "For a company to come
to a conclusion about something like that without a second opinion is dangerous. It's something that most larger firms do as a matter of course, but
that most junior mining companies don't always do."

Friedrich has helped Rubicon validate significant investments. One
example is that of Perry English, one of the key prospectors Rubicon
worked with in Red Lake, having optioned 14 of his 80 properties for a
combination of shares and cash. The rest were optioned to other companies with stakes in the region – Rubicon's competitors. When English said
he was thinking of selling his property interests, Rubicon was one of the
first companies he approached. "We thought, 'Well, this makes sense: we
buy our own deals back so we don't have to pay cash and shares to him.
Plus we also become the landlords of our competitors, so we own their
deals, they make payments to us, and we have potential production royalties so that if they find something, the royalties would be the real cash
cow – lottery tickets if you like, all further strengthening our grip in Red
Lake,'" Adamson reasoned. "We came to general terms on what we were
willing to pay and what he would be willing to accept, and we went to
Roman to do the analysis. Roman confirmed this to be a good deal that
should pay itself back in less than two years. So we did the deal. Last year
that deal made over $600,000 in cash plus share payments for the com-
pany, and the payments come from our competitors. We think it's a great
deal. It's an innovative deal. Plus it makes us a junior with cash flow.
Usually juniors are very good at spending money and we do that – we're
out there spending exploration dollars – but it's nice to get some income
which helps offset expenditures. Once again, our relationships with people in this one project, like Perry English, has paid off."

Once the basic focus was established for Rubicon with its Red Lake
and Newfoundland projects, continuing growth was the next direction.
But the company had enough grassroots operations, and wasn't interested in taking on any more. However, it wanted to stay in North America.

That set of criteria led, naturally enough, to Nevada.

"We've always had a desire to do something in Nevada and, back in 1997, we almost did. It just happened that more recently another ex-colleague from Lac Minerals, Bob Thomas, was based in Nevada, and came to us and said, 'Are you interested in looking at our portfolio of projects in Nevada?' We didn't want to go there like many Vancouver companies and imagine that we could find the next Carlin deposit, because it's incredibly competitive down there. The deals are expensive and it's tough sledding. So we didn't want to do that, nor did we feel we had the technical expertise in Nevada. We needed to hook up with that technical expertise. So here's a guy coming to us with a portfolio of projects, we know him, he knows us. He's not enthused about going public, didn't really want to walk Bay Street or Howe Street alone. We came up with a formula whereby we invested in his company, Toquima Minerals Corporation, going forward. They're about to file their initial prospectus so they hope they'll be public within a few months. So, for a modest investment, we'll own anywhere from 25 to 40 percent of that company. It's a way for Rubicon investors to be involved in Nevada exploration at very low cost and very low risk. If they find something, then 25 to 40 percent of that share value of that company should flow through to Rubicon. And the key was the technical expertise of the people in Nevada who we believed in. We went to Roman Friedrich again and Roman looked at it and gave it the thumbs up. We are growing the franchise – increasing investors' chances of success at low cost. We will continue to look at ways to do so."

Back in Ontario, another innovative means of partnering helped the company grow, too. In this case, Rubicon worked with a private outfit called Dominion Goldfields Corporation, owners of the McFinley Gold Project. McFinley had been mired in debt problems through the 1980s. DGC, who had purchased McFinley's debt after a lien was placed on the property, approached Rubicon intimating they wanted to find a way to do a deal that would rekindle exploration on the property. There was significant competition for McFinley, and some previous attempts to buy the property that had been rebuffed. Rubicon, through a combination of cash and shares, succeeded where others had not for a little more than $2.5 million, Adamson says. "We think it was an absolute steal. It already had a resource on it, it already had a head frame on it. The previous owners had spent $30 million on the property. Its neighbours were Placer Dome and Goldcorp – kind of like being offered Park Place on a Monopoly board for knock-down prices. But what really was the key driver for us, and for the other companies who had looked at it and were competing with us, was that there's a particular rock type there, called ultramafic. If you find ultramafic in Red Lake, a huge body of public domain data tells you that's where the deposit should be."

Goldcorp helped Rubicon to that understanding, having taken the unusual step of putting all the resultant data from its Red Lake Mine, some four kilometres to the south, into the public domain a couple of years earlier. It wasn't speculation or guesswork, Adamson says, but "here's the treasure map for free." Four kilometres worth of ultramafic on the McFinley property hadn't been explored. McFinley's original owners had planned to get the mine working, then use the cash it generated to do further exploration. Except McFinley's plans never got that far because of their defaulting on their loan, so the ultramafic, though clearly identified and mapped, hadn't been looked at.

"We've basically been there two seasons now we've explored it, and we're currently drilling it. Everywhere we've looked we have found high-grade gold and currently we're drilling a zone called the Phoenix Zone which has got economically significant intercepts and they're all hanging together. In other words, there's a continuous gold zone that we found right at the contact of the ultramafic. We've done one phase of drilling this winter which we've released results on and that the market liked. We're currently on phase two. It has the potential to be a great story and we're convinced the project has all the attributes that a major deposit should have. We own 100 percent of McFinley. We haven't dealt it, because we think it's worth more to keep 100 percent. McFinley is a key focus and a lot of our investors pay close attention to Red Lake and especially to McFinley."

With so many joint-venture partners, selling out might be a serious consideration in many of Rubicon's efforts. But Adamson says selling or maintaining ownership isn't decided by a particular formula. In fact, it's not really decided as much by Adamson, Gray and MacVeigh as it is by their shareholders. "It's a question of shareholder value, how best to reward shareholders. What are most shareholders investing in a junior mining company for? They're not looking for 10 percent on their money every year. They're really looking for that 10- or 20-fold increase that a junior company can and has historically recognized once it finds something. You get the best 'bang for your buck' if you discover it and you own a hundred percent of it. Therefore, keep all of your key projects. If you go into option joint ventures, fine. If they become discoveries, that's okay, but you're going to be discounted by the interest you hold in it. That's why we're judicious and don't do all of the option joint ventures. Our strategy is to hold on to our key assets as long as possible in order to maximize their value. We offer risk reduction and if we can maximize our discovery potential, we're in the right spot and I think people will come and pay top dollar for what we have.

"That's part of a corporate philosophy whose other ingredients include a North American focus and an understanding that gold is a commodity with certain special demands and opportunities. Staying primarily in North America means avoiding political turmoil and stress to as great a degree as possible. It also allows us to consider taking on more opportunities and risk going forward. Although sometimes – 9/11, for example – that kind of stability can be threatened. But even that kind of intrusion helps point out that in times of political turmoil, gold gets more valuable and in greater demand, something that doesn't happen with anything else."

"Gold, as a harbour of safety and stability will benefit as a result," Adamson says frankly. "Everything that should be going in gold's favour is pointing that way. We think the future for gold over the next little while is going into what is referred to as a secular or long-term bull market following 20 years of a bear market. That should bode well for companies with solid assets, but I still think that investors should look carefully and make sure the deposits work at $300 gold and that they don't need $500 gold to work."

The price of gold, as Rubicon sees it, can't be entirely counted on. That's why Rubicon makes sure its projects could turn a profit with gold at $250 per ounce. "If you were looking for deposits which require $450 gold, look out, because gold's at $400, although I think it's going to go higher," says Adamson. "But if you require it to go higher for the deposit you're looking for, be careful, because it may go lower again. That's important, because as the cycle gets more and more heated, more marginal deposits and more marginal exploration targets come to the table. Investors have to be careful about that. The debt issue in the United States and the decline in the U.S. dollar is the key driver for gold right now. We don't see any change in that situation anytime soon. We've seen the central banks reduce their selling. We've seen the decline of supply. It takes about six to eight years to bring an encouraging prospect to production. The producers which are mining seven to ten million ounces of gold a year, they've got big appetites. They need big appetites to keep that inventory going. Supply and demand is pointing towards an increase in price and the twin debt-deficit in the United States is a key driver, which we feel will continue to make gold a key place to invest in. There is a premium paid to gold: gold stocks, gold producers, but also even juniors that are involved in gold exploration because it's a financial instrument in times of crisis and it will be again if there's more crisis. In the final analysis, though, Rubicon cannot control these macro factors – we have to make sure our business plan can survive even in bad times. That's why we're still around.

Adamson summarizes: "I love this business. I love what I'm doing, we love and are enthused about the discovery process. You're right at the cutting edge. You're responsible for your decisions. You're out there trying to make money for shareholders. There's very few industries that give a person a chance to do that. I've got lots of technical education and am pleased to be able to practice my craft. But to be able to do it in a public company and to be out there really trying to make money is the most exciting job anywhere. I love it."

ST. JUDE
RESOURCES LIMITED

When Mike Terrell talks about the beginnings of St. Jude Resources Ltd., he is plain-spoken and doesn't mince words: "We did it from scratch. We did it the hard way." But as Terrell and his company illustrate, adversity not only makes each gain and triumph sweeter, it means lessons and knowledge that a person can rely on during difficult times, as well as a more thorough understanding of the challenges and opportunities than might be afforded someone who'd just lucked into success without a lot of hard work.

Given that – and given the company's development – its name is no accident. Saint Jude is known as the patron saint of seemingly lost causes.

"I prefer difficult cases," Terrell avers. "We've been lucky, and maybe it's because St. Jude's on our side; that's largely why we came up with the name. My name, which most people don't know, is Michael Arthur Thaddeus Terrell. Saint Jude's name is Saint Jude Thaddeus. And the deal with St. Jude is, if you get what you ask for, you're supposed to publish your thanks – if you look in the personal or the classified ads in any major newspaper, you'll always see, 'Thanks to St. Jude for favours received.' I believe in the power of prayer.

"It's always tricky to find a company name that means something to you and St. Jude is a name that people will remember. For all those reasons, I just thought it was a good name. This was a name that meant something to me for personal reasons, but also, in a funny kind of way, would be applicable, because if you look at the odds of being successful in the mining business, it's not that easy. I figured we could use all the help we could get."

Terrell grew up in Sudbury, Ontario, where the principal industry was mining and everything connected with it. "Most people in that part of the world have mining in their blood," he says. "My father was in the mining business and I spent my summers from elementary school and high school in the bush with him, staking claims and doing exploration. My dad had high standards and a great reputation, he gave me a lot of help and a love for this business. If it wasn't for him I wouldn't be telling this story."

That provided Terrell with a means of putting himself through school. As he earned his undergraduate degree at the University of Toronto and then a law degree from the University of Manitoba, he continued to work in mineral exploration. He and his father worked together often, and acquired a number of properties throughout northwestern Ontario. They vended most of those to other companies. But they held onto one of them, called the Uchi Lake project because of its location. It's also close to Red Lake, one of Canada's most significant gold mining centres. Terrell was practicing law in Edmonton in 1989 when he decided to switch to the mining business full time.

"I made the decision that if I was ever going to get involved with a public junior mining exploration company, I'd better do it sooner than later. We raised the seed capital and went public in 1990, almost 15 years ago. We worked on Uchi lake for two or three exploration seasons; we did some good work and had some good results. Unfortunately, we didn't get a lot of response in the stock market to those results. We weren't great promoters – as I said, we learned the hard way. We did the exploration, published the results and thought the market would take care of itself. I learned that you have to find out what the market wants."

So, in 1993, noticing the strikes in Venezuela and elsewhere, Terrell and St. Jude Resources started considering looking for gold projects outside Canada. That is what the market wanted. Venezuela, in fact, was where they began their search. Using consultants, they also looked throughout Central America and South America. But the increased interest in the region was driving up the costs of grassroots exploration projects. Eventually the search was expanded to West Africa.

"It wasn't as heated there, and we would probably be able to get a good project going for less than an arm-and-a-leg. We also felt the political risk was lower" Terrell says. "Uchi Lake was a nice project, but we felt dollar-for-dollar, we could have the potential to prove up a much bigger deposit for the same number of exploration dollars spent in Africa. After all, Africa was still one of those places where elephant-sized deposits could still be discovered. It appeared to be a better utilization of our capital. In 1994 I traveled over to Ghana to look at a couple of projects. One of the projects we'd optioned was a diamond and gold project that looked too good to be true. And as things turned out, it *was* too good to be true."

There were historical and geological reasons for focussing the search on West Africa. Ghana used to be known as the Gold Coast of Africa, and the region's Ashanti kings were renowned for their gold. Some of the continent's – and the world's – biggest and best gold mines are on the Ashanti gold belt. Terrell was also helped in reconnoitering the region by his early association with senior economic geologist, Bill Zilbersher.

"My father had a nose for good projects and good people. He helped me find good people, and one of the first I found was Bill Zilbersher, who came with me to look at that diamond and gold project. Bill was a senior consultant with a very reputable firm, Behre Dolbear. He's extremely reputable, he's advised the World Bank, he's done work for the government of Ghana and he's a really straightforward, honest, smart guy. More importantly he is just a hell of a nice person."

Terrell recalls, "After the first project turned out to be a dud I was ready to head back to Canada disillusioned. But Bill convinced me to stay and dig my heels in until we found something worthwhile. He said, 'Forget about diamonds. The real prize in this part of the world is gold. There will be many more quality gold projects discovered in West Africa.' We looked at 50 different projects when, out of the blue, my father sent me a fax that said, 'While you're over there, take a look at the Hwini Butre; it sounds like a sleeper but could have real potential.'"

Zilbersher also helped introduce Terrell to the man who is now St. Jude's exploration manager, George Flach. "Mr. Flach is a geologist with over 19 years experience in mineral exploration including 17 years in the country of Ghana. He leads one of the most successful and experienced exploration teams in West Africa, having discovered numerous deposits. These deposits have been mined by Golden Star, Ashanti Goldfields, and Gold Fields.

"George is one of those guys who has whatever it is that the local artisanal miners have," Terrell says. "He does have a nose for finding gold. It didn't take Flach long to find the sweet spots on these properties. He has delivered some of the highest grade results around. The average grade at a lot of mines over there is somewhere around 2 grams per tonne, and we've drilled holes averaging 78 grams per tonne over 12 metres. I wish I could tell you that the average grade of the property was this high. I can't, but my point is that George consistently gets interesting results."

The local artisanal miners – called galamsey – are admired widely by explorers like Flach and Terrell as savvy if untutored prospectors who know where to look for mineral deposits. Terrell says he doesn't think there's a mine that's been discovered in West Africa that wasn't first the site of some kind of galamsey activity. Smart geologists from North America know when they first arrive in a particular region to go into local villages and seek the chief, pay their respects and tribute according to local custom and then, instead of announcing their intention to use western or North American exploration techniques to locate the gold they seek, ask if anybody in the region or the village has seen any gold. Not long after that, usually, the explorer will likely be led to nearby sites of galamsey mining activity.

"They definitely have a sixth sense," Terrell says of the galamsey. "You can have a Ph.D. in economic geology from Harvard and that doesn't mean you're going to be able to find anything faster than a local galamsey miner – in fact, the locals probably find it faster. In their own way, they understand geological formations and the types of terrain that you should be looking in." Terrell says that he is quite impressed with the quality of the Ghanaian geologists who have proven to be intuitive, loyal and hard-working.

On the Hwini Butre project, St. Jude Resources has three deposits, which Terrell describes as 'pearls on a string'. The story behind how one of them, called the Father Brown Deposit, was found helps to illustrate the mix of instinct and science that marks mineral explorers and the way they work. Its timing was fortunate, too.

George Flach and Terrell were in Ghana, reviewing work they'd already done and considering drill targets they'd explore next. During an earlier visit to one of St. Jude's properties, Terrell had been shown an old European mining shaft. European shafts look different from the shafts sunk by local artisanal miners; they're square, whereas shafts dug by the locals are round. Terrell suggested to Flach that the two of them re-examine the site of the European shaft, where early sampling had delivered positive results. A few hundred metres from the shaft, they found some old rusty equipment – another encouraging sign.

"I'm leaning against this tree and I look down and see eggs and feathers and coins and jewelry, all in a big pile," Terrell recalls. "I said to George, 'What do you think this is? Who would have left this here?'

'Don't touch it!'

'What do you mean?'

'It's juju.'

"In these parts many of the locals are big believers in juju. It could have been there for a number of reasons. If they want to have good luck they will do certain things: they'll pour libations, leave gifts like what I had found. I don't understand all the history and the explanation for it. I said to George, 'You don't really believe in that stuff, telling me not to touch it.' He said, 'Well, not really...but I don't want to mess with juju, either.' So I reached into my pocket and took a few dollars worth of coins and bills and put them on the juju pile. It's bad luck to be superstitious, but I wasn't about to take any chances."

About a week later, George Flach called Terrell. He'd been thinking more about the site where they'd found the juju pile. The site didn't match certain elements of the expected geological profile. But that could have been because of successive rounds of small-scale efforts by local galamsey as well as early European miners. Terrell states, "We couldn't do any meaningful surface work because, at that time, this area was quite swampy."

He couldn't put his finger on it, but Flach had a good feeling about the area. Based on George's track record Terrell said, "let's take a shot."

So St. Jude proceeded to drill. Shortly thereafter, Flach called Terrell, telling him that some of the drill results looked 'interesting.' After sending the drilled material to two separate independent labs for verification, St. Jude released the results. "At that point those were the highest results we'd ever published," Terrell says. "The stock went from seventy cents one morning to three dollars the next day on millions of shares. It was a nice little hit along the way. Interestingly, the deposit is part of a long lens system, but that discovery hole was spotted right beside that juju tree."

"We've had good juju all over," Terrell says. "Fortunately every project we've acquired so far has been a property of merit and we've been successful in finding what we're looking for. That's a result of hard work, having great staff and key experienced people who know what to look for; and we wouldn't be where we are today if wasn't for our good exploration geologists. They should get a lot of credit for our success. Our key people like George Flach, Bob Griffis and Fred Somdah have been over in that part of the world for a long time. Heck, Bob Griffis, our General Manager literally wrote one of the the most comprehensive books that exists on the geology of Ghana. Our exploration team has been responsible for the discovery of a number of deposits. They've found the big ore bodies and it usually turns out that guys who find ore bodies continue to find more of them because they recognize them. Sure, there's been some luck involved. But, I believe you make your own luck...with hard work.

Today we are an advanced-stage exploration company and we are getting to the point where we're either going to be an acquisition candidate or a production company in the near future. That's the best way to describe our situation today. We've discovered approximately a million ounces just at the south end of our first concession within a strike length of approximately 1.5 kilometres. That concession is 20 kilometres long, with many other highly-prospective targets along that strike. With our next concession to the north, the Benso, we've got another 10 to 15 kilometres of potential strike and we've already found a number of rich deposits. We have not done an official resource estimate there, so I can't really talk about how many ounces are at Benso, but it would be safe to say that the potential to add a lot more ounces exists. We also have two projects in Burkina Faso and two in Niger. We are quite excited about the potential of these other projects to significantly enhance shareholder value."

Another example of fortune – as a result of juju or St. Jude – happened with St. Jude Resources' timing the way it dodged the Bre-X bullet that wounded so many other exploration and mining companies.

"We closed a financing with Griffiths McBurney two days after Bre-X blew up," Terrell says. "And I don't think there was another financing in this industry done for a long time after that. Somebody had to be up there taking care of us, because it would not have been unreasonable for the people who had committed, to back out because market conditions had changed. Our projects were starting to look interesting. But we certainly needed the money, and closing that financing allowed us to weather the storm the drop in gold prices precipitated. We worked hard and slugged it out for the next few years on those funds and picked up other projects and had great results. I am not suggesting that we went through these tough times unscathed. Our share price did get beat up along with everybody else. But we did survive and live to fight another day. Which is more than I can say for a lot of other less-fortunate exploration companies."

When discussing his shareholder base, Terrell comments that, "Not all shareholders have the same goals. Some of them are involved strictly because they see a trading opportunity. These traders have a different focus from those shareholders who really want to own the stock as an investment. A trader's main goal is to buy low, sell high. It's not uncommon if you have been in this business for a few years to get the odd phone call from unhappy shareholders. 'Why is your share price lower than what I paid for it? I just sold and lost money and it's all your fault. You can't blame people for being unhappy when the market cycles. That will happen from time to time. Unfortunately, I think that experience has proven that traders are lucky to break even; most end up losing money in the grand scheme of things. Having said that, we do have a lot of shareholders who were loyal and stuck with us. And I certainly appreciate those people. I would really like to acknowledge our long-term shareholders who said, 'Look, we got involved with this company for the long haul, we liked your story and what you were doing and who cares if the share price is down today? We're here for the long term and we'll see what happens.' It's not always easy to do right by those loyal, long-term shareholders. The people who stuck with us are just real good people. They come from all over the place. The shareholders that I've been talking to for ten years or more, oftentimes include people whose only mining stock was St. Jude. 'Bought the stock, liked the story, don't own any others and this is the one deal I'm going to stick with and I hope it works out.' These shareholders understand that you have to be patient when it comes to investing. It's like buying a really nice bottle of wine...you don't rush to open it. It gets better over time."

In addition to good projects and good people, Terrell feels that one of the other key factors in their success is the positive governmental and regulatory environments in the countries where they explore. Terrell says St. Jude Resources is fortunate to be working in Ghana, Burkina Faso and Niger.

"If you had to rate places in the world to explore today, we are in the top ten, maybe the top five. There is a rich mining history and prolific gold belts – good reasons to go there. The infrastructure over the years has developed where we have assay labs and drilling companies and mining schools where they train locals so you don't have to import all of your people. We've had a good experience with all of the West African governments. Found them to be quite reasonable and fair. They've been supportive of our initiative. You certainly get a much better reception over there than you do if you're in North America with your mining hat on. I believe, in life, that you should go where you're loved, and they love us over in West Africa."

In addition to being loved, it's conceivable and understandable that St. Jude Resources might be coveted and potentially courted by a larger company eager to gain access to the potential it's uncovered in West Africa. Terrell says any immediate plans for a joint venture would be premature, but that recent events are bringing more opportunities every day.

"We've been approached a few times. It's our opinion that for us to do a deal too early is equivalent to leaving a lot of money on the table. And from a management point of view, the time just has not been right yet. We certainly have projects that would be attractive to many of the majors, and they've indicated they would be happy to attempt to structure something with us, but so far we are still proving up more ounces. We realize that sooner than later we will have to decide where we want to be in the food chain – what we want to be when we grow up."

Of course, in many ways, it seems clear that Mike Terrell's St. Jude Resources is already mature in the way it does business and in its outlook.

"I have read everything there is to read on the subject and one thing is clear – nobody really knows what's going on with the price of gold," Terrell says. "I take a more practical approach and ask, 'What's the true cost of producing an ounce of gold?' You should factor in some of the costs of exploration and some of the costs of reclamation. If you bring in some of those sunk costs, many of the big guys will need to have a gold price of around $400 per ounce to justify being in that business. It's not easy. There are a lot of other businesses where you get to sit behind a nice desk all day long and go for long lunches and drive home to your family in the suburbs. A lot of guys in this business don't get to do that. They spend their entire lives slugging it out in the bush or on the road. It's not the easiest way to make a living. But the reason people stick with this business is because it's interesting – all the people in it are real characters. I enjoy the camaraderie. That makes it fun. That's why people will continue to be geologists and mining promoters. If you like taking risks and new adventures, it's a great business.

"There is a 'glamour factor' that attracts investors and people in the mining and exploration companies to gold," Terrell says. "But it's not the primary driving force in either case.

"From a junior company point of view, a practical point of view, it is possible to explore for gold, develop a project to the feasibility stage and go into production as a small company. Its been done quite a few times."

"The bottom line is that gold exploration is one of the few businesses where you can spend a few million dollars and find a few hundred million dollars worth of a commodity that people really want. It's the opportunity for the huge upside potential that drives us."

Terrell summarizes by stating, "We are in a great position. We have already drilled off quality ounces in Ghana and we have six great exploration plays with advanced targets. These projects cover over 2900 kilometres of one of the most prolific gold belts in the world. We have the knowledge and the financial resources to discover many more ounces.

" When you really think about it, the odds of being a successful gold explorer are actually pretty good. You do your homework, get good projects, get good people, good shareholders and add a bit of luck. We have been blessed with all of these. Thanks to St. Jude for many favours received."

At press time, St. Jude announced a measured and indicated gold resource on its Benso project of 487,000 ounces, plus an additional inferred resource of 11,000 ounces. At the same time, they also announced an updated estimate on their Hwini Butre project, where the measured and indicated resource had increased by 47.5%. This brings the total measured and indicated gold resources in Ghana to 1,316,000 ounces plus an additional 25,000 ounces in the inferred category.

SPARTON RESOURCES INCORPORATED

Lee Barker is a man who enjoys a healthy relationship with risk. He understands it, he is not afraid of it, but perhaps most importantly, he respects it. And since an element of risk is an inherent part of the mining business, it's a good relationship to have when you're the president and CEO of a junior mineral exploration company.

Barker sits at his desk in Sparton Resources' downtown Toronto office, having just moved up in the world – from the fifth to the sixth floor and into a larger space.

In typical Barker fashion, he unabashedly launches into a list of his vital stats right off the bat – 59 years old this year, a Leo, Type A personality and a self-professed 'contrarian'.

"If you tell me I can't do it, I will probably give it a try and show you," he says.

It's true there doesn't seem to be much that Barker hasn't tried at least once. Aside from being the sole person running Sparton's head office, he operates a mixed working farm outside of Toronto, still participates in athletic competitions, and is a pilot with his own plane. Which brings us back to risk and Barker's philosophy on it.

"I guess I like the thrill of the hunt," he muses. "I like solving problems, I like challenges, and I'm not adverse to accepting risk as long as I can perceive what the risks are and then deal with them appropriately. So I'm not paranoid about accepting risk in my job or in different situations."

It's obvious Barker would not be happy at a 9-to-5 job, sitting at the same desk all year long. He admits he needs to move around, be physical, and craves stimulation and variety. Fortunately, he is in the right industry for that. As a pilot, he was able to do his own geophysical airborne surveys during the seventies, which was the next best thing to his other dream of being in the air force.

"They wouldn't accept you in the air force in the fifties and sixties if you wore glasses. If you had glasses, you couldn't do anything. It was before affirmative action," Barker recalls.

There weren't nearly as many career choices back in the late fifties and early sixties as there are today, but Barker developed an interest in the mining business at a young age through some friends of his parents.

"They were mining promoters and I was hearing stories all the time about prospecting and the stock market. I thought it sounded rather glamorous," said Barker.

Despite being dissuaded by a high school guidance counselor ("It's a dirty business, why would you want to do that?"), Barker elected to pursue mining engineering because he was interested in surveying.

"I didn't know much about geology in those days. The uranium rush in the Bancroft area of Ontario had come and gone and the Elliot Lake rush was going on. To me, mining was prospecting, and I heard all these stories and there seemed like lots of romance."

But timing, as they say, is everything and it wouldn't take long before Barker's mining engineering path took an unexpected and fateful turn into geological engineering. At the end of his first year of university, Barker applied for at least 20 summer jobs at different mines as a junior engineer. He also applied for a job with the Ontario Geological Survey, since they were known to hire students as assistants on survey parties. Just when things were looking desperate with no job in sight, Barker received two job offers a day apart. He grabbed the first one, which happened to be with the OGS as a junior assistant with a geological mapping party.

"The next day I got a job offer from Quemont at about twice the salary, but I said I was sorry, I had already accepted another job. So that set my fate in becoming a geological engineer as opposed to a mining engineer," said Barker.

After two summers working with the OGS, Barker switched gears at school and ended up graduating in 1966 as a geological engineer.

"I enjoyed geology, I enjoyed field work, I enjoyed the romance of prospecting and the pot of gold at the end of the rainbow that everyone was trying to find. Coincidentally, at the time I graduated there was an upsurge in the mining industry. Metal prices had gone up, there was a shortage of people, and anybody with mining or geological engineer at the end of his name could have gotten a job in the middle sixties."

But rather than jumping right into a job, Barker decided to further his education and broaden his knowledge, going on to post-grad work at McGill University, nailing down an applied Master's degree and graduating in 1968.

"It was a very good course with all kinds of practical experience and mine tours and excellent ongoing education," he said.

Armed with his academic schooling, Barker was ready to begin a life and career in the mining business that would prove to be as varied and stimulating as his personality and character demanded.

It took decades before Barker would find his way to Sparton, but by the time he did, his vast practical and business experiences, not to mention the invaluable connections and contacts he had garnered, made the transition to president and CEO a relatively undaunting proposition. And Sparton wasn't new to Barker, nor was it new to the industry. It, in fact, had been around since 1979. Sparton Resources Inc., as it is now known, was formed in 1982 through an amalgamation of two companies – Cracking Stone Mines and Sparton Mining Co. Ltd. Although Barker didn't become president until the end of 2002, he already had a history with the company.

"In 1997, I'd been fortunate enough to make some money during the days of the diamond boom through my old relationship with the Aber/West Viking discoveries at Diavik in the Northwest Territories, and with SouthernEra. I actually participated in a financing of Sparton in 1997 and invested a considerable amount of money in the company, partly because I thought the company had some potential, but also because I realized my future down the road wasn't going to be with SouthernEra for the rest of my life."

After years of experience that had taken Barker from Alberta and the prairies to the U.S. and Mexico, to Greenland, the Northwest Territories, Uruguay, Brazil, Venezuela, Angola and countless other countries and climes, he ended up back in his home province.

After working with companies like Inco Shell, Denison Mines, Duval Corporation (Pennzoil), Lacana Mining Corporation (which merged with Corona Corporation), Aber, Platinova, West Viking Exploration and SouthernEra, he is now running his own show.

And having looked for everything from petroleum to uranium, potash, silver and gold, and following extensive and successful work with diamond exploration, Barker is once again looking for the pot of gold.

All those experiences led Barker to Sparton. After making a personal financial investment in the company, Barker decided to also invest his considerable expertise and his future.

"If I positioned myself with a share position in a company, I figured it would basically force me to do something with it to try and realize the value back. I made the investment. Now I'm basically trying to build value into Sparton and ultimately I'll be able to gain some personal benefit as well."

With Barker's benefit, comes shareholder benefit. And he has no desire to let himself or anyone else down.

"It's not a charity," he points out. "I invested a lot of money in the company and hope to get it back and make a profit. And that's why I've begun some of these more aggressive projects and taken the company into China and picked up some new things. With the market revived in late-2003 we have also, fortunately, been involved in some serious financing."

Although China is currently the big lure and most exciting prospect for Barker, he's also been busy filling up Sparton's portfolio with other assorted and promising projects. Because Barker doesn't believe in 'being a specialist and putting myself in a box', he doesn't expect it for his company either.

About a year ago, he picked up some gold properties in the Hemlo area and sealed a joint venture with Beaufield Consolidated Resources,an old associate in the business. According to Barker, they acquired some properties, raised some money, did some drilling, but weren't particularly successful in finding anything new.

"I also picked up a diamond property in the Otish Mountains where there had been some exploration success with Ashton. They were finding some diamondiferous deposits there, which I think have the potential to become commercial. So Sparton still has some activities there," he said.

In the meantime, China had reopened itself to foreign investment in mineral resources, deregulation and control of precious metals. A company called Southwestern Resources had acquired a project in China, began drilling, and produced spectacular results. According to Barker, their share price jumped from about two dollars to over forty-five dollars, prior to a two-for-one share split.

"It was the darling of the junior mining industry, so China became very hot. It became a great place to go, everybody was excited, and everybody wanted a project in China. You could finance things over there."

It was 2003 when Barker decided to check it out, right in the midst of the SARS scare. But aside from having his temperature taken three times a day, and constantly filling out forms stating where he had been and where he was going, Barker said the Chinese handled the situation extremely well and exercised great control.

"It was a non-issue basically, because there was no SARS in the provinces I visited," he said.

Yunnan province was where Barker set his sights. A progressive province, Yunnan had been allowed by the central government to participate in independent foreign investment transactions with outside mining companies. Because of this independent status, Barker found Yunnan to be the most appealing place to work.

"I looked at a number of projects there, and one of them caught my eye," he said.

Geologically, the technical aspects of the project were extremely similar to a number of gold discoveries Barker had worked on in Nevada when he was with Corona and Lacana, six or seven of which were brought into production. The geological similarities to the famous Carlin Trend gold-producing area in Nevada were especially significant. For Barker, the familiarity was reassuring.

"I had the benefit of that experience and I was able to recognize geology very similar to a number of those deposits," he said.

By September 2003, an agreement was in place on a project in Yunnan called the Luxi (prounounced 'Looshi') gold project. By the end of the year, a joint venture was finalized with the partner who held the exploration licences and operated a small mine within the area. The Yunnan Nuclear Geological Exploration Brigade 201 is the name of Sparton's Chinese partner.

"They have 20 percent of our project. They're a provincial group that has now become a private organization. They were state-supported in the past, but the central government let them loose in 1999 and they had to fend for themselves," explained Barker.

"These guys operate a small gold mine in the center of our area. They've been very successful, they make lots of money with this mine, they buy hotels, office buildings and restaurants with the money they make, and they're our partner in the whole exercise," says Barker.

But aside from acknowledging their partners' expertise and past successes, Barker is pleased with the relationship on a personal level as well.

"I think our partners are very honourable people. They're excited about working with us and I think we've developed a sense of trust with them," says Barker.

"We're not the type of company that makes under the table payments to get things done. I wouldn't do that personally, and I wouldn't do it for the company with its money, and the shareholders' money. So far, everything has been very positive."

Having just received their business licence, which allows work to proceed, it's all systems go for Sparton on the Luxi project. Barker had a diamond drill shipped over to China, and drilling began late in the first half of 2004. Not only is it in Barker's nature to be hands-on, he determined it's more cost effective in the long run.

"I elected to do that because I like to do things myself or deal with people that I trust and know can do things well. There was just a huge savings over a two-year period and we still own the equipment. The Chinese love that because they're anxious to get modern equipment over there to do the work."

And that's the trade-off. While Sparton supplies financing, technology, and new ideas, their local partners will be contributing a skilled work-force and mining expertise for the surface oxide deposits.

"Our objective for the long term is to determine how much gold is in the primary material," says Barker.

Although the mine is an open surface operation, they'll be drilling the material underneath the surface soil deposit that contains mineable gold. Finding a large deposit is the obvious goal, and one that Barker is opti-mistic about.

"There has to be a source for this gold, it's in the rocks. We've sam-pled the rocks and determined good gold values, but nobody's ever drill tested them or done a comprehensive evaluation," he points out.

The potential is as huge as the area, which covers more than 250 square kilometres. Until now, the local miners have found a number of small surface deposits, mined them and made money. There is, in fact, one operating mine in the area that has produced around 210,000 ounces of gold since 1991. But again, it's all from oxide surface soil and virtual-ly nothing from primary rock.

"They're happy, but now they realize those deposits are starting to become depleted and they don't want to invest the capital to develop or explore further themselves to look at the primary material. A foreign investor is their long-term potential," says Barker.

Although Barker is aware there is the potential for several million ounces based on geological merit alone, he remains cautious about pro-moting it. To make a mine, he says, there are three things you require – location, grade and tonnes. As it happens, location is optimum.

"The infrastructure is wonderful. There's a paved road within about five kilometres of most parts of the property. It's the old Silk Road that runs from China into Myanmar (Burma), and there's power everywhere, so there's no problem with that," says Barker.

Now it's only a matter of grade and tonnes, the latter of which is abundant.

"Certainly we have the tonnes. There's obviously a lot of rock there, we just have to find the local zones of economic grade gold mineraliza-tion," says Barker, adding they currently have at least a dozen targets including whatever is underneath the existing mine itself.

"It's one-third owned by our partner and has a very restricted vertical limit. So, the primary ore in that mine beneath a certain level is within our exploration licence areas."

That potential, Barker says, is the most obvious in the short term. In the long term, he characterizes Sparton's team as 'explorationists not operators'.

"We do have good senior operational experience on Sparton's board, but I think our prime goal in life is to find things to the point where they become attractive to somebody else. Then we could benefit the company and create value for shareholders by either doing joint ventures with those people or by actually merging the company into a new vehicle that creates more value."

In the end, Barker would like to identify enough gold to make the project attractive to a senior mining company.

"In other words, if a Barrick or a Newmont or a Placer would be interested in developing a deposit of this type in China, larger than a million ounces for instance, then I think that would be our best objective."

But until that happens, Barker is thrilled to be operating in China. He points out that China is getting the Summer Olympics in 2008 which will put them front and center on the world stage, and he's impressed with the country's cutting edge technology and adherence to the rule of law.

"Universally, it has tremendous respect for rules and regulations and that's how they maintain control over society. There are a billion-and-a-half people living in China, but they've all become little independent entrepreneurs in many ways and the country is technologically very advanced. They have a cell phone system that covers most of the populated parts of the country."

In the last year or two, the Shanghai gold exchange opened which allowed Chinese people to independently buy and sell gold at world prices. And fortunately for Sparton, there's a three-year tax holiday on new mines in Yunnan province, after which they can enjoy two more years at 50 percent of the corporate tax rate. Barker agrees this system is also a great incentive.

Sweetening the pot, there is no import duty on equipment brought in for mining as long as it's not used for commercial purposes. This also suits Barker just fine, particularly since he's bringing in his own drilling equipment.

If all that isn't enough to make China an attractive place to work, there's always the weather. Yunnan is known as the 'springtime province' which makes working conditions not only bearable but greatly extends their scope.

"The weather is never really extreme, it's always springtime. You have a rainy season and a dry season and we can work 24 hours a day, 12 months a year. They seem to think the rainy season is an impediment, but it's nothing compared to what it's like in parts of Africa where I've worked," notes Barker.

Having recounted all the positive aspects to working in China and specifically on the Luxi project, Barker sits back and seems almost amazed at his good fortune.

"I can't complain a bit. I keep waiting for something bad to happen, but so far everything's gone very well," he says.

"In my career, I've worked all over the world – and you're always waiting for something to go wrong. But so far I've been very gratified by this whole exercise in China."

Although China is Sparton's number one priority at this point, it's certainly not the only thing on the go.

"You can't have a one-project company, and we have our projects in Ontario which we have joint ventured with a number of other companies. We have one in Newfoundland, and all these things at this stage are still active," says Barker.

And just for something completely different, back in 1997 Barker purchased an interest in Chebucto, an oil and gas field in offshore Nova Scotia. It's part of the Nova Scotia offshore gas project developed by Exxon Mobil over the last few years.

"There's a reserve there, but we don't know when it's going to be developed because it's a third priority type of situation. But eventually that gas is going to come out of the ground, it's going to flow through the pipelines and Sparton will realize some value on it," says Barker.

In fact, Sparton is the only public junior exploration company in

Canada that owns a percentage of a major natural gas reserve in the off-shore Nova Scotia gas production area region. Although it may take years to realize the value, this discovery remains a key element in Sparton's portfolio in Canada.

"It forms a bit of an underpinning, rather than just having a group of mineral claims in a swamp somewhere. There's actual value there that can be calculated, but nobody really takes it into consideration when we are examined as a junior resource company. We're not an oil-and-gas company, we're a junior mining exploration company and it's those projects that people put their expectations on when they buy the shares."

So, oil and gas aside for the time being, shareholder expectations for mining can focus on more than China. Barker has recently been eyeing up Mexico, specifically the promising Santa Rosario project in the Sierra Madres.

"We had a lot of experience working in Mexico with Bill Gross and Ed Thompson and a string of contacts in the mining business – some people we've been associated with since the 1980s," says Barker.

"They offered us a number of opportunities there and we decided to option one of their projects. They had already done a lot of grassroots work and identified this area with gold and silver mineralization that had never really been systematically evaluated by a mining company," says Barker.

Therein lies the attraction for Barker and his team.

"It hasn't been beaten to death by somebody else. It does have some significant indications of mineralization, but it's basically virgin territory in many ways."

There has been some artisanal mining activity and exploration, some gold and silver production from the area by local prospectors called gambisinos, but otherwise it's a relatively new area and Barker is eager to see what lies in wait. The joint venture is with a company called International Northair, and Sparton will earn an interest by spending money in what Barker characterizes as a 'standard type agreement'.

Based on their portfolio, Barker believes Sparton's stock is currently undervalued. Their treasury sits at a comfortable $2.5 million and there is no debt. Today the stock price is around 40 cents, compared to only 10 cents a year ago.

"Last year when China was really hot, in the fall when we were doing these deals, we raised about $3.5 million or more through private placements, mostly organized by Haywood Securities. The stock actually got up to $1.70 with all the hype around China and a number of newsletter writers mentioning the company in the U.S. The stock peaked and then fell back to a dollar, and now everything's quietened down and people are waiting for us to generate some news on the technical front," explains Barker.

All of which is why he sees the stock price as currently being undervalued, something Barker acknowledges and accepts.

"I'm the kind of person who would rather promote based on technical value. When I see real technical value, then we'll talk about it and let the market know that we really do have something here."

Barker won't be content to sit behind his desk, waiting around for results. Although he has hired two extremely skilled and trustworthy geologists to work with Sparton's Chinese partner and perform the bulk of the field work, no doubt Barker will be getting his hands dirty too.

"I still like to go out into the field and I thrive on physical activity. I went in the field last winter, doing geophysical surveys in the bush on the Hemlo project and in the Otish Mountains," he said.

But whenever he's seated in Sparton's head office, Barker is pretty much flying solo.

"Well, the company doesn't really have many employees...we have very low overhead," he says.

He currently shares the office space with two other companies and John Paterson, a Sparton director, is associated with both. One floor down is Ed Thompson, the chairman of Sparton, who has a long working history with Barker and runs a consulting business representing a number of other junior companies.

"So, we have everybody in the same place here," says Barker. "We have a very strong board of directors with a balance of geologists, engineers, entrepreneurs, and two lawyers. Our senior legal director goes back to the original formation of the company, as his father was the person who was behind Cracking Stones Mines.

"There's nothing very new here, we are all seasoned professionals."

And that's something shareholders can put their faith in, because that's where Barker's putting it.

"My position is that we're all mature people, we're not new in the business. At this stage in our lives, we're not all personally concerned about the next five dollars. We're not a bunch of guys who will flip their stock as soon as it goes up. We really believe that if we can create value, we'll all benefit.

"We're not traders, we're investors. I guess that's the difference."

Setting his sights on China, Mexico, and some scattered North American projects, Barker has his hands full and wouldn't want it any other way. Recognizing opportunity when he sees it, embracing the challenge of exploration and discovery, and naturally respecting the parameters of risk, are what drive Sparton's president and CEO.

"I have never been cavalier about it, but I do enjoy a challenge. The particular project in China I have grasped onto is the kind of situation that is difficult for someone in our business to come across close to home.

"So I think the opportunity is a good one, I've put a lot of energy into it, raised money and financed it, and we have a good chance for success. If we get lucky on the first few drill holes and find something really super, that will be wonderful and it will drive some momentum for us. If we don't, we have the funds for two or three years of exploration to carry on with systematically testing all these things. The Luxi gold belt is not a one-shot deal."

But all Barker's enthusiasm for China doesn't diminish his hope and optimism in Sparton's other projects. It's just a matter of priorities and knowing when to focus on what.

"The project in Mexico has a lot of blue sky because it's never been evaluated before by anybody else. It's not a high-cost item and it gives us some diversity. The diamond project in Quebec, the Otish Mountains, we'll grind away at that and hopefully come up with some more positive results this year. The other projects...their time will come. We'll do our best to try and realize all of them."

No matter what the outcome, Barker is a great believer in taking responsibility for both the positives and the negatives – "If I make a mistake, I'll admit it. I'm not paranoid about that."

That's how it has to be when your hand is in everything, when the vision is yours. But because he has a good sense of management, much experience, and a highly credible team, Barker doesn't foresee a lot of extreme swings in fortune.

"I'm analytical enough before I pursue something, that I'm not going to make a huge mistake and have a big train crash. And I don't get narcissistic about things. I know when to cut bait and fish somewhere else. There's a law of diminishing returns that sets in often on some of these projects and you have to face that it just ain't there. I guess my ego is not necessarily driven by that."

Barker's sense of responsibility extends further to the shareholders who have put their faith and money in Sparton just as he has.

"I feel responsible for the shareholders' money, I don't want to waste it. I'd rather try and spend it the most efficiently and technically productive way I can," says Barker.

"The things that make me feel good are basically executing objectives in a successful way. If you recognize something with potential and you can realize that potential, I think that's how you should be judged as being successful by your peers. And by doing a good job along the way."

And as if Barker didn't have enough to keep him busy, he tries to spend at least a few days a week with his wife on their farm just north of Cobourg, Ontario. He has a small herd of beef cattle, a couple of horses, and cash crops with corn, soy beans, oats, barley, "whatever happens to be saleable." He contracts the crops, but not surprisingly bales his own hay.

In an amusing twist of fate, one of Barker's mares is currently being bred with a horse belonging to a very familiar name in mining circles.

"She's been bred to one of Chuck Fipke's stallions," chuckles Barker, referring to Fipke from his past Diamet days. His name is 'Not Impossible', a good frame of reference for people in the exploration business.

"It's kind of ironic. I've known Chuck since the early-1980s before the diamond game became his primary focus."

When asked if this is yet another promising joint venture, Barker laughs.

"Yeah, my old nag and his hot stallion."

It's not surprising that paths will cross in ironic ways, given Barker's years in the industry. Even Tindale Drilling, a small independent Canadian contractor Barker has worked with all over the world since the early-1980s, has a close connection.

"Two of the drillers that are going to China are my godsons. They're ex-rodeo cowboys from Western Ontario," he says with a laugh. "They've both been drilling for a number of years for an independent drill contractor, Mark Tindale. I don't like to invoke nepotism in corporate structure, but I don't think this really is. These guys are good solid drillers and if they don't work out, they get fired, the same as anyone else. They're very hard workers and I'm sure they'll do well."

When all is said and done, it's easy to see why Barker thrives on challenge and respects the boundaries of risk. To be otherwise, he couldn't raise cattle and crops, fly his own plane, and run a company like Sparton. Although he wasn't involved when Sparton was named, he has his own ideas about what it stands for.

"I don't know who named the original Sparton Mining and Development Corporation. They probably named it Sparton because they wanted to adopt the philosophy of the Spartans from ancient Greek society," notes Barker.

"They were efficient, creative and tough, they didn't waste money, and they were productive and entrepreneurial. We try to maintain that kind of philosophy here, too."

At the time of publishing, it looks as if Barker's Luxi gold project in China may well be on the way to proving itself up to his expectations. The first two drill-holes reported values of 2.85 grams of gold over 33.4 metres, and 2.58 grams of gold over 59 metres, with even more good results hopefully to come.

STEALTH MINERALS LIMITED

The original logo for Stealth Minerals was a simple design featuring three solid black pyramids sitting beside each other on a thin horizontal black band. According to chairman and chief financial officer Bradley Jones, it represented a Stealth bomber from a head-on perspective, a starkly impressive image. Jones liked the symbolism which, to his mind, represented strength and gave an impression the company was strong.

"I rather liked it. I even have a picture in my office of a Stealth bomber to remind me of the potential power of one of those things," he said.

Sadly for Jones, not everyone shared his enthusiasm.

"It was brought to my attention that it was politically incorrect, that the Stealth bomber invoked fear factors and therefore should be dispensed with," he said, obviously reluctant to relinquish the powerful image.

Luckily for Jones, Stealth's CEO Bill McWilliam stepped in to save the day and the logo. All it needed was a twist, literally. The bomber was flipped, shaded in grey and pasted in underneath the original logo as a shadow image. Now the logo appears as a mountain range reflected in water, a perfect symbol to represent Stealth's massive mineralized property in British Columbia.

"Bill took the concept of the Stealth bomber and turned it into a mountainscape," says Jones with admiration, adding, "But look, if you put a piece of paper over the grey ... !"

And the Stealth bomber sneakily reappears, much to Jones's delight.

It's fitting to mention this anecdote because it aptly reflects the mutual respect these two gentlemen have for each other's abilities and ideas, and the teamwork that is at the core of Stealth's successes. Although Jones works out of a Toronto office handling financial concerns and McWilliam is on the other side of the country managing B.C. operations, their energies are focussed in exactly the same place – north central B.C. wherein lies Stealth's 970-square-kilometre Toodoggone Project and the significant discoveries and riches it may host. According to McWilliam, it's the largest land holding of its kind in B.C., perhaps the largest in Canada, excluding the diamond properties in the Northwest Territories and Nunavit.

"What's important about this land position is that we essentially control a mineral district, a volcanic arc that is densely mineralized," points out McWilliam. "It's a position a junior company never gets to – never. And we've succeeded in doing that."

Much of their success is due to highly-respected talent, without which Stealth's dream would likely not have come this far. Jones emphasizes the importance of having both financial and geological expertise, and the ability to differentiate between the two.

"If you're lucky enough to find a person such as Bill McWilliam who has an extensive background in the financial side of mining and also has an incredibly deep geological base, this is the key type of person any junior mining company must have to succeed," Jones affirms.

"That's not to underestimate or devalue the worth of a financial person, which obviously is essential. But you need that combination of knowledge and skills otherwise one will dominate the other and if the geological side dominates, disaster is often the result."

McWilliam nods his head.

"I totally agree with that," he says, adding, "Not just because I'm sitting here, but because I've experienced it so many times."

With his extensive background in corporate finance and having worked for years as a mining analyst in the brokerage business, McWilliam knows what he's talking about.

"I've seen the pattern recur and often there was never a realistic or reasonable balance between the money and the geology. Brad and I made a real effort to get them as separate things because they're quite different businesses," he said.

"Management has to recognize that and know how to relate to both sides. Then you've got a chance to build a decent company. It's very important."

For his part, McWilliam fell in love with stocks and the market in university when he started up an investment fund and promptly lost a borrowed twenty-five thousand dollars. This made him even more determined and intrigued. Through a broker, McWilliam was introduced to George Tapp, who ran the Vancouver branch of a Toronto company called Doherty Roadhouse & McQuaig, one of the original mining houses in Canada, later becoming Midland Doherty. Expanding its operations across Canada at the time, McWilliam was hired on as a research assistant and his path in mining had begun.

"I finally ended up running that part of the business in Vancouver and got more and more interested in the rocks side of the business and travelling with geologists and learning the business from the field back to the academics, rather than the other way around."

After leaving Midland, a stint at Odlum Brown in Vancouver doing oil and gas research followed, after which McWilliam ended up at Dominion Securities. His next step was starting the research department at Canarim, now Canaccord, working for Peter Brown. Before leaving Canaccord, McWilliam hired his successor Graeme Currie, now a highly-respected and sought-after professional.

All this experience has certainly stood McWilliam in good stead as he brings both his financial and geological expertise to bear at Stealth, managing a highly-skilled team of geologists.

"The varied experiences crystallized the view of what the right business model should be. I was practicing it every day. In 1984, I think Canarim did over 200 underwritings, and I knew a bit about all of them," he said.

"Bill saw virtually every mining property deal in Canada, in B.C. certainly, for a number of years," says Jones. "That was what formulated a lot of the background technical knowledge that has been applied to what we have there. It's helping us now make the correct decision about where to spend this money that we have raised."

And money is Jones's forte. Born and educated in Quebec, he received his degrees from Bishop's University and McGill University. A chartered accountant, Jones is also a LMD (Limited Market Dealer), registered with the Ontario Securities Commission. After spending 14 years as a senior partner in KPMG (formerly Peat Marwick), and later at Coopers & Lybrand in the corporate finance arena, Jones decided to embark on what he dubs 'an entrepreneurial career'. This choice got Jones involved with investment banking groups in Toronto, taking him into the hi-tech industry as a director for Softquad International, and other various corporate finance endeavours that saw him also spending some time in the bottled water industry for Nestle's.

"Subsequent to that, I became involved almost by chance with an associate in B.C. to start Stealth Minerals Limited, formerly known as Stealth Mining. It was basically a shell company used to go public," Jones explains.

And that's how the story begins. From Stealth's inception in 1996, to McWilliam coming on board in 2001, it's been a long journey to get to this point in 2004, but it's been worth it. If the enthusiasm generated by McWilliam and Jones is any indication, the fun is just beginning.

"Now we're on the verge of something enormous," said Jones.

Stealth's official history began in 1996 when the initial funding took place, followed in March 1997 with an IPO done by Global Securities in Calgary to raise $750,000 and bring the company public.

Stealth's initial joint venture agreement, signed in October 1996, was with Electrum Resource Corp., a private British Columbia entity.

"The ERC joint venture was the principal asset of the company, which consisted of 491 land claim units in north central B.C. And that's how we started off," Jones said.

Since McWilliam joined the group, the property has been built up from those 491 land claim units to 3,718 and Jones credits his partner with being the catalyst behind this growth. In fact, before McWilliam brought his business expertise to bear on the situation, Jones said Stealth's team was looking pretty grim from a geological perspective.

"You have to picture the situation ... the initial financing group being made up entirely of chartered accountants, basically partners or former partners of the major firms in Toronto, and a couple of lawyers for good luck. Their knowledge base, geologically-speaking, was quite marginal to say the least."

That said, Jones gives the group credit for recognizing that acquiring a land position in northern B.C. close to the newly commissioned Royal Oak mine operation, the Kemess mine now run by Northgate Minerals Ltd., would be a good concept in a hot junior mining market.

"Little did they realize that the hot junior mining market was about to get very cold very fast. So the decision at that point in the company's history was, after you've completed the initial financing, what do you do? Do you pack up and go home or do you basically hang in there?"

Fortunately, they hung in there but even today Jones scratches his head when he thinks about what it took.

"That's where you have persistence and you have stubbornness and stupidity and luck, all involved at the same time – because between that time and before Bill came in as CEO, we raised millions of dollars through these private individuals to continue the company and maintain its land claim base without really having a clue what we were doing.

"Basically we just thought the showings looked good and the property had potential and we were damned if we were going to walk away from this thing."

Jones laughs at what some may describe as dumb luck, but meeting McWilliam in 2001 would turn out to be an equally serendipitous occasion.

"I had a meeting with someone else, not Bill. But Bill happened to overhear parts of our conversation, and he quietly said to himself: 'These guys really have something, in spite of themselves.'

"So he basically overheard us, thought about it, went in and did some research on his computer, and came back and said: 'That's quite an impressive land package you've accumulated. How did you do it and what's the plan?'"

It was a happy irony, but Jones acknowledges that those depressed years were actually a contributing factor to their acquisition of the land package due in part to a lack of competition.

"The few junior mining companies that were stubborn enough not to walk away from B.C. were able to build quality land positions with virtually no competition. As they were building those land positions, they put themselves in the position either to fail even more miserably than they thought they would, or to be very successful. Nobody could predict when public money would be available again."

McWilliam concedes he was rather astonished when he overheard the fateful conversation that would steer him into the Stealth family. "There's a lot of work you have to do to make sure a company controls or acquires a property of merit. That work had already been done. And there were many prospects with gold and silver values on open ground in the area of the current claims, and I was shaking my head and thinking: 'You have no idea the position you're in here.'

"The first thing I saw, after deciding I liked Brad and that he was a good guy, was the opportunity to execute a plan that fulfilled a junior's dream. I saw that immediately.

"So we put a plan together, decided to raise the money at whatever price was available, and executed that plan."

But before McWilliam began planning anything, he illustrated his confidence in Jones and Stealth by offering a sizeable financial show of good faith. Jones was impressed.

"In this day and age of paper and regulatory handcuffs, Bill's first move was to contact me and ask if he could send me $100,000. To which I said, 'This would be good'," Jones says with a grin.

"And Bill sent me $100,000 with no paper, simply my word that I would translate it into stock. That was good enough for him. That's how the relationship started. It was a risk on his part, obviously, but it was a show of incredible faith and a judgment call that he made. In this business you have to move quickly at times, and that's where trust and relationships are so important."

McWilliam not only trusted Jones, he was thoroughly impressed with the Toodoggone's densely-mineralized volcanic arc geology.

"They're rare, they're limited, and very few of them exist in B.C., especially with so many mineral occurrences."

Added to that was the unfavourable political climate at the time, characterized by McWilliam as overly restrictive and overly regulated.

"A lot of mining companies left B.C. and let their claims lapse in this particular area, and elsewhere. So when I got involved and did the initial research, a lot of these claims with gold showings in outcrop were on open ground, available for the cost of staking.

"I know what it costs a junior company to find a gold showing on surface – it would be in the neighbourhood of $100,000 or $200,000 for one showing. And there were many, many showings available just for staking costs, which are typically two percent to five percent of the cost of actually having to option a property, issue shares, pay the cash, do the investigation, and get the report. It's a lot of work."

But by the time McWilliam came on board in early 2001, Stealth and its group of finance people had already done some of that work and it was full steam ahead.

It sounds simple enough, but Jones is all too aware of the sacrifices and persistence needed not only to get a project or company off the ground, but make it fly. He has nothing but respect for the people involved in Stealth's story, as well as any other company in the junior mining community.

Jones elaborates, "The key issue for any junior mining company is persistence and relationships. Anybody who thinks that all you have to do is stake some property, basically stick a few holes in it, and you're going to be wealthy, is very, very mistaken. It always requires an enormous amount of time, an enormous amount of money and sacrifice.

"Relationships are strained, friends are lost, money is very tough to raise, and people are put into very difficult situations. If you put the overwhelming burden of the regulatory environment on top of that, it's a very difficult thing to accomplish. Anyone who is successful doing that, is extremely deserving because they have probably sacrificed a lot in their lives, both personally and financially to get to that point."

McWilliam agrees with that assessment, and recognizes that although Stealth now has an asset that puts them in the position to get valued properly by the investment community and start soliciting third-party money, it took six or seven years of commitment to get to that point.

"The mine discovery myth that exists in the public is the lottery idea ... you find a gold-showing one day, you put a drill-hole in it the next day, and then you sell it for a billion dollars the day after that. You become overnight millionaires, right?

"The truth is, this business is no different than any other good business. It takes really good people, it takes money, it takes persistence, a good focus and a good plan."

The only difference, according to McWilliam, is a lack of revenue. The currency at this point in time is equity and the company has to sell shares to finance its operating and exploration capital.

"We're focussed on keeping the whole ship going, on one thing, which in our case is drilling the discovery hole. That's really what we're trying to do – drill the hole that may lead to the development of a mine. It takes years not weeks to do this.

"We're focussed on the fact that we have to continue to sell our equity to what has been a very strong and solid group of core investors who have supported this company through a diffficult period. That is astonishing to us."

And that's something both McWilliam and Jones can't say enough about – the loyalty of those people who stuck by Stealth through the dark days.

"People can get impatient, so when you have a group of individuals who stick together through thick and thin and put up 10 million dollars over time, there's a lot of faith in the people that they're working with," says Jones.

"It's not to be taken lightly."

Obviously the loyal investors have faith in Jones and McWilliam, and Jones and McWilliam have put their faith in the Toodoggone River district. The persistence and hard work has paid off and they now find themselves in a position to become a property generator and introduce a revenue concept like any other business.

"Now we can option a property to a Placer Dome or a Barrick or XYZ junior company, they pay us cash to earn an interest in our properties. We can do the work on these properties and get a fee for that. Most junior companies never get to this position," notes McWilliam.

Stealth's attraction for the majors is its dominant land position and control of a mineral district. Several of their prospects appear to have the magic – the discovery hole potential. "That's what major companies strive to do – get control of a major mineral district. Then they can take their time, their diligence, map it properly, understand the setting and focus on exploration in a systematic way over several years.

"We're in a position now, where we control a very large land position in a densely mineralized area, and we have the money now to take our time and execute the plan properly. That's the first thing," says McWilliam.

"But the business model we are really pursuing here, is we're now in the position to generate prospects for joint ventures to other people, including majors. We have several major companies interested in what we're doing here and the nature of the mineralization and the size of the structures that we have identified on a preliminary basis are all very promising. It's a huge achievement."

Another bonus about the Toodoggone location is its close proximity to Kemess, Canada's second largest mine run by Northgate Minerals Ltd., a mid-tier public company. Jones gives a lot of credit to Northgate for developing a complete infrastructure that enables the Stealth personnel to access their property easily.

"While we were out staking and claiming all this land, in a very dire metals market, the infrastructure was being financed by Royal Oak. We have a lot to be thankful for in that area," Jones said.

"Kemess is a huge operation, very complex, highly efficient – one of the best mines in the world. It's an incredible operation and it's right beside our property."

McWilliam adds: "If that infrastructure wasn't there, we wouldn't have done this. Period."

Before the infrastructure was put in place, it was expensive and time consuming to get in and out of the property. Helicopters were used, and according to Jones, they'd "fly in, collect a few samples and get the hell out."

Back in 1999, three years after optioning its land position from Electrum, Stealth's exploration geologist Dave Blann staked two claims about 10 kilometres north of the existing properties. Thanks to a geo-chemical survey done by the B.C. Government that identified an interesting RGS silt sample, Blann staked claims JC-1 and 2, where he believed the extrapolated source of that gold anomaly existed. But due to the expense and logistics of accessing the remote harsh terrain, not much was done for another couple of years.

"That was an infrastructure issue in this remote area," McWilliam notes. "Everything was helicopter supported, it's pretty rugged country, and it's expensive and Stealth was under-capitalized. This area was under-explored and was actually considered as the B.C. Frontier."

Due to the lack of infrastructure, the grade had to be 10 grams of gold equivalent or higher to make anything worthwhile returning for. Back in the 1980s, McWilliam points out that a lot of samples did assay between one to four grams of gold, and consequently were never followed up.

"So all those showings existed in the historical assessment reports, which was a benefit to us in 2002," he says.

Two year after Blann's 1999 staking, he was back at it, scouting around the area, prospecting on the slope of Griz Bowl when he found a rock that McWilliam describes as 'quite interesting'.

"It ran eight grams of gold and 2,200 grams of silver which is ore grade material anywhere in the world, doesn't matter where ... infrastructure or not, if you can find it in volume."

But again, despite the interesting rock and very high values, another two years would pass before it was followed up.

"Partly because of lack of money, partly because there was limited infrastructure in that part of the country, and just inertia, it wasn't that important. But Stealth kept the claims in good standing," McWilliam said.

This is where McWilliam enters the picture. One of the first things he did when he joined forces with Stealth was meet Dave Blann and take a look at his rock. Having spent some time in the Toodoggone back in the 1980s during the area's main exploration phase, McWilliam was familiar with the territory and geology.

"I looked at the rock and I had seen nothing like that, this was something totally different. I said, 'Are you sure it's from there?' And he said, 'Yeah.'

"That was the next important thing for me. Aside from the fact that the ground position was basically open and having many, many showings ... that rock was in a place somewhere in a vein and if we could find it, it would be a major achievement," said McWilliam. "That rock really got me excited."

On August 20, 2003, a date forever etched in the minds of Jones and McWilliam, Stealth prospectors found that mineralization in place.

"Ron Bilquist came into camp and tabled some prospecting samples. I looked at them and realized this was the same style of mineralization as the rock Blann had found. I left the next morning to get a rush fire assay on it.

"It ran 8 grams of gold and 2,040 grams of silver. Subsequent to that discovery, by prospecting, we've extended that zone for 6,000 metres on surface. In world terms, it could be a major discovery," said McWilliam.

"No drill holes, but it's got all the signs of being real big and real important ... Eskay Creek grades, only more strike length."

Eskay Creek, one of the major gold and silver discoveries in B.C. and Canada, saw its stock go as high as $67, according to Jones.

"I'll emphasize that I'm not a geologist, but as an accountant I'll tell you those grades produced that kind of result – the same grades as we're seeing in the preliminary sampling of our property.

"That's the exciting thing about it. I can tell you that when you look at Eskay Creek and you look at what we've got, there are some similarities – high silver concentrations – and Eskay may be known as a gold mine but also it's a huge silver deposit."

"Third largest silver producer in the world," points out McWilliam.

In fact, Stealth has the benefit of experience in its highly respected chief geologist Dave Kuran who used to work on Eskay. Last year, Kuran shared in winning the Edgar Schultz medal, a distinguished prospecting geological award in B.C. McWilliam and Jones are chief amongst Kuran's admirers, and Jones recognizes the necessity of having good geological talent on board.

"One of the key things in any junior mining company is the quality of its geologists and what I call the management of the geological ego, which is what Bill's principal responsibility is," says Jones, sliding a glance at McWilliam who nods his agreement.

"Geologists have egos just as large as lawyers, or doctors, dentists, accountants, in fact even more so. Their main goal in life is to drill and they really want to develop a property. We are blessed with people like David Kuran who was one of the developers of the Eskay Creek mine, and is now our head guy."

Also getting a nod from McWilliam are two PhD geologists, Dr. Kenneth Dawson and Dr. Tom Richards, both valued components of the Stealth team.

"These are highly-respected people in the Canadian and South American geological communities who are working as a team under Bill's direction. We've had incredible results from this association," Jones said.

All that talent, managed by McWilliam, has nicely coalesced into a team that works well together for a common goal, egos aside.

"It's not an easy thing to do. It's like putting five superstars on one hockey team," says Jones.

"So, having said that, we have built a geological team based on fairness. We've compensated these people with stock options and gone out of our way to give them an environment they want to work in. We have made some tough decisions with people who have not been willing to play as a team. And again, the key is having a financial geologist type person around, which is Bill."

After the discovery, Stealth got busy. Within the volcanic arc, that runs 110 kilometres in length and 30 to 40 kilometres in width, Stealth now controls the main piece of land. With a property running 82 kilometres north-south, and roughly 20 kilometres across, they've nailed down 80 percent of the most prospective geology and currently own 100 percent of all their properties.

"We staked these properties after that discovery. I just put my pen on the paper and said to Dave, 'Let's look at this corridor up here.' It's never been systematically prospected, the silt geochemistry which showed gold, silver, and copper hasn't been looked at since 1985, nobody's been there, it's all open ground," said McWilliam.

"It was a no-brainer. We staked the most prospective ground."

In October 2003, the Stealth team was up there in the snow, keeping it quiet until they had finalized its land position. You might say they went in under the radar, much like a Stealth bomber would. The main camp is in place, and this summer they have 36 people there and seven prospectors working in fly camps on the northern claims.

And again, thanks to the proximity of Northgate's open-pit Kemess mine, its infrastructure and accessibility, the threshold for discovery has dropped significantly.

"It lowered the bar for exploration in the area and that's another thing the street didn't realize," McWilliam pointed out. "I told them we had this great property in the Toodoggone and they said, 'Oh, it's too far away, there's no access, and the deposits are small.' That's why they didn't stake it."

For its part, Northgate didn't scoop the property surrounding the Kemess mine because they were under the control of Brascan at the time and dealing with an extremely tight budget, according to McWilliam. Northgate's inability to execute was Stealth's gain.

"We're in an incredible position," Jones says. "Basically it's very simple, because of the infrastructure which was partly financed by the taxpayers of B.C., we now have the ability to create an economic resource at a grade much lower than originally required. The interesting thing for Stealth is that we are sitting right beside Northgate Minerals, a profitable and highly-efficient operation with lower-grade ore. We have the potential for significantly higher-grade ore and the math is easy to do."

Currently the math shows Stealth sitting with a $5 million treasury, no debt and no liabilities. Their stock is way undervalued, according to Jones, as they head into the next exploration program in good financial shape with exciting prospects. And although the potential for gold is the big news, Stealth's shareholders recently approved transfer of some of the company's major porphyry properties in the southern part of their holdings to a new company called Cascadero Copper Corporation. A new public company, Cascadero will be a Stealth subsidiary, with Stealth owning 70 percent. Jones acknowledges it's the best solution for their shareholders.

"There's no equity dilution for our shareholders, only property dilution. We're moving some of the properties into another vehicle and if they are successful, our shareholders will obviously benefit because it is a subsidiary of Stealth Minerals," he explains.

"We feel quite strongly that the possible grade levels of gold and copper in those properties will exceed the threshold grade and that makes us a very attractive candidate for Northgate Minerals."

And the northern properties, wherein lies the Aug. 20 discovery, certainly have the potential to excite the majors.

"We are counting on a Barrick or a Placer Dome, who are constantly searching for those five million ounces each year, coming to us. They're well aware of what we're doing and they're going to see, based on our efforts, that a large-scale mineral system exists, which will merit their attention. If that's the case, they'll be extremely aggressive. We need a discovery hole to trigger their interest."

All of which takes Stealth nicely into its plan to become a property generator and receive revenue from its total B.C. holdings of 970 square kilometres.

"Our property is so vast it offers many possible economic opportunities. We have no intention of developing a mine of our own, but we can take the prospects to a certain point where they make attractive joint ventures, or to a more advanced level where they may be acquired," says McWilliam.

These countless possibilities give Stealth a lot of 'kicks at the can', and as such, they're not going anywhere. "It's so big, and it's such a huge mineralized system that many people have difficulty even conceptualizing it ... they just say, 'Oh, bullshit.' But that's what time will prove. We're around for the long haul, or until Barrick says we would like to buy you at multiple dollars a share. Then we'll go on to another project," says McWilliam.

Even the B.C. government had difficulty fully believing Stealth's Sickle Creek discovery, and McWilliam shares an amusing story that illustrates nothing is impossible when you've got the right people who are willing to step outside the box and not accept common wisdom. Two weeks after Stealth's Sickle Griz discovery, McWilliam phoned Tom

Schroeter, manager of the Ministry of Mines and Energy in Vancouver, to tell him about the news. Knowing Schroeter was a big fan of the Toodoggone District, McWilliam couldn't wait to share the details of Stealth's new discovery with someone who would appreciate it.

"I said, 'Tom, this is a brand new discovery.' He basically said, 'You're full of baloney. This is impossible. There's no way...the entire Toodoggone has been prospected and you're not going to find something that somebody hasn't found before.'"

Jones quickly interjects with: "Tom's a great guy."

"And a great believer in the Toodoggone," adds McWilliam earnestly.

Now that we've been assured Schroeter's disbelief wasn't unexpected, McWilliam continues his story. He duly emailed Tom the GPS coordinates of the discovery and then went down to his office to study the original 1982 and 1985 staking maps of the district.

"This map was 15 feet long, a huge map all taped together. And we're looking for it, and he gets the GPS and its different coordinates, and we're still looking...," says McWilliam, a grin creeping in, the punchline imminent.

"He looks and then he goes, 'Holy mackerel!'"

As fate would have it, the GPS coordinates placed the Sickle Griz discovery directly underneath the map's legend, sitting on the top right-hand corner.

"There were no claims there, or the legend wouldn't be there!" said McWilliam, re-living the moment.

"So Tom says, 'Well okay. It's never been staked, it's a brand new discovery, and it's got some size.'"

Jones breaks in: "Isn't that amazing? You couldn't even see it!"

This revelation ensured the support of Tom Schroeter, Larry Diakow and other B.C. Ministry of Mines people who, according to McWilliam, are just as driven and excited as the mining companies when it comes to new and major discoveries.

"They've been so supportive, so positive, and so helpful to us in our efforts," notes McWilliam. "Contrary to common beliefs, our public-private partnerships with UBC, GSC and the B.C. Ministry have been excellent and very productive."

The Sickle Creek discovery was subsequently bestowed with a MIN file number by the B.C. government, a designation that recognizes it as a mineral discovery.

"Sickle Creek was given the MIN # 239. It's the first one issued in 15 years. So the government has recognized it's something that's never been staked before and no work has been done," explains McWilliam.

"That alone is a major achievement."

Another achievement, and one that thrills both McWilliam and Jones, is how another fateful rock was found in outcrop. Jones especially, being a self-confessed 'non-geologist', finds it fascinating.

"The gold discovery at Sickle Creek is hosted in a volcanic unit and the quartz-carbonate vein system that contains the high-grade massive sulphide veins has a very subtle alteration signature. You can't really see where the vein starts and where the hangin or footwall rocks begin. You can fly over it, walk right up to it, but if you don't bang on it, it keeps its secrets. Newly exposed mineralization can be massive and anybody that knows anything would likely have assayed it, if found. The Sickle Creek discovery triggered a focussed prospecting and sampling effort by Stealth for the next 20 days until the snow came to the high-alpine. We covered the immediate area, some 3 to 4 kilometres to the north and to the south. This produced another fateful rock that did not look all that interesting at first glance as it was an unusual mixture of quartz and calcite.

"This was from an outcrop about 1.9 kilometres north of the Sickle Creek discovery. It consisted of quartz-carbonate alteration and had very fine wispy, bluish-grey speckles in it that lacked clear epithermal textures. In fact the texture looked mostly like single phase bull quartz, which usually doesn't produce any joy. This was a new style of mineralization to me for sure. We looked at it and kind of shrugged the collective shoulder and decided to put some in a bag and get it assayed.

"I returned to Vancouver with several other samples but the rock that looked like nothing stole the show as it assayed 18 grams-per-tonne gold and 865 grams-per-tonne silver. Once again we were on to something new. It was a very exciting addition to an already exciting prospect."

McWillam gives credit to Tom Richards for preaching that things are not always what they seem and that there are fewer liars in the assay lab than anywhere else. "It's an amazing business," McWilliam continues. "Tom is still a young man but he has experience and knowledge well beyond his years. This is due to his diverse training and his exposure to many geological environments. He is a geologist at heart but a prospector in soul, which I believe is a perfect combination. He also says it is impossible to be both at the same time because geologists are sort of tied to academic models and prospectors are keen on finding something different.

"But the really neat thing we are trying to do with Stealth is to provide the geologist and prospector with as much time as possible in the field banging on rocks, the old fashioned way. This is the fundamental separation between geology and business that we are adopting as a major component of our business plan. Some people look at rocks full time and some people raise the money and provide the administration and support. We try not to get these activities confused because we know that the more time we spend in the field walking and banging, the more successful we will be."

The Sickle Creek discovery was also given due recognition earlier this year at the B.C. Prospectors convention. "It was highlighted as one of the two major discoveries in B.C. last year because of the showings of gold and silver and other base metals, and its Eskay Creek potential," says Jones.

If all that weren't enough, the Stealth team has a large-scale prospecting and claim staking initiative underway in Argentina. McWilliam explains, "Brad and I along with some long-time associates financed some ideas about Argentine geology advanced by Tom Richards and his team of Ron Bilquist and Les Allen. Tom's group is a team within a team. Ron is an outstanding prospector as he is 50 percent eagle, 50 percent goat and 50 percent gazelle. Les is capable of getting the teams in and out with no problems. We formed Watch Lake Resources as the corporate vehicle.

"We partnered with some Argentine geologists, lawyers and other executives to form Salta Explora Ciones S.A., a wholly owned subsidiary of Watch Lake Resources Ltd. We staked several prospects, grew the business and added Brian Fagan, an old friend, as a partner. Brian quickly saw the opportunity and moved to Salta to manage the business. It was a great day for us when Brian agreed to get involved as he is one of the most conscientious and meticulous people I know, as well as being a good prospector."

With the massive Toodoggone district to investigate and navigate, the start-up of its Cascadero Copper subsidiary and the Argentinian project looming in the background, the Stealth team has its hands full. To help ease the burden and get more accomplished, McWilliam decided to try something new, an idea inspired by Richards. He posted an ad in universities, seeking interested geological students to help work in the field. After interviewing 40 applicants, he hired 20 students, from second-year to newly-graduated geology students.

"We've got the kids up there in the bush right now, a mix of guys and girls. They're working with the old guys who have been all over the world on mineral properties. All this very valuable information that Ken and Dave and Tom and all their buddies have, you can't teach it and there's no one to pass it on to. There's a real generation gap," McWilliam said.

"So they thought, 'Well, we've got a huge property, here's an opportunity to hire some students, give them a shot at not acquiring the burden of a student loan, give them some practical experience ... and get an energetic, devoted, intelligent workforce instead of hiring a bunch of bums out of the bars, right? It looks like it's going to be a huge success."

Success can be defined in many ways and both McWilliam and Jones have their own ideas about it. On a purely personal level, it's the excitement of discovery that drives McWilliam.

"When I got the assays back from Sickle Creek, I nearly fell off my chair. The rock they handed me in the exploration camp was the same one that Dave Blann showed me two years before that. It was an incredible rush. I came running out of my office, yelling ... 'We found it!'"

From a business perspective, McWilliam is driven by a sense of morality whereby he wants to ensure the opportunity matches the risk.

"When I'm managing this project, I know the money is putting our shareholders in a position of maximum leverage. We're in that position with Stealth and also in Argentina right now, where the money that's gone into these projects has created the opportunity for enormous discovery leverage.

"Mother Nature is capricious, it's extremely risky ... but that level of satisfaction and morality is fundamental to my existence and I couldn't do it any other way."

Jones loves being part of a team and watching the evolution of a project into a successful accomplishment, with everything it entails.

"It would be a wonderful thing to say that we were involved in the discovery of a mine. To say there's a mine in northern B.C. that Bill McWilliam and Bradley Jones had something to do with discovering. To say that I was part of that, and it's going to be there for awhile, I think that would be magnificent," enthuses Jones.

The thing that drives McWilliam and Jones to these goals is their belief that it's not only possible, it's probable. Not only do they visualize one mine, they see the potential for several in the Toodoggone district possibly surpassing the output of metal from Highland Valley.

"And also, we have honoured our obligation to those people who have invested their savings in the company," Jones says.

"We intend to create wealth for them."

TUMI RESOURCES LIMITED

Stories about mining companies typically end – or at least run out of steam – when they reach the part about a major stock market setback. For obvious reasons, plunging share prices, panicking promoters and stampeding investors have long been viewed as harbingers of doom in the resource sector, heralding the beginning of the end for companies reliant on outside financing. The story of Tumi Resources Limited, on the other hand, begins with a stock market crash. Though this comes as a bit of a surprise, it actually makes a great deal of sense, particularly given the nature of the company's president, director and chief executive officer David A. Henstridge, a man who has spent a lifetime conducting business successfully, if perhaps a bit differently.

A Melbourne, Australia-based geologist whose Vancouver, Canada-based junior exploration company operates exclusively in Mexico, the time-zone traversing Henstridge is disarmingly candid as he reclines in a high-back swivel chair during one of his frequent visits to the company's Vancouver office, casually recounting the circumstances that led to the formation of Tumi Resources.

"The starting point for us was the 1987 stock market crash," he says matter-of-factly, with an unmistakable pinch of irony. "The crash of '87 brought about the demise of the junior exploration industry in Australia for quite some time – in fact, it almost brought about the end of it. From that point on, up until the early-1990s, it was very difficult to get consulting work, find jobs, or do anything in the resource sector, let alone try and raise money in the industry. It was a really lousy time in terms of job prospects.

"I was given the opportunity to come to Vancouver near the end of 1992," he continues. "Vancouver was considered to be the heartland for raising capital in the junior exploration industry and was known world-wide as the place to be if you wanted to take a crack at running your own company in the gold and silver business. I got the opportunity to come to Vancouver through an Australian company called Xenolith Gold, which was run by Graeme Robinson and had a Vancouver subsidiary called Kookaburra Resources Ltd. That got me into Canada and gave me a starting point. Canada gave myself and my family an opportunity that we very much appreciated, and we lived here for about nine years, until the end of 2001."

Kookaburra Resources Ltd. ("Now there's an Australian name, for you," Henstridge quips) was involved primarily in copper exploration in South America, a pursuit Henstridge considered mostly a stop-gap measure between bigger and better ventures. "My colleague and I had this idea that we should get into gold exploration," he says, "so we purchased a listed vehicle with the principals of Xenolith Gold and Kookaburra Resources Ltd. and renamed it Peruvian Gold. That was the starting point for me being involved in the junior exploration industry in this part of the world."

The company operated successfully on mineral exploration in Peru from 1993 until it was taken over in 2001, "by people who were interested in its large cash treasury," says Henstridge. "As an aside, this takeover was made easy because of a lack of share control by the prinicipals. I made sure that the current director and friends of Tumi control a significant percentage of the share capital of the company so that a takeover cannot be undertaken so easily. It is ironic that the principal of the takeover company for Peruvian, Robert Atkinson, has subsequently become a friend and big supporter of Tumi's activities. In 2000, we were approaching the bottom of the exploration cycle started by the collapse of Bre-X in 1997 and saw the advent of the dot.com boom. Even though things were very slow, I and my fellow director Nick DeMare – who is an accountant here in Vancouver – decided that we would set up a capital pool company and see if we could find a new business venture in the dot.com sector to vend into this listed vehicle. And that's exactly what we proceeded to do."

Unfortunately, in the time it took to get this particular company up and running – raising approximately $300,000 – "the dot.com industry was already dead," says Henstridge, "So we were basically left with nothing. Though of course we didn't realize it at the time, almost none of the dot.com companies that were operating with the idea of selling things over the Internet, or associated with Internet activities, had any kind of a business plan, let alone the muscle to make a serious listing for a public vehicle in Canada. It just never really happened."

As a result, Henstridge and his colleagues put the company on the backburner until 2002, "when we recognized the early signs that precious metals were really coming back and that the world was really noticing," he says. "Subsequent to that, we've seen that the precious metals market has come back, with both gold and silver prices increasing dramatically since that time.

"We were lucky," Henstridge continues. "Thanks to the respective backgrounds of myself and my fellow directors, Nick DeMare and Harvey Lim, we were able to change this particular capital pool company into a vehicle for the mineral resource exploration industry. We successfully managed to turn it into an exploration company, and we were one of the first to do so. But it was certainly a novel way of doing this in those days – to turn a non-profitable capital pool company into a successful venture resource company."

Renamed Tumi Resources Limited, the company was eventually listed on the Toronto Venture and Frankfurt Exchanges, as well as the OTC Bulletin Board (TSXv: TM.V; Frankfurt: TUY; OTCBB: TUMIF). A qualifying transaction was required, however, to make the leap from dot.bomb loser to resource industry contender. "We had to enter into a joint venture partnership," Henstridge explains, "which we did with BHP Billiton on a large land area in northern Peru that abutted Manhattan Minerals Corp., who had discovered the large base metal deposit known as Tambo Grande. BHP Billiton had leases around the Manhattan property, and they had located several geological anomalies during the course of airborne gravity surveys. At that point, we decided we would drill the property on behalf of BHP Billiton."

It was a risky proposition, Henstridge concedes, though the romance and mystique – as well as the potential financial rewards – of following in the footsteps of the ancient Incas cancelled out any concerns. "I think the public is generally aware of the problems of working in northern Peru," says Henstridge. "The locals around Tambo Grande are quite vocally against any mining taking place in the region. Nonetheless, we had our drill rig organized and were essentially checking out the area to see if we could begin drilling. That's when the locals told us in their own singular way that our lives would be in serious jeopardy if this program started. As a result, our main area of interest was rendered unexplorable and we were essentially finished overnight. We subsequently withdrew from that project without ever having the opportunity of drilling our selected targets."

Tumi, however, soldiered on, convinced that gold and silver were going to be profitable commodities in the foreseeable future. "It was very easy for me to make the decision that I wanted to get into the silver industry," says Henstridge. "It was the one resource that really interested me. It was also clear that silver demand continues to exceed production – as it has for many years – and this bodes well for a commodity that is used and not stored like gold. Silver demand will continue due to its unique properties and applications. For example, of all metals, silver is the best electrical conductor and is used in circuit breakers, switches and fuses, and is found in all common domestic appliances, such as dishwashers, televisions, microwave ovens and computers. Besides its known common usage in jewelry, photography, batteries and coins, silver is less well-known as one of the world's most powerful bacteria killers. In fact, early pioneers used silver coins to keep water barrels free of algae. Silver sulfadiazine is used to kill bacteria for burn victims and also in some types of hospital catheters. It is clear that with existing uses for silver and new applications, including water purification, band aids and reflector properties in window glass, we will see continued growth in the silver demand.

"I thought that with silver trading at around $4-plus an ounce," Henstridge reasons, "it was pretty cheap. I expected there would be quite a dramatic price increase as time went on." He was ultimately proven correct, as the price of silver rebounded to well over $6 an ounce. "We've watched the price of silver increase more than 50 percent since that time," he says, beaming.

Henstridge is quick to add, however, that the decision was not his alone, and he credits his colleagues at Tumi for the company's eventual turnaround. "Thanks to the collective minds and backgrounds of the directors of this company, we were able to identify some very interesting silver plays in Mexico," he says. "We were also fortunate to know a fellow named George Barnett, who is a principal of Minera San Jorge in Mexico and who represented these particular prospects. His assistance enabled us to get our first joint venture agreement signed up, and it allowed us to get active in Mexico.

"Once we'd made the decision to pursue silver," Henstridge continues, "we had it in our minds from the beginning to go into Mexico, because silver and Mexico go together – it is the number-one silver producer in the world today. From a geological perspective, if you are going to look for silver, then you might as well go to the place where it's commonly found and mined. There was certainly no point in going to my home country of Australia, because we have very few silver projects in the country at all – silver is mostly produced as a byproduct in base metal mines. But it is relatively easy to find silver just about anywhere in Mexico, and the country has a long-term history of producing the precious metal."

Tumi therefore entered into joint venture partnerships on two substantial tracts of land in Mexico: the Cinco Minas and the Gran Cabrera Projects. "Cinco Minas was a relatively easy target to decide to have a go at," he says, "because it is an epithermal vein system that is known to extend for more than five kilometres within the lease area. It is historically interesting as it contains an old silver mine that was founded by Marcus Daley, one of the cofounders of the Anaconda Mining Co. Daley operated the Cinco Minas Mine from the period of about 1920 to 1930, until it was shut down by the Mexican Revolution."

Located in the state of Jalisco in west-central Mexico, the 600-hectare Cinco Minas silver-gold project is part of the historic Jalisco silver belt, a northwesterly trending zone of underground-mined, bonanza-grade, silver-gold, vein-and-stockwork epithermal deposits, occurring within an area approximately 40 kilometres long and 10 kilometres wide. An advanced-stage silver-gold project, the project area is immediately accessible from the nearby town of Cinco Minas (which means 'five mines'), northwest of the city of Guadalajara. Further detailed channel sampling of the underground workings and initial drill testing are taking place, and this data will likely prompt early stage pre-feasibility studies.

"The production figures from the Cinco Minas Mine," says Henstridge, "are quite intriguing. It produced 97,000 ounces of gold and 15 million ounces of silver from 1.08 million tonnes of ore, which averaged 3.2 grams per tonne gold and 476 grams per tonne silver – quite a high grade. It fascinated me because these old timers generally only mined stope widths of about two metres, but the vein itself averages 14 metres – meaning there were 12 to 14 metres left of this vein which were mineralized, but had never been touched. We could walk along the vein for at least 400 or 500 metres and physically feel that the surface was, I believed, a very good drill target. We have since undertaken three drill programs in the upper levels of the Cinco Minas vein, and issued a resource calculation that estimates there are 12.5 million ounces of silver equivalent resources. We feel that number will definitely increase following the recent completion of our third drill program. It has proven to be a rather interesting project and will probably be a small mine sometime in the near future."

Located nearby and part of the same land package assembled by Minera San Jorge's George Barnett is the Gran Cabrera project. "It, too, is close to the city of Guadalajara," says Henstridge, "so it's quite accessible. It's not difficult to work there, and it has a very good work force located nearby. Gran Cabrera intrigued me because it was a zone of about 4,000 hectares of land and had 20 old silver mines on it. All of these old silver mines have been mined by underground techniques, picking up the high-grade silver-bearing ore and shipping it off to recover the metal, but the mines have never been looked at for modern mining methods or with modern exploration technology. We've got a pretty good program underway in the area to define what is controlling the zones where these 20 silver mines occur. Hopefully, we will have this information in the next year or so and be able to get substantial drill programs up and running, looking for a large silver ore body."

The Gran Cabrera properties are centered on three large silver-gold epithermal systems: the San José, Espada-La Deseada, and Las Caridades. The systems consist of groupings of rich, historic mines located in the Hostotipaquillo mining district. The Cabrera mega-system contains stockworks, breccia-hosted ore bodies, and large vein feeder subsystems at the intersection of the Sierra Madre and the Trans Mexican Volcanic Arc. These old mines historically and sporadically produced high-grade silver-gold ore over a period of more than 350 years, beginning with their discovery by early Spanish Conquistadors.

Within the prospective area, pervasive alteration by quartz and vuggy silica in veins and stockworks produced very hard, silicified host rocks which could not be economically mined or processed by either the early Spanish miners or the Americans during the first quarter of the 20th century. Modern mining equipment, however, can handle this type of ore and these zones are therefore immediate exploration targets for the company.

Consulting geologist Kent Ausburn visited the area in 1997 and undertook some sampling, concluding that "early indications of broad zones of potentially bulk-mineable silver-gold mineralization have been delineated in several locations. These results show the prospectivity of the mineralized zones and justify an immediate start to exploration."

Initial work on the Gran Cabrera properties will consist of data recompilation, geological mapping, and verification (or extension) of earlier sampling on the vein, stockwork and breccia-hosted mineralization, seeking ore-grade mineralization suitable for open-pit mining. Once target areas have been identified, a drilling program will commence.

"Both the Cinco Minas and Gran Cabrera projects are joint venture opportunities," says Henstridge, "whereby Tumi can earn a 60 percent interest with the right to buy the remaining 40 percent interest by investing a certain amount of money on the properties over three years. I always felt, however, that I would like another project in which the company could earn a 100 percent interest. After conducting a great deal of research, we acquired our third project, Jimenez de Teul, also using the extensive background knowledge of George Barnett in Mexico. I liked that area in particular because it has the potential to contain a larger deposit. The core area of the claims covers an alteration zone mapped for over one kilometre in length, and numerous pits and adits have been recorded. Sitting right it the middle of it, there is a higher-grade vein that we've sampled underground and recorded grades of 0.2 grams per tonne gold and 318 grams per tonne silver over a width of 15.3 metres on an exposed face. The vein definitely has the potential for higher-grade tonnage but the overall area will be explored seeking a larger, lower-grade silver resource.

"The Jimenez de Teul will be coming online later this year," Henstridge continues. "It will be a relatively straightforward exploration project, where we simply put in the grid, map and sample the surface in detail, and do some geophysics to see if we can identify the zones of interest. Then we'll know exactly where to drill."

Given Henstridge's background and 34 years of experience, it is easy to believe him. Born in Australia in 1948, David Henstridge graduated with an Honours Degree in Geology from Adelaide University, before spending his early years in the industry doing field exploration work in Australia. "When I graduated out of school and got my qualifications for university," he says, "I was strong in math and science, so I went into the science program in year one. I was told when I started that the basic science subjects were math, physics and chemistry, and that – to fill in the first-year requirement of four subjects – the easiest subject was geology. I took it and was glad that I did. I just loved geology and went on to graduate in it. But I really had no idea when I first started that it was what I would end up doing in life."

In time, Henstridge would leave Australia and hone his discipline in wildly disparate locations all over the world, subsequently working for a variety of mining companies throughout South America, Europe and the United States. A fellow of the Australian Institute of Mining and Metallurgy, and a member of the Australian Institute of Geoscientists and the Geological Society of Australia, Henstridge held numerous positions with Central Pacific Minerals N.L.. Then, in 1987, he began working and consulting for several different mining companies on advanced exploration and feasibility projects in Australia, Papua New Guinea, North and South America, Fiji and China.

"I was very lucky to have highly respected and qualified mentors in Australia," he says, "including Sir Ian McFarlane, the legendary Queensland mining entrepreneur who, in his very early days, actually ran a junior exploration company out of Vancouver. He later became a financial guy that worked for Morgan Stanley in New York, in addition to setting up his own mineral exploration companies in Australia. He definitely provided me with the insight and background on how to run public companies. I still model my work on the things he taught me back in those early days.

"At the same time," Henstridge continues, "Sir Ian's exploration manager, John Ivanac, was my geological mentor. He taught me a lot about the ins-and-outs of geology – he's an extremely good technical geologist. You always remember these people from your younger days because, if you're taught correctly, you carry their wisdom with you throughout your entire career."

Relocating to Vancouver after the aforementioned market crash of 1987, Henstridge helmed Peruvian Gold Limited from 1993 to 2001, before overseeing the evolution of Tumi Resources. Married with three children, he returned to Australia with his family shortly after solidifying Tumi's future, and he now works from his home office in Melbourne, paying regular visits to the company's properties in Mexico, as well as its head office in Vancouver. "What you find with most Australians," he says, "is that they love their country so much, it doesn't matter where they go and live in the world – ultimately, they always go home again. I wanted my children to grow up there, and my wife and I would eventually like to retire there in the place that we love."

Needless to say, the digital revolution made Henstridge's globe-trotting work schedule considerably more manageable. "Electronic communications certainly makes it easier to live in Australia, work in Mexico and have our main office in Vancouver," he says. "Initially, I thought it would be more difficult, because I'd lived in Vancouver for nine years. I thought maybe it would be a bit of a negative to try and conduct business that way, but in fact I've found it's much easier to keep up-to-date with what is going on via email. I still visit Vancouver quite frequently, plus, I'm a very technical person, so I like being onsite in Mexico, supervising and making sure that our technical programs are going ahead smoothly."

Henstridge states emphatically, however, that without the key people in place, Tumi Resources would never have gotten off the ground, let alone into it. "The people that are key to this group are key to the industry," he stresses. "Without the right people, it is hopeless, it is impossible- as I've discovered several times in the past during my long-term career in this game. Tumi Resources is not a one-man band – without these other people, I wouldn't be here doing what I'm doing. As far as I'm concerned, my colleagues are the most important aspect of this business to me. I have been extremely careful in making decisions about the people I want to work with, and I've made sure that I have identified the people that I want to go on with – particularly with regard to our staff in Vancouver. I have faith in them and they are unbelievably good. I'm lucky to have such terrific support in Vancouver by people who are experienced in all areas of the mining exploration business because, without these people, this company would never succeed."

Specifically, Henstridge points to his fellow directors Nick DeMare and Harvey Lim. "Nick and Harvey are both chartered accountants and they know the ins-and-outs of exploration companies," he says. "They know how to get through the approvals process, and how to do whatever is required for the Securities Exchange Commission and the stock exchanges." DeMare, who earned his Bachelor of Commerce degree at the University of British Columbia, is a member in good standing of the Institute of Chartered Accountants of British Columbia. Since May, 1991, he has been president of Chase Management Ltd., a private company that provides a broad range of administrative, management and financial services to private and public companies involved in resource and venture capital activities. He also serves as an officer and director of various public reporting companies.

Harvey Lim likewise graduated from UBC with a Bachelor of Commerce degree and is a member in good standing of the Institute of Chartered Accountants of British Columbia. Employed by Coopers & Lybrand (now PricewaterhouseCoopers LLC) from 1981 to 1988, Lim worked as controller with Ingot Management Ltd. from 1988 to 1991. Since then, he has served as controller for Chase Management Ltd., and acts as an officer and director of assorted public reporting companies.

"I can't help but mention my personal assistant Mariana Bermudez," says Henstridge, referring to Tumi's corporate secretary and investor relations/communications person. "Mariana looks after all the material that comes in and goes out of Vancouver." Beginning as Henstridge's executive assistant at Peruvian Gold Limited, Bermudez weathered the lean years with the company, and is well-versed in both the resource sector and securities industry. "She has been with me for over 10 years now," says

Henstridge, "and she is vital to handling the company's day-to-day affairs."

John Nebocat, the company's professional engineer and qualified person in accordance with National Instrument NI 43-101, "has worked extensively in this part of the world," says Henstridge, "and he is one of the world's best in my opinion for project evaluation and project supervision in the field. Once again, without these types of people, our company would not succeed. You have to be surrounded by a good team."

Which is precisely why Tumi hired financial and marketing consultant Nick L. Nicolaas, the man responsible for getting the word out to the media and the general public. "How do you get your name out there so that your company stands out from the pack?" Henstridge asks. "There are thousands of mineral explorers in the world, and you want to make sure that you're recognized. That's why we contracted Nick. He is a very important and valuable asset. It's a good feeling to know our company has somebody who is dedicated and focussed on getting our name out there to the worldwide community.

"Another integral part of the junior mineral exploration industry is the people in the Canadian Brokerage Houses," Henstridge continues, "who support the belief and the people in the industry, and are prepared to help fund companies – even sometimes when things are not the best. I acknowledge Bill Anglin, formerly of Research Capital, who singlehandedly financed the capital pool company, now Tumi Resources, and Ian Gordon of Canaccord who undertook the major financing of Tumi Resources in December 2003.

"Also, I cannot let the moment pass without saying that probably none of this would have happened without the total support of my wife Sandra. Geologists' wives get it tough, continually moving their families to where jobs are located and being a sole parent for long periods while husbands are away travelling."

Foremost among the facts Tumi wants to get across to the public is that Mexico actively encourages foreign investment and mineral exploration. "The political climate is very stable," says Henstridge, "and we don't have any problems with land tenure. Although it's somewhat complicated to figure out, it stands up well. Plus, the people are unbelievably good. We employ a lot of contractors and consultants, and we use

Mexican people whenever and wherever we can. During peak season on the three properties, there are up to 20 people on each site working full-time. The entire workforce on our exploration projects comes from the nearby communities, and they're all extremely good, hard workers. If and when we get a mine going, we'll be able to use any one who wants a job. There's no point finding people elsewhere if the locals are good at the job. We have had absolutely no problems anywhere in Mexico, unlike other places in the world where I refuse to work – such as Colombia – for obvious reasons."

And though the company is well-funded and always on the lookout for new projects, "we've been careful to never rely solely on any one single project," says Henstridge. "We always have our eyes open to new possibilities." Having said that, he adds that Tumi Resources has no plans to diversify, either in terms of location or commodity. "I've found in my life that the average investor is more attuned if you stay in one country and stay on one commodity," he says. "Sometimes I think investors get a little lost if you are involved in a lot of countries, looking for a lot of different things, because they keep on saying, 'Well, what's your real direction in life?' Our investors know what we're trying to do and trying to achieve without getting sidetracked into other areas.

"Further to that," Henstridge continues, "Mexico has not been picked over to any extent because there has never been much emphasis put on silver anywhere in the world, up until the past couple of years – mostly because the price has been pretty low and nobody has been interested in it. Consequently, exploration companies haven't made a great deal of effort to be in Mexico until recently. These days, you've got a much larger number of junior explorers from Vancouver who've moved into the country and who are having a crack at it. There are quite a few of them there now, actively and literally trying to turn resources into mines. That's a positive step forward for both the country and the commodity.

"Mexico has hundreds of old mineral occurrences and vein-type deposits that have been mined historically, then not mined, and then looked at again. Some of them are still going. At Cinco Minas, we were the first company in almost 70 years to take a serious look at reassessing that vein. That shows you that not too much effort went into looking at these areas in the past. But things are changing very quickly. If you intend to turn prospects into mines, there are a lot of things that come into play, notably infrastructure. You need the right environment, you need water, you have to be aware of the environmental concerns – everything has to be considered."

As for taking Tumi's Mexican projects into production, Henstridge is cautiously optimistic. "At this point," he says, "there is definitely the possibility of the company going into production on these properties – if we ever get to that point in time. But we have a lot more work to do yet. We have to continue doing mining studies and see if we get to full feasibility. In some of these areas, we need to find out where the water is coming from, we need to reassess the metallurgical characteristics, the infrastructures and so on. Everything has to be looked at in detail and it simply takes time to get to the bottom line. Can we start or can't we start? If we can get there and ultimately raise the money to go into production, we most certainly will – it's all part of the game that we're in."

And what has kept David Henstridge in the game these past 35 years? "The mineral exploration mystery is what keeps me going," he answers, without missing a beat. "The luck of finding that next deposit. That's the reason I'm still here today – the reason I have to be here today. You really get that taste in your blood when you are trying to find a deposit in the earth – it is a bit like hunting for buried treasure. There is no doubt about that. Once you're an explorer, you're always an explorer, and you're always trying to find the next deposit.

"I've always been fascinated by gold and silver," he says. "These things have a wealth of connotations for me. But I also think you can create a lot of work and fulfillment for the people on your team. The individuals who are around you can get a lot of fun out of what they're doing. You can't be doing something if you don't like it. If, at the same time, you can be financially successful, then it's a reward. Certainly, there are times when it's a real struggle, and I know many people in my profession have gone by the wayside over the years. For those of us who have been able to get through the difficult times, the good years have rewarded us. That, of course, is an important aspect, as well.

"Those tough years were a real struggle for this profession," Henstridge reflects. "There were no funds available for junior exploration companies. It was hard to get a job and make an income. But it is never difficult to get investors interested and involved when the market is moving. We waited and waited patiently through the hard times, and when we saw the first upswing in gold and silver prices in early 2002, the investors came flocking back again. There was absolutely no difficulty with that. Ultimately, they are supporting what we're doing, and we are supporting their interests and investments. It is a mutually beneficial and rewarding relationship, and that is exactly the way it should be."

VIRGINIA GOLD MINES

If anyone was seemingly born to the job of running a junior mineral exploration company, it's Andre Gaumond. Before this geological engineer was even 10 years old, he was fascinated with digging things up and constantly bringing home his collections of rocks, minerals and skeletons. When other young lads were dreaming of becoming firemen or cowboys when they grew up, Andre was torn between being an archeologist, a paleontologist or a geologist. While it's true that many boys enjoy scavenging, how many of them unearth an entire cow's skeleton and painstakingly put it back together, bone by numbered bone?

Gaumond recalls how as a lad in Quebec, he made his earliest discovery of buried treasure.

"When I was between 10 and 12 years old, I heard that a cow had died 10 years before and was buried in a field two kilometres away from my home. So I knocked at every door on the street near the field to see if anyone could remember where the cow was buried," says Gaumond, recollecting the beginnings of a major project that ended up garnering media interest.

After discovering the approximate location of the long-dead cow, Andre grabbed a friend and a couple shovels and set to work. They dug for days, eventually creating a hole that was 15 feet by 15 feet and four feet deep. One day, their shovels hit the skull of the cow and they excitedly began uncovering individual bones, bringing them all back to

Andre's basement – each bone numbered and in a bag. There were boxes and boxes of them.

"My mother was wondering what kind of crazy project I was again working on," says Gaumond with a grin.

By the end of the exercise, which took days of careful cleaning and identifying, he was faced with hundreds of bones lying on his basement floor.

"Then I decided to go to a butcher and I made copies of skeletons and pictures of cow's anatomy that they use to cut the meat. Eventually, I rebuilt the complete cow's skeleton."

Andre's father constructed a glass case in which to display the re-created animal and local interest filtered to a journalist who showed up and wrote a story about it. Following the story, a high school called and asked if Andre would donate the skeleton to its biology department.

"My mother, who always supported me but who still probably does not understand the fun and passion behind digging and cleaning bones from the ground, thought donating the cow's skeleton was a very good idea."

The cow went to school and so did Andre, continuing his education for years to come and indulging his passion for exploring and digging in academic settings as well as geological fieldwork. His cow project would only be the first of many thrilling finds he had yet to discover.

But that anecdote is a good place to start when talking about the president and CEO of Virginia Gold Mines, because it's a testament to his personal passion and perseverance – two qualities that he hastens to share with the entire Virginia team. All Virginia's successes, which include two exciting gold deposits, one nickel play, and a new VMS polymetallic property, several joint ventures and strategic alliances with major mining companies, a healthy treasury and promising future, are attributed by Gaumond to his team who he describes in glowing terms.

"We're long-term builders, we know what we're doing, we are considered honest, straight shooters, hard workers and we also have a reputation for being perseverant. But having said that, I like to underline that I say we because Virginia Gold Mines is not Andre Gaumond. Virginia Gold Mines is an entire team and I'm just part of it. Virginia Gold Mines would continue, if I disappeared tomorrow. So it's not a one-man company."

There's no getting around it. Gaumond is not only eager and willing to share the credit for all Virginia's successes, he insists on it.

"I think the people make the company. The right people find the right projects. That's how you build companies – you build them on people.

"That said, if one property doesn't work out but you have the right people behind the company, they'll find another one and eventually one of them will end up being a big winner for the shareholders and for the company."

And because of Virginia's solid reputation as exploration experts in Quebec, the company has earned a respectable niche within, and support from, Gaumond's home province.

"In exploration, we play a very important role in Quebec," says Gaumond. "It's still a very small part of the industry and the economy obviously, and we don't hire thousands of people. However, the Quebec government and the mining industry have put a lot of hope in us and our team. They tell us that continuously."

On a personal note, Gaumond says he would love to further fulfill Quebec's faith in Virginia Gold Mines and make the province proud.

"My dream since I was in school, is to discover a mine one day and create 200 to 300 jobs. I would love to cut the ribbon one day and say: 'I have been born for something. I am creating 200 jobs in Quebec, I am creating wealth'."

To this day, despite Gaumond's vast experiences, he still seems amazed and delighted with the industry, and the treasures to be found deep within his home turf.

"The beauty about discovering a deposit is that you create millions of dollars – from time to time, billions of dollars – of wealth, from scratch. From nothing! It's a treasure.

"It's not something you transform and add value to, it's something that was not there and suddenly it's there – bingo – billions of dollars of wealth. By doing that, you're participating in the development of the country, the development of the province, the wealth of the community, the society, and you create well-paid jobs.

"So that drives me. To be the best team in Quebec in terms of performance – I'm very proud of that. But the day you stop pushing, it's the end. Someone else will take your place. You have to be sure, to not sleep ... at all."

Although Gaumond was definite about his direction from a very early age, he made sure to investigate and learn about all aspects of the industry along the way – a route that was circuitous at times but ended up giving Gaumond a well-rounded and thorough education and knowledge of what it takes to run a company.

It started, not surprisingly, by taking geological engineering at university. While still engaged in getting his Bachelor's degree, Gaumond got the opportunity to work for a gold mining company that later became Lucien Belliveau Mine.

"They asked me if I would do my Master's degree on that mine and be paid at the same time. So I could continue to go to school and be paid by the company. Obviously that was very interesting for me, so I did it in a-year-and-a-half instead of two.

"In fact, my Master's degree was very instrumental for the reopening of the mine. It was because of my thesis that they checked the recovery and added a new circuit for the processing of the ore to recover gold by gravity. By doing a gravity circuit, they would be able to recover more gold and they tried it. Then the mine became profitable and they put it into production. I was very pleased with the conclusion."

Moving on from there, Gaumond began paying his dues working in exploration jobs and for consultants in the Eastern Townships as a geologist. While he was busy garnering all kinds of geological field experience, there was another aspect of the industry that he was interested in but not getting any practical knowledge about. The financial end of things, the stock exchange, the market, and trading shares had always held appeal for Gaumond but wasn't taught in school. During school, he had even created a small investment club and made his first profit with a gold mine called Golden Knight.

"I made a nice profit with that. At the time, it was a nice profit. We invested these dollars and I also lost a lot, but for me it was a way to learn the business and how it works," he said.

Then, while working in the Eastern Townships as a geologist, Gaumond heard about an opportunity that would give him the chance to learn the financial aspect of the mining business. Word got to him that the Caisse de Depot had instituted a training program for financial analysts in Quebec.

"Instead of having all the analysts from Toronto, they wanted Quebec-based analysts. They didn't have a lot of them in Montreal, so they were offering a program where they would pay 50 percent of the salary to a brokerage firm if they wanted to train analysts, to a maximum of $25,000 a year."

Gaumond recalls it was a Wednesday in January 1987 when he got a call, asking if he would be interested in moving to Montreal to work for a company called Pemberton Securities Ltd. He would earn $25,000, a salary to be split between Caisse de Depot and Pemberton. At the time, Gaumond was earning $75,000 as a geologist in the field, just one year out of school.

"I was earning this very wonderful salary, my wife was pregnant, we had a young child, and it was perfect. They had even furnished me a home, I didn't have to pay for anything. It was wonderful for me, because I was starting a life."

And what did Gaumond do when he got the analyst training offer?

"I accepted right away," he says, grinning.

"My wife said: 'It will be tough but we can do it.'"

With the same clear vision he had always possessed about his path in life, Gaumond didn't hesitate to take a huge pay cut in exchange for additional learning experience. There's a French word he uses to describe his decision: tremplin. Translated literally, it means trampoline.

"Something to jump, you know? An opportunity in my career, an opportunity to learn. It was like going back to school for me."

It was also a chance to take the Commission Securities course, the same course potential brokers have to take.

"So I followed that course, not to become a broker but to become a financial analyst, specializing in the mining sector," explains Gaumond.

Some people might have seen Gaumond's move as a gamble or a risk. But the mining industry itself has its share of risk attached and as most people involved in the industry will attest, a risk is nothing more than an opportunity.

"These are the types of opportunities in your life that you have to jump on," says Gaumond.

"If I didn't jump on it, my life or my career would have been completely different if I had said no to that call. It's very important. When you have an opportunity, you have to recognize it and react."

And that's exactly what he did. His game plan was to be a mining analyst for two or three years, learn all about the financial community, get contacts with major and junior mining companies, figure out how to raise money in the stock exchange, and basically discover everything there is to know that would help him in the future.

"That's exactly what happened," Gaumond says.

In less than three years, he got back into the exploration business working with a mining group comprised of three junior companies. But he still felt like he had more to learn and once again, it wouldn't be as a geologist in the field. In this new capacity, Gaumond found himself being general manager of one company and vice-president of exploration of another company.

"I told my wife I would like to stay three years with them, if it's okay, and learn about the corporate business," he says.

And learn he did. Gaumond's continuing education now revolved around activities like attending board meetings, being a director, figuring out the accounting end of things, learning what is involved with being a public company, annual reports, press releases – in short, anything and everything one needs to know about running a public company.

"You have to know how to deal with auditors, accountants, lawyers and agreements. Negotiations with majors, things like that."

Once again, he accomplished what he set out to do. The mining group, Corpomin, enjoyed good technical successes. They discovered a gold deposit and a base metal deposit during Gaumond's time with the group. One company was a takeover situation, bought by a major, and another put a gold mine into production.

To sum it up, in Gaumond's words: "It was very successful."

It was, in fact, through his work with Corpomin that Virginia Gold Mines came into being, as a reorganization of a shell. Gaumond decided to exchange his ownership in the Corpomin Group against the control of Virginia Gold Mines. The year was 1992 when he left the group, with Virginia in hand.

A shell company, about to be unlisted on the Montreal stock exchange because of inactivity, Virginia was so named because it used to have properties in Virginia in the United States. Gaumond decided to keep the name, for a couple of reasons. For starters, it's complicated and expensive to change the name of a company and Gaumond wasn't sure it was worth the trouble or expense.

"The second reason was that my strategy was to go into virgin territories. So I said: 'Virgin territories. Virginia. Let's keep the name. Keep it simple.'"

Now Gaumond finds himself with a company, but no team, no money, and no property. Fortunately, there was enough interest and confidence in Gaumond to get things rolling. A broker by the name of Louis Parquette said he would finance Gaumond to the tune of $100,000 to organize Virginia Gold Mines on the condition Gaumond move to Quebec City and join a mining group called Vior-Mazarin, which he did in 1993. Gaumond agreed, on the condition he would be allowed one year free of expenses during which time he could organize the company.

"I was from Quebec City, so that was okay. I had a free ride for one year, which helped me to build the working capital necessary to build a company, acquire properties, and put the money in the ground instead of anywhere else.

"I started with one property, then two, three, and now we are the largest landowner in Quebec – the most land in terms of numbers of properties, in terms of activities, and dollars spent in Quebec per year – Virginia and our partners, obviously."

Ten years later, and the Vior-Mazarin group has disappeared, leaving the Virginia group with Gaumond as its leader.

As with all mining exploration companies that have stuck it out through a couple cycles and weathered the Bre-X scandal, Gaumond saw

Virginia's stock fluctuate over the years. When the company was first organized, the stock was a mere eight to 12 cents. In 1996 it was up to $4.00, and dove back down in 1998 to about 40 cents. Gaumond is philosophical, understanding the nature of the business and the market cycles.

"We went through bad and good times because of the gold bear market. Now our stock is $1.50, but that means nothing right now."

Although Gaumond is obviously proud of the work done by Virginia and its team, he admits to being a bit uncomfortable if pressed to boast about his accomplishments.

"In this business, one thing I've learned is humility," says Gaumond.

"It's like a hockey player. You're only as good as the last goal that you scored. But when you have to talk about yourself, you always have to talk about extraordinary things to separate you from everybody else and to show you're a little bit different.

"And that's the thing I don't like. But that's probably the name of the game, eh?"

So rather than talking about himself, Gaumond chooses to speak about the company's strategy – a five-point strategy that begins with "focus, focus and focus." The way it breaks down is simple enough: focus, partnerships, diversification, expertise, and an excellent financial situation. Gaumond explains.

"By focussing we develop an expertise which is now recognized all across North America and brought us the interest of major mining companies, which by signing deals with these majors, brought us recognition from the mining community that recognized our group as a pretty good group of explorers, especially in Quebec.

"We have our own technical team and because it's in place and has a very good reputation, we've been able to keep the operatorship on most of our joint ventures. It's very unusual for a junior to retain operator status with a major mining company like BHP, but we've kept it because of our renowned team," says Gaumond.

Virginia's exploration team has, in fact, been recognized in the mining community as one of the best in Canada and has an enviable expertise in Quebec. To that end, it has received numerous awards in Quebec that underline not only its expertise but also its contribution to the geoscientific knowledge of northern Quebec.

It's one part of the five-point strategy that has nicely parlayed itself into a diversified portfolio of gold, nickel and base metals.

"I always say that I'll take what Quebec offers us," says Gaumond. "Quebec is the best territory on the planet for exploration and mining. And Quebec is the only territory in Canada where the majority of the territory is covered by aboriginal treaties, which is a very good thing."

In fact, in the summer of 2000, Gaumond was the only white man invited to the Grand Council of the 13 Cree Nations of Quebec in Waskaganish. The purpose of the meeting was to discuss the Cree's strategy and interest in the mining industry.

"I also negotiated with the Kangirsuk community – Inuit negotiation in Innuktituk and had a wonderful fishing trip on a sacred island with the Inuit people," Gaumond notes.

True to his company's name and mission, Gaumond and his team have ventured deep into virgin territories to see what they can find. Before settling on northern Quebec as Virginia's stronghold, Gaumond spent a year travelling around the world and looking at mining opportunities. After all that, he ended up back where he began.

"I finally realized, after travelling all over the world, that the northern part of Quebec was totally unexplored. I also saw the possibility to benefit from the hydroelectric infrastructures that were built in the 1970s in that area," says Gaumond.

"Since no exploration was allowed in the vicinity of these hydroelectric dams in construction, we decided to have a look at the area's potential and realized that nobody was there."

The Virginia team discovered that not only was the area open for exploration, they also found numerous volcanic belts that were practically untouched.

"They had the same geological setting as the rich southern Canadian belts, similar to the ones that made Canada's reputation as one of the richest mining countries on the planet," says Gaumond.

"That was it. As simple as it may seem, we considered that northern Quebec would be the best place to explore for years to come and it would become the niche of Virginia."

As promising as these volcanic greenstone belts are, Gaumond isn't all that picky about what lies within.

"If they have the potential to find gold, we explore for gold. If they have the potential for nickel, we explore for nickel."

Thus far, Virginia's portfolio is diversified with approximately two-thirds in gold potential properties, and one-third base metals.

"That's what we found so that's what it is," says Gaumond.

Whatever it is, it's good news for Virginia, its shareholders and Quebec. Gaumond may be loathe to take complete personal credit, but he's obviously done something right. As of March 2004, the company has a yearly exploration budget of $7 to $8 million of which the Quebec government reimburses 50 percent through incentive programs and the rest partly financed by partners, $18 million in cash, no debt, and is richer than ever in terms of dollars in the bank.

"We are actually the richest junior in Quebec in terms of working capital," notes Gaumond.

"So we are the most active and the main landowner in Northern Quebec. The government puts a lot of hope in what we are doing up there and considers the area to be the future of the mining industry in Quebec."

Virginia's pioneering spirit brought the team to the far-flung James Bay area of northern Quebec where they staked all the best areas on the huge, 500-kilometre-long La Grande greenstone belt. Gaumond estimates they control about 150 kilometres within the belt. Although no mines are currently in production in the new territory, Virginia has discovered two promising gold deposits on its properties – La Grande Sud, with 350,000 ounces of gold, and Poste Lemoyne, whose first resource calculation in 2003 was over 100,000 ounces of very high-grade gold. Also promising new gold discoveries located 70 kilometres away on the same belt is Corvet, that needs further work to prove the presence of significant gold resources.

By exploring these virtually untouched territories, Virginia bumped into some nickel in a totally unknown ultramafic volcanic belt, the Gayot belt, which hosts spectacular base metals mineralization. Because of the extremely rich mineralized zones found at Gayot, one of the largest mining companies in the world, BHP Billiton, has shown an interest in developing Gayot with Virginia. Gaumond compares this nickel play with the Raglan Mines, an extremely rich Quebec mine.

"It's very exciting, very rich," he says.

There's an expression used by the Virginia team whenever good results are obtained from the field or the lab – "Es-tu bien assis?"

Literally translated, it means: "Are you well sat?"

For non-Francophones, it translates as: "Are you sitting down?"

Gaumond knows that whenever someone in his company uses it, he can expect to hear about exceptional results.

"Every morning we wake up and go to work hoping to hear that expression," he says.

When Zone 32 on La Grande Sud was discovered, Gaumond heard it. He heard the same thing for Poste Lemoyne and Gayot.

If all that weren't enough to pique the interest of shareholders, Virginia has two base metal projects that, according to Gaumond, could become 'a company maker for Virginia'. The first project, MegaTem, is a strategic alliance with Noranda and Novicourt (a subsidiary of Noranda), using a state-of-the-art technology called MegaTem. That technology can detect semi-massive to massive mineralization up to a depth of 250 metres. This strategic alliance illustrates Virginia's determination to stay on the leading edge of the world's best technologies and apply them to the Quebec territory through strategic partnerships.

As well, Virginia discovered a new virgin volcanic belt called the Coulon belt, that hosts spectacular base metal mineralizations and could reveal positive surprises for years to come.

Although a lot of drilling has already been done to find the two gold deposits, Gaumond says it's all relative and the scope of possibilities is huge.

"Compared to the immensity of the territory, we have done virtually nothing. Compared to the Abitibi greenstone belt, a volcanic belt located further south, we are just at the beginning. Val D'Or, Rouyn Noranda were not formed in a couple of years. It took decades to develop these mining camps."

Although Quebec is extremely busy with mining, Virginia doesn't have much company nearby. Most of the big rich mines and mining camps are located in the southern part of Quebec, and because these camps are controlled by major mining companies, all the necessary infrastructure, mills, and smelters, are present. Gaumond believes this is one reason Virginia doesn't have a lot of competition further north.

"We think we were the first one because the big companies didn't want to go there since they wanted to feed their infrastructures in the south. You can't feed your infrastructure in the south if you find things too far away. So we decided to go outside the known mining camps into uncharted territories further north and we found the same geology as in the south ... but nobody was there."

The flipside to such a unique position is obviously a rougher terrain and conditions. But it doesn't faze Gaumond, who is accustomed to the wilds of his province.

"It's rough, but it's part of Canada and Canadian miners and explorers have been coping with mining and rough conditions everywhere in Canada. We know how to do that, so it's not an issue. It's just a little bit more expensive, but nothing else."

Presumably one way of determining the worth of a company is to see who else has joined forces with them. Aside from having several properties owned 100 percent, Virginia boasts three deals including two strategic alliances on the nickel side of things with BHP Billiton, one of the largest mining companies in the world, three deals with Noranda Novicourt, a deal with Soquem, some joint ventures with other juniors, and several new deals signed at the annual PDAC (Prospectors & Developers Association of Canada) convention in Toronto in March 2004. With that kind of credibility, it looks like Gaumond isn't the only one who has faith in Virginia.

"We have among the best partners in the world, which is an independent objective opinion on the quality of our properties. If the major mining companies did not share our view that there is potential on our properties, they would not proceed with us to spend millions of dollars on our properties.

"So this is confidence, coming from a major. And majors are looking for big takes. It proves there is potential to find big things on our properties."

Adding to that investor confidence is Virginia's excellent financial situation, which has enabled it to be one of the most active explorers in Quebec, and able to obtain additional financing allowing the company to continuously develop new high-potential projects. In short, it ensures a long-term presence on the territory and bodes well for stability.

"The fact that we're very active, we have no debt, and $18 million in cash, means we will still be here 10 years from now," says Gaumond.

His geological expertise, his hard work and his education in every aspect of the business, have all prepared him for this moment. Virginia's strategy is clear, and Gaumond's passion intact. He's in it for the long haul.

"You want to be there," he says intently, leaning forward. "You want to be there when you find the jackpot ... the big one."

As his eyes light up with the possibilities, you can picture that same expression on the face of a 10-year-old boy, digging for buried treasure in a farmer's field in Quebec. Whether he's digging for gold or the skeletal remains of a cow, it seems clear that Gaumond won't give up until he's found it.

WOLFDEN RESOURCES INCORPORATED

Ewan Downie doesn't fit the typical profile of a successful junior mineral exploration company president and CEO. At 37 years of age, he's certainly younger than most. His degree isn't in the traditional field of geology – it's in commercial diving. And Wolfden Resources's head office is not perched in a big city skyscraper – it's in a modest three-story building in the northern Ontario town of Thunder Bay. But once you get to know this leader of the Wolfden pack, it all makes perfect sense. Ewan Downie didn't get where he is today by backing down from a challenge or playing it safe.

Here's a tip: If you want Downie to succeed at something, simply tell him it can't be done. Not only will he prove you wrong, he'll thrive on doing just that.

"Never give up," he says emphatically. "And never wait for an opportunity to come to you, because they seldom do."

Downie would characterize this spirit as determination.

His father and co-founder of Wolfden, geologist Iain Downie, has another name for it: stubbornness.

"He doesn't get it from me," the senior Downie says, shaking his head. "His mother's exactly the same."

But no matter how he came by it, Downie's fearless tenacity has paid off handsomely for Wolfden Resources. As of mid-2004, the company is sitting pretty with a healthy CAD$35 million treasury and zero debt. Its portfolio boasts several valuable and key properties including High Lake in Nunavut, a project in Red Lake near Thunder Bay joint ventured with Placer Dome and the Ulu property near High Lake. Both High Lake and Ulu are 100 percent owned by Wolfden. As for joint ventures with majors, these include two with Placer, one with Teck-Cominco and one with Bema Gold, as well as several joint ventures with juniors.

As a general philosophy, Downie likes to look for gold and copper so as not to be a one-commodity company.

"By having multiple projects, it gives us more kicks at the can and just multiplies our potential for success," Downie says.

The occasion for meeting Wolfden's affable CEO is the annual Prospectors & Developers Association of Canada (PDAC) convention in Toronto, held March 7 to 10, 2004. With more than 10,000 delegates registered it's the biggest turnout yet, and miners are swarming the Metro Toronto Convention Centre. While waiting for their booths to open, delegates pack the lobby restaurant, some buttoned-up for business and others, like Downie, attired more casually. Passionate talk of gold and diamonds filters over from nearby tables, and Downie, for his part, is a self-professed 'gold bug'.

But although he shares a common passion with the other delegates, Downie has been singled out this year. Wolfden is being awarded the PDAC 'Prospector of the Year Award' for its West Zone discovery in 2003 on the High Lake Property. The West Zone is now the largest zone on the property and is situated less than 1.5 kilometres away from the existing deposits that were known when Wolfden first purchased the property. The award is bestowed for the best discovery of the year and can go to anyone – a major, a junior or an independent prospector. It's no small honour for the Wolfden team.

"It's one of the most prestigious awards given to someone in our capacity," says Downie.

"I think it's a real testament to what our entire team has done, and to me, it's a great kudos to my father who ran the explorations project for us. The West Zone is now our biggest zone in High Lake and, in my opinion, it's taken us over the threshold of not being economic to having enough tonnes to be economic."

Downie can afford to be pleased about this recognition. Wolfden is a top junior performer with a promising future, led by a young guy whose journey to this point wasn't without his detractors. There are many people, and Downie will happily list them, who didn't think he could pull off a viable company, let alone be so honoured. Fortunately, many of those people are now his biggest fans. And Downie thanks those early naysayers with as much earnestness as he thanks his lifelong supporters. But if it wasn't for his 'Never give up' philosophy, it's certain none of this would have happened.

Although he is always quick to credit his team of professionals, a highly credible and experienced board, and anyone integral to Downie's initial learning curve and subsequent successes, arguably no one has been more influential or challenging than his father, Iain Downie. Sometimes volatile but always valuable, the father-son relationship plays no small part in Wolfden's current status and achievements. It was the elder Downie, a professional geologist (P.Eng), who first gave his young son a taste of life in the bush. As a senior geologist running exploration programs for major mining companies, Iain let his son tag along on drilling programs. These forays into the wilderness made an impression on young Ewan.

"I enjoyed going out into the bush with him, staying in tents, I like to go fishing. I remember a driller, when I was young, who gave me a rabbit once. A drill set-up scared a rabbit family away except for one little baby. The driller gave it to me and I had a pet rabbit. Those kind of things had a big effect on me."

Those things also had an effect later on, when Downie was looking for a company name and discovered a wolf den behind a showing on their first property.

"I called this little outcrop the wolfden showing and when trying to come up with a name for the company, I liked the ring of it. And I've always been a big fan of wolves. They're my favourite animal."

In his teens, Downie continued his outdoors education and worked summer job programs with his father during his high school years. Furthering this education into university by taking geology would seem to be a given. Ironically, it was his own father who dissuaded Ewan from pursuing the path he himself had chosen.

"My father urged me not to get into geology due to the cyclical nature of our industry," Downie said, eyeing his father for confirmation.

Iain Downie, who is at the PDAC convention holding down Wolfden's table in the Core Shack, nods his head.

"I tried to get him to stay the hell away from it," he agreed. "But he didn't become a geologist. He did it the right way. He's raising money and making money."

"So are you," Ewan points out.

"Just as a sideline," deadpans Iain.

Although Iain has since resigned from Wolfden, clearly the father and son share more than just a common interest in the same profession. There's an obvious affection and respect on both sides, but getting them to admit it doesn't come without verbal sparring.

"He's done a helluva job, but he just ignores everything I say," says Iain.

"No, I just ask the same question over and over again until I get the answer I want," returns Ewan.

"Never work with your kid," Iain says, shaking his head. "It keeps you honest."

"But there's no one's opinion I value more," offers Ewan.

"Well, I'm not always right but I'm never wrong."

This is ribbing such as you'd expect to hear from a father and son who have a working history. But Ewan admits it wasn't always so good-natured and they both suffered their share of friction that eventually led to Iain's resignation.

"I can see it from his side – wanting to do something and actually having to okay it with your son would be, y'know, I couldn't do it. Sometimes he would want to do something and I'd say, 'Well, not yet...later,' and then we would get into a big blow-out fight, not talk for three weeks, and my mom would get upset and I guess we figured it's not worth it. I respect and trust his opinion more than anybody else, but it's not worth fighting over a company."

You've got to respect Downie's candour. It's refreshing and has a ring of honesty to it that no doubt has played a role in winning over investors and colleagues.

Despite butting heads with his father over work-related issues later on, Downie took his advice about schooling and rather than pursuing geology, he got his diploma in commercial diving. But after graduating, Downie quickly discovered he was about as fond of that type of work as he was of 'taking orders'. Back to school he went, still avoiding the academics of geology. This time around, he took business at Lakehead University in Thunder Bay. During his last two years of university, something happened that sealed his eventual fate. The government came in, gave a presentation and offered 'student venture loans' to young entrepreneurs. That was all it took. Downie jumped on it.

"Since I have a difficult time working for others, I decided to try this out," he says. "Together with a loan from dear ol' mom, I bought a couple of tents, a couple of chainsaws and an axe, incorporated a service mining exploration company, and went out looking for contracts."

With that, Vytyl Exploration Services was born and once again, the elder Downie was instrumental. Iain and his mining buddies gave Ewan a shot at a couple of contracts. Each time a new school semester rolled around, Ewan put off returning in favour of fulfilling contracts or potential contracts. After a year, he knew that finishing his business degree wasn't going to happen.

"That was that. I decided I would learn the mining business in the bush rather than in a book," he said.

And learn it, he did.

"I did everything and anything. I staked claims, line cut, and worked with big companies like Noranda and Placer Dome. I got to know what we were looking for and made some pretty good recommendations. Placer made a couple of finds following projects we did, and we're still pretty friendly with the guys from Placer."

In fact, one of Wolfden's current joint ventures is with Placer Dome, on their East Bay property in Red Lake.

"I actually staked it for them, so if you went to the shores of East Bay you'd see my name on the claim post. And now we're drilling on claims that I staked.

"The company – Vytyl – founded by me and mom became one of the largest of its type in Ontario. But after a few years, I found myself chasing workers as much as I did working, as we constantly had multiple contracts on the go."

With this first successful experience under his belt, Downie was ready for the next person who would impact his life – Perry English, a client and well-known Red Lake prospector who was finding properties that Downie would stake for him. After spending a couple of years together in the field, English made Downie an offer he didn't refuse.

"Perry convinced me to partner up on a few properties, taught me the world of prospecting and looking for yourself rather than for someone else – to me, a much more rewarding proposition. At the end, we had 30 or 40 properties, a lot of projects. In some ways, next to my father, Perry became my mentor and, in working with Perry, he also became one of my best friends."

Armed now with field experience, some successful recommendations, and buoyed by his increasing independence, Downie was bursting with ideas. He would tell anyone who would listen and fortunately one such person was John Pollock, another friend of Iain's.

"He was looking for claims in Red Lake and called me about doing some projects for him. I think he optioned one off Perry and me, and then I started calling him and giving him all these ideas. I want to do this, I want to do that, they were wild ideas."

But even though Pollock didn't share the same boundless enthusiasm for Downie's never-ending ideas, it didn't stop Downie from suggesting them. It might be fair to say Downie wore him down, prompting Pollock to finally offer his own suggestion.

"He said, 'Well why don't you start a junior? You start it and I'll finance it.' Looking back on it, I think he was basically kidding," says Downie.

But if Pollock was bluffing, he obviously didn't know Downie very well. You don't issue a challenge like that and expect Downie to let it ride. His persistent confidence is a crucial element of his character, and one that Wolfden shareholders would do well to be grateful for.

Downie mulled over Pollock's suggestion for about a week. He didn't know anybody in the brokerage community, or in investments, or anybody who could help start a company.

"So I phoned up one of the other juniors I worked for and I said: 'Well? How do you start a company like this?'"

They were helpful and put Downie onto Sheldon Huxtable, a mining legal firm that set up the company and got everything going. One of the senior guys at the firm was Henry Knowles, a former chairman of the Ontario Securities Commission, and a very credible name within the industry. When approached by Downie to join him on board at Wolfden, he accepted.

Next step: going public. Next hurdle: financing.

It was time to see if John Pollock would back up his offer.

"I phoned John and said, 'I started up the company, hired the lawyers, I put my own money into getting it to where it is, and you said if I started one, you'd finance it.'"

Downie sits back in his chair, reliving the moment and Pollock's answer.

"His response was ... 'Are you kidding?'"

"That's when I really knew that his first comment wasn't serious. But I said, 'no I'm not kidding.' I thought it was a really good idea."

John Pollock's answer: "Well I'm a man of my word."

Now his father's friend John Pollock was on board, who brought in Jones Gable, a local brokerage firm run by a fellow named Don Ross. At first, Ross and Downie clashed.

"Don and I got off to a rocky start because I had no clue about what it took to make and run a junior mining company and Don often reminded me in his oh-so-gentle manner."

The year was 1997, and it probably didn't help their relationship that Downie was young, and refused to wear a tie or cut his long hair.

"Now Don and I get along famously and he's probably one of my bigger fans. I really like and respect him. But still to this day, I think if you asked him, he'd tell you he didn't think the company would go anywhere."

And that's how Downie does things. If he doesn't know how to do it, he'll ask and learn. If someone tells him he can't do it, he'll get it done. And because he's always the first to admit when he needs help, he surrounds himself with good people who can offer it.

"There's Henry Knowles, John Pollock who ran four TSE-traded companies, John Cook who was formerly a senior officer at Lac Minerals and also a former vice president of operations at Goldcorp. These guys had the credibility on the street that I didn't have.

"All these guys ultimately gave me the opportunity to get this thing going and then it was up to me to make it or break it."

Credibility is no longer an issue for Downie or Wolfden, both being rightly recognized for their achievements within the industry. But it wasn't always easy and the timing, as it turned out, couldn't have been worse.

"We launched our IPO (initial public offering) just days after Bre-X was officially announced as a scam. Days!" exclaimed Downie.

"We almost didn't raise the minimum in our IPO and almost didn't make it public. It took years to lose the stigma of that scandal as it had a big part in leaving a bad taste in the mouths of investors when it came to mining shares and perhaps even gold as a commodity."

But now, in the spring of 2004, with a great gold market, interest is at an all time high for Wolfden. A relief, after having struggled through the darker days.

"We started trading in the midst of the fall in the gold price, and struggled through a price that nearly hit $250 an ounce. At a convention several years back, while most of our peers were flocking to PGEs and dot-com fiascos, I was once asked why we were still looking for gold – 'It's only good for doorstops and bookends'– I might even say that I loved the low prices for acquisitions."

To give Wolfden a leg up in the early days, Downie and his father invested their own money and their trust into the fledgling company. After the Downies put their seed financing in place, Ewan made that call to the man-of-his-word, John Pollock. One by one, others fell in line beginning with yet another father-son relationship. Pollock's son, Rob Pollock, who just happened to work at Dundee Securities, one of the bigger brokerage firms. It was a fortuitous link, and through a CMP fund (flow-through fund), Rob bought a small position in Wolfden.

"At that time, CMP was really the only source of money for Canadian explorers. It was that bad," Downie says.

"Then we drilled our Monument Bay property and we hit some pretty good values. Our stock went from a quarter to $1.70 or something."

The next thing Downie knew, he was being called to a meeting with the head of Dundee, Ned Goodman.

"Ned Goodman is an icon in Canadian mining. Dundee had had a meeting about the CMP fund and Ned asked who the top performers were in the CMP fund. Rob Pollock said, 'Wolfden.' And Ned said, 'Who the hell's Wolfden?'"

Armed with that less-than-stellar recognition and a pile of maps, Downie took a meeting and did what he does best.

"I came in and I didn't have a computer presentation. I had all my maps – you know, typical prospector – and I rolled them out. I think Ned liked that I came in with the maps instead of a fancy projector."

After Downie left the meeting, Ned apparently looked at Rob and said something that is music to any prospector's ears:

"Finance that guy. Make sure he always has money."

Going public in 1999, Downie concedes that the first couple of financings were as tough as the market. But while gold was tanking and others were off chasing more likely prospects like skyrocketing platinum/paladium, Downie dug his heels in and persevered.

"The first sample I ever picked with visible gold made me fall in love with gold. While everybody else was going off elsewhere, I was out buying gold deposits or base metal deposits. And we actually built a very, very solid portfolio of properties, however our stock was still down and we remained unrecognized."

Then in 2001, Wolfden entered into a joint venture with Bema Gold on its Monument Bay property and Downie used this alliance to get some face time with Canaccord, one of the largest independent brokers in Canada.

"I had tried to get into Canaccord forever with zero luck. But they were a big supporter of Bema so I phoned one of their mining analysts and asked if I could come in."

As fate would have it, Bema had recently been in the Canaccord offices talking about the Monument Bay property and Downie was invited to come in and clear up some lingering questions they had. Never one to let an opportunity slip by, Downie pushed his luck and Wolfden's agenda.

"I said I'd do that, but only if I get to pitch the whole company and not just talk about the Bema joint venture. The analyst said okay."

Also present at the meeting was Jens Mayer, the head of corporate finance at Canaccord. At the time, Downie wasn't entirely aware of how important it would be to impress Jens.

"I presented the company and I thought, based on their reaction, it was a meeting that didn't go overly well. But by the time I got back to my hotel room, there was a message from Jens Mayer to come down the next morning. John Cook, on our board, said: 'You cancel all your other meetings to see Jens.' That's when I found out who he was."

As things would turn out, Jens was impressed with Wolfden's portfolio of gold and base metal projects, and introduced Downie to yet another highly important person to have in your corner: Peter Brown, the head of Canaccord. A successful meeting ensued and by the time the dust had settled, Downie and Wolfden had the support of two of the biggest backers of mining companies in Canada – Ned Goodman and Peter Brown.

"I think Peter and Jens are still two of our biggest fans as I always hear about them promoting our company. They have been huge backers of Wolfden and they've had the biggest influence on us, especially in terms of raising money. They have allowed us to be more aggressive in our explorations and acquisitions and the success of our company is largely, when it boils right down to it, built around the support of the brokerage community. Without them, we're really nowhere."

Now that things have progressed from nowhere to somewhere, Wolfden has worked with several other brokerage firms including BMO Nesbitt Burns, GMP Securities, Pacific International, Desjardins Securities, Haywood Securities and Jennings Capital.

"We have $35 million in the bank that has come from financings. Our two biggest supporters continue to be Dundee for source of funds and Canaccord for actually helping to create a market. We now have five analyst buy recommendations and good support from the brokerage community. It is now easier for us to get meetings, our stock has been one of the top performing juniors in recent years, and it took a lot of things to get there. It took the relationships from my father to the relationships I've formed."

Wolfden has come a long way since the days when Downie ran the company out of his truck with nothing but a single cell phone and a lot of heart. Now he's picking up an award for best discovery of the year that lies in the ground on Wolfden's High Lake property in Nunavut, just south of the Arctic Ocean. Wolfden purchased the property, a high-grade copper deposit, in 2001 from Kennecott. Once again, it was Ewan's father who indirectly had a hand in the deal.

"One day I was here, at this convention, with a gentleman my father worked with at Kennecott. We went out drinking one night at the PDAC suites, and I met up with this friend of my father's. We hit the suites together and I told him I wanted one of Kennecott's properties. Again, it was my father's relationship that opened the door and they sold us the project.

"When my father looked at it, he said: 'We don't want that.' But I liked it because it was promotable. We could promote it and maybe raise money, so I took it anyway."

At the time, the property was about five or six kilometres long and two kilometres wide, but now, with all the subsequent acquisitions it measures around 40 kilometres in length. Initially there were a couple of deposits of copper or zinc, both of which were drilled and then cut off. Although they weren't big enough to go into production, they were high-grade – two of the highest grade deposits of their type in the world with one zone averaging over 5 percent copper. Downie's instincts had been correct: they were promotable.

"High Lake is what Canaccord really liked. We now had nice high-grade copper deposits and after we acquired it, my father decided to get into it and found some potential extensions."

The deposit was extended, but once again cut off. A beltwide consolidation was called for, something that required a lot of money during times when the market was still tough. Enter Teck-Cominco, one of the biggest base metal producers in the world, with financial help.

"Teck-Cominco came in and they liked the idea and the good grades. They wanted to partner up somehow and we worked out an arrangement where they helped finance us in exchange for a first right of refusal if we ever decided to sell it or joint venture it."

Wolfden decided to go with a regional exploration program to examine the entire belt. Because the volcanogenic massive sulphide deposits typically occur in clusters, and with two already found on the side of a hill, the senior Downie suggested flying over the area in a helicopter and doing an airborne survey.

"Having Teck-Cominco come in and finance us helped to give the project extra credibility, and it became easier for us to go to brokerage firms and raise the rest of the money we needed. The support of Teck-Cominco and the brokerage community allowed us to begin a beltwide exploration program.

"My father was running the exploration and he wanted a specific airborne survey. When we flew it, we had a big anomaly less than a mile away from our existing two deposits where there were some sulphides around. So the geophysical anomaly looked really prospective. We drilled it and we hit the zone."

The third zone was the charm. It is currently the biggest deposit on the property, with high grades in copper, zinc, gold and silver. The precious metal credits, Downie estimates to be four to five times the world average for this type of deposit. On a per tonne basis, if the West Zone were in production today, it could very well be one of the highest-grade mines of its type in the world.

And things are hopping up there in the mining camp. During peak times, there are probably 30 to 35 people working. To keep market interest high, Downie implemented a winter drilling program in 2003 – a difficult and challenging proposition in the Arctic with its lack of daylight hours, frigid temperatures and blowing snow.

"It was tough. Ian Neill, our project manager, basically spent eight weeks up there in a horrible season, but he's very dedicated to the project. It's my job to manage the market and keep the momentum going. Once you get the interest of the brokerage or financial community, you want to keep it. One mistake, you lose it. And it's almost impossible to get it back."

Although High Lake could become Wolfden's biggest mine, East Bay in Red Lake has the potential to be the first one to go into production. Situated a little closer to home, Red Lake is about a five-hour drive outside of Wolden's home base in Thunder Bay. The area already hosts two of the richest gold mines in the world, those of Goldcorp and Placer Dome. Getting in on that action, Wolfden joint ventured one of Placer's properties and is currently drilling off a pretty high-grade gold zone.

"Actually we recently announced a new discovery where the first assay of this intersection is over 11 ounces per tonne, which is extremely high. We have six drills on the property right now, we're drilling 75 holes this winter, and it's shaping up to be a fairly decent discovery."

But East Bay is only one of two properties in the promising mine trend in Red Lake. When Downie took it upon himself to research all the patented mining claims owned by companies in the area, he was surprised to find five that weren't in either Placer or Goldcorp's name situated right beside the mines. Further research revealed they were owned by Martin McNeely Mines Ltd., a company that had been defunct for some 20 years. In order to find out what had happened, to see if the claims could be purchased, would require a letter from the defunct company allowing a look at their corporate records. Downie figured this roadblock probably stopped Placer and Goldcorp from doing further research on the property.

But it wasn't going to stop Downie. He could smell a challenge and a potentially amazing purchase for Wolfden. Going back, the trail appeared to begin with an oil company called Neomar that had dabbled in mining exploration. Following several amalgamations, mergers and acquisitions, it became part of Marathon Oil in the States. Downie hit the phones to see if this Martin McNeely Mines had anything to do with Marathon Oil.

"I ran into dead end after dead end. Most people I talked to at Marathon Oil said 'If we did own a mining property, we don't care and we'd rather just give it up.' They assured me Marathon Oil had nothing to do with Martin McNeely."

Downie didn't believe them, but did believe he needed to talk to the legal department. Stretching the truth ("it was a fib, not a lie"), he called back and said he was a joint-venture partner of Marathon Oil and he needed to talk to the female lawyer working on his case. It was a wild guess, but it paid off and he was given the direct line to a female lawyer. Too bad for her. In Downie's own words, he began to 'pester' her with phone call after phone call. Was Marathon Oil formed out of Martin McNeely? Was there any record of this?

Despite the lawyer's denial of any such relationship, Downie didn't give up. "Are you sure? Can you check your records again? I'll wait on the line..."

There was in fact some urgency on Downie's end, because the claim would have been open that year for anyone to stake.

"I kept bugging her and bugging her and, after many calls, I was about to give up."

But then, surprisingly, she phoned him and said his persistence had made her curious. She looked into it, and lo and behold, Martin McNeely is part of Marathon Oil. That's all Downie needed to hear. He typed up a formal offer for $10,000 and sent it to her.

"She phoned me and said 'Look, we won't even lift a pen for $10,000 and besides, my higher ups want nothing to do with it. Maybe if you gave us $100,000, we'd think about it.'"

Not deterred, Downie promptly sent in another offer for $50,000.

"She phoned me back and this time she said: 'You're a persistent prick, aren't you?' I said, 'Listen, I'm not going to leave you alone until those claims are in my name.' She said, 'Okay, if you give us $60,000, we have a deal.' So I said: 'Done.'"

After going through the government to reinstate the claims to Marathon, they then sold them to Wolfden and it was a done deal.

"So the claims are now reinstated. We bought them for sixty and, as soon as we announced it, Goldcorp and Placer phoned us and said: 'What are you going to do with those?'"

Downie decided Placer was the logical partner, not only because it had direct access to the property but also because Wolfden had joint ventured one of their properties in Red Lake.

"As a return favour, I decided on Placer as a partner. We joint ventured to Placer where they pays us $180,000, or three times what we paid, and they spend the initial exploration on the property with the right to carry us to production. So if they go to 60 percent ownership of the property, we'll never have to spend a penny on the ground and we'll be carried forever."

Late in 2004, Placer will be drilling into those claims from their mine underground. Because they've never been drilled from underground before, Downie has high hopes.

"If they hit anything like Goldcorp has, watch out! We're in the same neighbourhood where you could find a bonanza-type gold deposit."

According to Downie, Placer believes they'll find the best potential below 5,000 feet, a depth they're already mining right beside the claims. Goldcorp is also mining at that depth and is currently putting in a shaft down to 7,000 feet.

"Goldcorp's high grade zone, which essentially gives them a $3 billion dollar market cap, was found at 5,000 feet deep. Placer mines essentially the same deposit – Goldcorp's on one side of the boundary and Placer's on the other side and then they dip southwest. South of the Placer ore body is our five claims," says Downie.

If all that weren't enough, Wolfden's most recent acquisition and most advanced stage gold project is its Ulu property situated 50 kilometres from High Lake.

"It hasn't been mined before, it has a high grade 12.9 grams per tonne gold deposit, and previous operators actually went underground and drifted into the deposit so it's basically a ready-to-go mine," says Downie.

"Ulu is now one of our top priority properties. High Lake and Ulu are 100 percent owned by our company and will be the focus of our company going forward."

No matter what the eventual outcome, Downie understands the importance of keeping market interest keen. With a stock that opened between 24 and 40 cents and seesawed back and forth for years, eventually reaching a high of $7.70 a share with the West Zone discovery, Downie knows what it takes to stay healthy.

"Our share price closed on Friday at $5.95 so we're not too far off our high. Every year we've drilled High Lake we've hit new highs and we hope to duplicate that again this year with another new high."

Shareholders can rest easy that Downie will pursue the best economic route, no matter where that leads, even if it means getting taken out.

"Our High Lake project's grade is extremely rare and it's starting to get to the size where a lot of the bigger companies will start thinking they should maybe own it. If the right deal came along, sure. But I'd have to think it's good for my shareholders because at the end of the day, I'm working for them."

Also reassuring is Downie's hands-on approach that reflects his own personal stake and confidence in Wolfden. Often it is Downie himself who will answer the phone when it rings in the Wolfden offices.

"I am of the opinion that this up front and personal nature will attract more loyal investors. I run the company and do all of the investor relations work. I am a large shareholder in the company – when I talk about the reasons for owning Wolfden stock, these are the same reasons that I am a shareholder. In fact, I likely own as many shares today as the day we went public.

"When I talk to you about our company, I am putting my money where my mouth is."

Now, that's a claim shareholders can stake their belief in.

X-CAL RESOURCES LIMITED

Many are the myths surrounding gold mines, potential, producing and otherwise. Like most myths, however, they are often difficult to substantiate, their very nature calling into question the ultimate relevance of concrete evidence. When myths are linked to real-life figures, however, particularly ones who have attained near-mythical status in their own lifetimes and chosen disciplines, the tale is lent not only truth but tangibility.

Such is the case with X-Cal Resources Ltd. (TSX: XCL), a Vancouver-based exploration company with a significant pair of gold projects in north-central Nevada, U.S.A. Founded by president, CEO and director Shawn M. Kennedy in 1981, X-Cal's roots dig back far deeper, into the legend surrounding world-renowned prospector and geologist, Dr. Franc R. Joubin (1911-1997). The man responsible for discovering Ontario's massive Elliot Lake reserve in the 1950s, Canada's largest uranium mine, Joubin went on to define equally extraordinary mineral deposits on five different continents during the ensuing two decades he spent with the United Nations, assisting developing countries in mineral exploration and thereby bolstering not only their natural-resource infrastructures but, by extension, their economic, social and political ones, as well.

"I was very lucky to be adopted by Franc Joubin in 1982," says Kennedy, a thoughtful and intuitive man, whose scholarly demeanor reveals a deeply philosophical bent that makes the paternal reference to

Joubin seem almost literal rather than metaphorical. "Franc was one of the most successful mineral explorers that ever lived and my apprenticeship with him lasted from our initial meeting in 1982 until his death in 1997. He was an extremely demanding taskmaster and I thought perhaps I had failed the apprenticeship until, in 1996, he asked me if I would go to Winnipeg and accept an award on his behalf – one of many he received in his lifetime – because he was unable to attend. At that point, I figured I must have earned at least a passing grade.

Though Kennedy finishes his self-deprecating quip with a chuckle, his reverence for the late Joubin is unmistakable. "X-Cal is a very unusual type of company," Kennedy explains. "We've been funded by mostly long-term, blue-chip investors, and Franc was directly responsible for capturing the interest of many of the European financial institutions that hold stock in X-Cal. Though we're in the high-risk end of the investment spectrum, our shareholders have been very loyal to us and we've been very loyal to them."

A native of Ontario, Shawn Kennedy was reared in Toronto, where as a kid he collected scrap metal in his wagon and sold it to local junk dealers for $1.50 or $2.00 a load. "They probably thought I was quite humourous," he says with a laugh, "but even then I had this entrepreneurial streak." His far-reaching vision, creative instincts and natural gravitation toward hard work impressed his stepfather – a successful businessman in his own right – who appreciated that young Shawn was bound for a future that promised considerably more than a lifetime spent punching someone else's time clock.

The self-described 'black sheep of the family', Kennedy headed West in the early-1970s, shortly after finishing school. Smitten with the lay of the land and the bountiful resources British Columbia had to offer, he toiled aboard fishing boats, in logging camps and on oil drilling rigs – gruelling, often dangerous work that not only built character but instilled in Kennedy an appreciation and respect for both the country's natural resources and the pioneering spirit of his forefathers. "I'm not a geologist," he says. "I'm a prospector/entrepreneur educated by apprenticeship to people I admired and sought out for various different reasons. I moved to the Bralorne area of British Columbia in the fall of 1974 and first became seriously infected by the prospecting bug when I met an old miner near the site of the old Bralorne-Pioneer Gold Mine. He passed on some of his wisdom to me and explained the best methods for staking claims. I acquired a prospector's license at that time because the area itself is a known gold area. Initially it was a lark. I was young and adventurous and a prospector's license gave you certain rights. I enjoyed the Bralorne area, enjoyed living there and wanted to be in a less-densely populated area."

Though Kennedy would not cross paths with his future mentor until 1982, it was in this selfsame neck of the woods that Franc Joubin learned the ropes of the mining trade in the 1930s. The son of French immigrants who relocated to San Francisco in the wake of the Great Earthquake of 1906, Franc Guy Renault Joubin was born in the Bay City in mid-November 1911. (There is some confusion as to the exact date, owing to the celebratory drinking binge undertaken by his father upon Franc's arrival – the elder Joubin had yet to sober up before reaching the registry office and subsequently entered the wrong date on his son's birth certificate.) Less than three years later, the family, with Franc's baby brother Gerald in tow, landed in Victoria, B.C., where his patriotic father immediately enlisted in World War One and shipped off for the frontlines in France. Seriously wounded in battle, Joubin's father eventually returned to B.C., but required constant medical attention at convalescence facilities. Complications from the injuries took their toll and he died in 1918.

Left with two small children and no financial assistance, Joubin's mother succumbed to a nervous breakdown. She was hospitalized and the two boys were shuffled off to foster parents and later orphanages – Franc to a Protestant one, his brother to a Catholic one, where the younger boy suffered corporal punishment and frequent canings. Franc rescued his sibling and ran away. By the age of 11, Franc Joubin was fending for himself. When the Great Depression came crashing down in 1929, Joubin found himself in a hobo camp near the Bralorne-Pioneer Gold Mine in B.C.'s Lillooet region, 140 miles north of Vancouver, awaiting any job that came available. Hired to build a rock garden for the mill manager, Joubin soon entered the world of mining and found his calling. In the 1950s, he masterminded the largest staking operation ever conducted in Canada at the time, resulting in the Elliot Lake uranium discovery, halfway between Sudbury and Sault Ste. Marie in western Ontario. Stock prices skyrocketed from $1 to $135 a share in 13 months and, after sell-ing off his 10 percent interest, Joubin walked away with $11 million.

"This was in the late 1950s," says Kennedy. "He could have gone off and spent the rest of his life in the Hawaiian Islands, done whatever he wanted to do. Instead of that, he became a global representative for the U.N. He would go into a developing country with a four-man team, map the mineral potential of the entire country and set up an agency within the country to develop that mineral potential. They made discoveries all over the world. He didn't need the money – he wanted to help people in other countries. Franc used to open his talks by saying, 'Mining is a business – you need trucks and cash flow and engineers. Mining exploration, on the other hand, is a romantic adventure. I've always preferred the latter over the former.' Franc was one of the most successful economic prospectors who ever lived and one of the first inductees into the Canadian Mining Hall of Fame. His philosophy is very much the philosophy of X-Cal Resources."

Not entirely surprisingly, X-Cal's ascent began in the early 1980s with claims in the area of the Bralorne-Pioneer Gold Mine. "It was where Franc started his career in the 1930s and where I lived for 18 years," says Kennedy. "I was fascinated with mineral claims and with watching small companies drill. I had acquired a series of small claims at the time when gold went to $800 an ounce and I saw a lot of staking activity in the area. Then the gold market plunged. At that point, I was knowledgeable about the entire area and I thought people were going to start losing their claims. I thought I would try and pick them up while they were at a low, so I took the mineral-inventory map of known mineral occurrences and started putting squares around known mineral occurrences in conjunction with David Brace, a consulting geologist. I didn't realize at the time how much money this can encourage you to spend."

Maps in hand, Kennedy attended a prospectors' convention in Toronto, hoping to find buyers for his claims and possibly keep a key par-cel for himself. "At that point, I think I had 17,000 acres in maybe five or six different locations in the Bralorne area," he says. "As a prospector, I was green, but I thought I would start my own public company with the one claim I kept for myself. At the conference, someone told me that because I had claims in the area, I should meet Franc Joubin. In fact, a geologist whom I was working with said, 'I'd give my eyeteeth to meet that guy for five minutes.' So I looked up Franc in Who's Who and realized he was someone quite out of the ordinary. I phoned his office and got connected to his assistant – the appropriately named 'Mrs. Wolf,' who vigourously screened everyone who wanted to speak to him – and somehow or another I got to talk to Franc. I started naming off creeks and mineral claims at various locations in the Bralorne area which, of course, Franc knew very well. He listened to my pitch and said, 'Come and see me and bring lots of maps.'" Kennedy did just that.

"I had the geological maps of area," Kennedy continues, "which I really didn't know how to read at the time. Franc began pointing at the maps and asking if certain markings were geophysical or geochemical anomalies. I didn't know – but he did. That's when he turned to me and said the words that changed my life: 'I judge you to be more of a promoter than someone who is technically knowledgeable about the area you're involved in. My first advice to you is to gain more technical knowledge – but if you come back here with your geologist, I'm not going to see you. So be quiet and I'm going to tell you some things that I could be telling to a major mining company, but I won't – I'm going to tell them to you.' On that note, he leaned over my maps and started explaining things to me. As it turned out, Franc had written the definitive papers on the Bralorne region in 1948. He started lecturing me at that meeting in 1982 and never stopped until his death in 1997."

Joubin imparted his considerable knowledge to Kennedy in rapid-fire bursts of weighty import. "By the time we'd finished that first meeting," says Kennedy, "he'd bent my mind. He told me where I should go and look, and he gave me a plan of what he would do. I remember stopping outside the door of his office immediately afterwards and saying to myself: 'I know that with each step I take from this spot, there is room for doubt to creep in – but I believe what took place in that room and I'm going to run with it.'"

Kennedy dug into his research and discovered that almost all the land Joubin wanted to secure was open. "We thought we were going to have to go and make deals with people," he says. "Instead of that, the money came out of my own pocket to hire seven guys and a helicopter to do the staking. I had 17,000 acres and took an additional 21,000 acres on bank overdraft. Nine days after leaving Franc's office, I had this whole parcel wrapped up and I sent him a note saying, 'I've got it!' The next thing I knew, the phone rang and it was Franc Joubin calling. I couldn't believe it – it was like somebody learning to play the harmonica suddenly getting a phone call from Bob Dylan. When you are used to aspiring to things, you don't think you're going to get a reciprocal response. As a prospector in the early stages, you just assume you're going to take a lot of losses. Instead of that, I had Franc Joubin calling me and telling me that he was sending me a letter saying that he felt these properties were important and should be explored."

The letter in question granted aspirant prospector/entrepreneur Shawn Kennedy access to a whole new world and a whole new level of business opportunities. Through his stepfather, Kennedy had become acquainted with Vancouver-based Royal Bank executive Doug Gardner. "Doug would always take the time of day for me," says Kennedy. "He was my devil's advocate and I think, to a certain degree, he was entertained by me." That is, until Kennedy turned up one day with Joubin's letter in hand. "Doug knew I had some mineral claims," Kennedy continues, "but when I showed up with this letter from Franc Joubin, he was stunned. He said, 'How did you get this?' Then called in the Royal Bank's mining analyst, who also knew who Franc was. The analyst said, 'Not only does Franc still have all his marbles, he's as smart as a whip.' At that point, I had the mineral claims in Bralorne, a petroleum lease, and the letter from Franc Joubin. Those things – and three years of hard work – raised the first $500,000 for X-Cal. We went public on the Toronto Stock Exchange in 1985."

With Joubin's assistance, influence and encouragement, X-Cal Resources soon took an interest in Nevada. The state produces more than 7.73 million ounces of gold annually and 81 percent of the gold in the United States, making it one of the world's most prolific mining districts. X-Cal zeroed in on the famous Battle Mountain Trend and secured two substantial projects, the 20,000-acre Sleeper Gold Property and the 640-acre Mill Creek Gold Property. The former, located in the Slumbering Hills area of Humboldt County, remains the company's primary focus today.

"Our mineral exploration goals led us to the Sleeper Gold Property,"

Kennedy explains. "It was well-known at the time it went into production for Amax Gold in 1986, yielding ore of such a spectacularly high-grade that armed guards were stationed around the pit. Within six months, capital costs of operation were paid off and Amax reinvested its cash flow into projects all over the world." Unfortunately, the new Amax projects – including the Fort Knox Mine in Alaska, the Refugio in Chile and the Kubaka in the Soviet Union – all ran well over capital costs before generating any money. Amax subsequently wound up in serious debt and the company's holdings were divvied up in a series of mergers.

"In the meantime," says Kennedy, "X-Cal had been involved in the area and had acquired ground adjacent to the Sleeper Mine. We brought our mineral claims up against the Amax holdings so they had contiguous boundaries and we then made an exploration agreement with Amax that combined the properties. We put a lot of money into documenting a mineral system that exists within the claim's boundary. We now have 30 square miles of property, and the Sleeper Mine is a part of that mineral system."

The area has a rich and prodigious history with gold production dating back to 1914. In the 1930s, both open-pit and underground operations at the Jumbo Mine (located approximately four miles southeast of what would become Sleeper) recorded production of 30,000 ounces of gold in 1986. Assays at the newly developed Sleeper Gold Mine ran as high as 195.0 ounces per tonne from blast holes 20 feet in depth. Twenty ounce-per-tonne material was common. Amax began exploration in 1982 and delineated the mineable reserve that would eventually yield approximately 1.7 million ounces of gold and 2.3 million ounces of silver before ceasing operations in 1986. During operations, Amax discovered a high-grade vein in the eastern pit wall that necessitated the relocation of the mine office (hence, the Office Pit). Furthermore, it was discovered that the mill stood on low-grade leachable ore and that the leach pads were located on the probable extension of the high-grade vein to the northeast of the main pit.

"I looked at various other properties in the area and first visited the Sleeper in 1990," says Kennedy. "In 1993, we began our land assembly at Sleeper with an initial land lease. We began to expand our land holdings, eventually coming up against the Amax lands. We recognized that the

Sleeper Mine, along with the Jumbo and Alma mines – which had both been past producers – might delineate a northwest trend, contrary to the conventional view that Sleeper was primarily associated with a north trending range-front fault.

"We were encouraged by the initial exploration results," Kennedy continues, "and X-Cal subsequently staked nearly all the remaining ground around the Sleeper property. We realized that Amax was busy elsewhere in the world and had their hands full. Sleeper had been the engine that provided Amax with the cash to launch their other projects. They dug it up until they were confined by their infrastructure, which you can see by looking at aerial photographs of the site taken in the mid-1980s. When you look at it historically, you realize that Amax was confined by their debt at the same time the pit was confined by its own infrastructure." It was becoming apparent to the X-Cal team that the mineralized system at the Sleeper Mine was far from being exhausted.

"Amax just stopped drilling," says Kennedy, "the system didn't stop. They planned for a pit of a certain size, they rushed it into production at the time they began, and they made money hand-over-fist. But you can see from looking at the data that they had to stop for reasons other than lack of gold. In fact, the reconciliation studies show that Amax actually dug up more than 4.5 million ounces. They sent 1.7 million ounces to the bank, which they got paid for, and the difference is still sitting above ground, onsite. They managed to average $158 an ounce because of the high-grade ore being run through the mill. They piled up the low-grade ore in a very inefficient heap-leach operation that was recovering less than 42 percent. It was what they ran through the mill – the legendary Sleeper high-grade – that paid for everything. It launched them into those other projects. The pit bottomed in ore, there are targets throughout the district. In short, the Sleeper Gold district hasn't been fully explored."

Of the 20,000 acres (30 square miles) at the Sleeper Gold Project, X-Cal Resources Ltd. now owns 50 percent in a joint venture with the New Sleeper Gold Corporation. Thus far, six favourable project domains have been identified. "X-Cal spent US$12 million to assemble the land and document the mineral system at the Sleeper Gold Project," says Kennedy. "Our partners, New Sleeper, have put up US$20 million to establish a 50/50 joint venture with us. It is because they understand the scale and scope of this project. We are currently spending US$500,000 per month to explore the district together.

"Look at what happened at Red Lake," he adds, comparing the untapped wealth at Sleeper to the Ontario project resurrected by Goldcorp Inc., a project now considered to be one of the richest gold mines in the world. "They thought it was mined out."

In addition to Sleeper, X-Cal Resources likewise secured the 100-percent owned Mill Creek Gold Property, an important holding in nearby Lander County, Nevada. Located within the Cortez Joint Venture Area, where Placer Dome has the Pipeline Gold Deposit and recently made a new discovery called Cortez Hills, it, too, lies within the Battle Mountain Trend. "At Cortez, Placer has 5.5 million ounces within an area that is 1,500 feet long by 750 feet wide," says Kennedy. "You can't just find these things easily but if you go back into the history of the area, you find that gold reserves were well-known in this region before the turn of the century. At the time we began work in Nevada, the Battle Mountain Trend wasn't even considered to extend as far north as the Sleeper Mine. This was the same thing that happened at the Carlin Trend in Nevada. Until Ken Snyder discovered the Midas Mine for Franco Nevada – now Newmont – nobody thought the trend extended that distance.

"Deeper rocks forced to the surface provide what geologists call 'windows,'" Kennedy continues. "In a sense, they are like the knuckles on your hand – there is one set of rocks and then another and then another. It is the alignment of these windows that outlines the Battle Mountain and Carlin Trends. Some of the higher-grade mineralization is present in these lower plate rocks. It ties into your basic gold-exploration theory, which is that fluids carrying minerals come up from down below. The mineral fluids have to have a structure to carry them up and then they get deposited in a number of ways.

"In the early days of the Carlin Trend, for example, geologists had a theory that these things were epithermal, surface deposits – the mineral would come up, circulate near surface and make a pod of very consistent but low-grade, bulk-mineable mineralization, and then it would go back down again and leave nothing in between. That turned out to be an erroneous theory – like the world is flat – but a whole series of geologists subscribed to it. Newmont had drilled four mines on the Carlin Trend at that time, but only to a certain depth. Everybody kept thinking that this was the way these trends behaved: they're shallow, they're bulk-mineable. People thought because Newmont was big and experienced, if there was anything else there, they would have found it. Well, along came Barrick Gold Corp. who discovered a deposit called Betze. Barrick drilled deeper and went beyond the theory that these epithermal deposits were shallow. No one until then had drilled beyond a certain point. Now, 40 million ounces of gold later, you've got Barrick on Carlin Trend. To put it in perspective, if Nevada was a country, it would be the fourth-largest gold-producing country in the world."

It was no coincidence that the man who drilled off of Barrick's Betze – respected professional geological engineer Larry Kornze (the 'ze' in Betze derives from his surname) – is an integral part of Shawn Kennedy's X-Cal Resources team. A top-notch team is part of Kennedy's greater vision. "Like the film Field of Dreams," says Kennedy, referring to the fantastical 1989 flick, "assemble the right properties and they will come. Franc was the original geologic brains of the operation and I was the legs, for a number of years. Now Larry Kornze, Ken Snyder and Win Rowe – all successful mine-finders – are part of the X-Cal team. In addition, we have established good relationships with some of the larger companies in the area, such as Placer Dome. When you look at our head office, it's pretty small and we have low overhead. We are able to keep it that way because we generally work with well-seasoned and well-known subcontractors and consultants."

Employed by Barrick Gold from 1985 until his recent retirement, Larry Kornze managed the company's exploration projects in Mexico, Central America and the United States. Prior to joining Barrick, he held various positions with Newmont and Getty Mining Co. in North America and has 34 years experience in the international gold exploration and discovery business. Dr. Kenneth D. Snyder – whom Kennedy calls "the most humble Ph.D. you'll ever meet" – likewise brings outstanding credentials to the company and, in fact, Newmont's Midas Mine is also known as the 'Ken Synder Mine', owing to Snyder's discovery of the project. Winthrop 'Win'A. Rowe, M.Sc., joined X-Cal as a special consultant in 1996, having worked as director of exploration for Pegasus Gold, where he was responsible for that company's exploration in Chile and led the team that discovered the extensions of the Florida Canyon Mine. Prior to joining Pegasus in 1990, Rowe was employed as Nevada manager for Coeur d'Alene mines and also worked for Freeport McMoRan and Hanna Mining. To date, his teams have been credited with the discovery of more than 5 million ounces of gold reserves for major mining companies. Rounding out X-Cal's outstanding list of personnel are Keith Blair, MSc, and Larry Martin, Geo., key parts of the team who are well on their way to establishing themselves in the mining world.

"You can tell the calibre of the company and its properties by looking at its people," says Kennedy. "It all goes back to my mentor Franc Joubin, a very recognizable name with a legendary track record. Franc would go to local indigenous people and ask, 'Have you seen any rust-coloured rock or anything unusual.' He knew what to look for and how to find it. Both Ken Snyder and Larry Kornze are accomplished mine-finders and have documented their opinions of the Sleeper Gold Mine. Both of them have summarized the potential of the Sleeper Gold Project. They have provided succinct overviews of one of X-Cal's projects. Beginning with a man like Franc Joubin and moving to a pair of very prominent and well-known Nevada mine-finders like Larry and Ken is very encouraging.

"The people that we have in our history – Franc Joubin, Larry Kornze, Ken Snyder, Win Rowe – they've been a big part of putting the Sleeper Gold Project together, which for me is, once again, like Field of Dreams – assemble the right property and they will come. We have a team of very good technical people who have been responsible for putting together the data pack that shows we control a large mineral system at Sleeper. The Sleeper joint venture is now drilling and adding to the known gold at Sleeper. Plus, New Sleeper has added more able people such as Adrian Flemming, James Crombie and David Fennell to the mix.

"I'm a prospector and entrepreneur," Kennedy continues, "so with guys like Franc, Win, Larry and Ken pointing me in the right direction, I go get the claim tags, find the money and find the technical people to document it. As Ken Snyder has said, "of all the currently active district-scale plays in Nevada, the Sleeper mine has the highest potential for major success." He is a major-league guy and he has personally rated this project higher than the others, with the potential for both high-grade and high tonnage. Snyder's recommendation is to continue exploring along the same course, and Kornze seconds that opinion. In addition to Sleeper, we have the Mill Creek project in the Cortez Joint Venture Area. Mill Creek is a very interesting piece of property. We've held onto that property for 10 years and this year we're beginning to drill it."

When asked to compare Sleeper to Midas, Ken Snyder answers: "I believe that there is much more potential at Sleeper. Midas is essentially a single-vein, very high-grade ore body. There are more veins at Sleeper. It is a district with many targets – there is much more potential at Sleeper."

Venerated financial analyst Frank Veneroso concurs: "Our research team has tracked X-Cal's progress with Sleeper over a several-year time frame. Our team has been thorough and diligent in its research and analysis. The establishment of the sleeper Joint venture by X-Cal with its partner, New Sleeper Gold was the last missing piece. X-Cal has put together a major league gold play with top geologic people involved and lots of upside. Our opinion of the potential is evidenced by the shares that we hold."

Both passionate and realistic about the ongoing success of X-Cal Resources, Shawn Kennedy clearly demonstrated his mettle by refusing to buckle when times turned bad. "We rode through a very difficult period of low gold prices through the past several years," he says, echoing a post-Bre-X sentiment that separated the serious players from the fly-by-nighters in a hellish bear market. "When other companies were pouring everything they had into dot.coms or the high-tech sector, we were continuing to explore this property on behalf of our sophisticated, long-term investors who have backed the company for many years.

We have had private institutional European investors backing us since 1988 and to give you an idea what they're like, they prefer to have information presented to them in black-and-white – that is why our annual reports are in black-and-white, not colour. The reason behind this is quite simple: they believe the more gold there is on the cover of the annual report, the less gold there is in the ground."

This kind of common-sense approach is what makes X-Cal Resources Ltd. the unique and singular entity Shawn Kennedy envisioned upon leaving Franc Joubin's office for the first time 22 years ago. He smiles assuredly before concluding: "We've really only touched the surface."

CORPORATE CONTACT INFORMATION

AFCAN MINING CORPORATION
Stock symbol: AFK - TSX
Head Office: Suite 850 - 141 Adelaide Street West
Toronto, ON   M5H 3L5
Telephone: (416)360-3415 • Fax: (416)360-3416
Website: afcan-mining.com

AURIZON MINES LIMITED
Stock symbol: ARZ - TSE
Head Office: Suite 900 - 510 Burrard Street
Vancouver, BC   V6C 3A8
Telephone: (604)687-6600 • Fax: (604)687-3932
Website: aurizon.com

BRALORNE GOLD MINES LIMITED
Stock symbol: BPM - TSX
Head Office: Suite 400 - 455 Granville Street
Vancouver, BC   V6C 1T1
Telephone: (604)682-3701 • Fax: (604)682-3600
Website: bralorne.com

CANDENTE RESOURCE CORPORATION
Stock symbol: DNT - TSX
Head Office: Suite 200 - 905 West Pender Street
Vancouver, BC   V6C 1L6
Telephone: (604)689-1957 • Fax: (604)685-1946
Website: candente.com

CASSIDY GOLD CORPORATION
Stock symbol: CDY - TSX
Head Office: Suite 220 - 141 Victoria Street
Kamloops, BC   V2C 1Z5
Telephone: (250)372-8222 • Fax: (250)828-2269
Website: cassidygold.com

EMGOLD MINING CORPORATION
Stock symbol: EMR - TSX
Head Office: Suite 1400 - 570 Granville Street
Vancouver, BC   V6C 3P1
Telephone: (604)687-4622 • Fax: (604)687-4212
Website: emgold.com

ENTRÉE GOLD INCORPORATED
Stock symbol: ETG - TSX
Head Office: Suite 1450 - 650 W. Georgia Street
Vancouver, BC   V6B 4N7
Telephone: (604)687-4777 • Fax: (604)687-4770
Website: entreegold.com

ETRUSCAN RESOURCES INCORPORATED
Stock symbol: EET - TSE
Head Office: 48 Gerrish Street, PO Box 2020
Windsor, Nova Scotia   B0N 2T0
Telephone: (902)798-9701 • Fax: (902)798-9702
Website: etruscan.com

EVERTON RESOURCES INCORPORATED
Stock symbol: EVR - TSX
Head Office: Suite 201 - 290 Picton Street
Ottawa, ON   K1Z 8P8
Telephone: (613)241-2332 • Fax: (613)241-6005
Website: evertonresources.com

FREEGOLD VENTURES LIMITED
Stock symbol: ITF - TSE
Head Office: 2303 West 41st Avenue
Vancouver, BC   V6M 2A3
Telephone: (604)685-1870 • Fax: (604)685-8045
Website: freegoldventures.com

FRONTEER DEVELOPMENT GROUP INC.
Stock symbol: FRG - TSX
Head Office: Suite 1640 - 1066 West Hastings Street
Vancouver, BC   V6E 3X1
Telephone: (604)632-4677 • Fax: (604)632-4678
Website: fronteergroup.com

GOLDCORP INCORPORATED
Stock symbol: G - TSE
Head Office: Suite 2700 - 145 King Street West
Toronto, ON   M5H 1J8
Telephone: (416)865-0326 • Fax: (416)361-6403
Website: goldcorp.com

HIGH RIVER GOLD MINES LIMITED
Stock symbol: HRG - TSE
Head Office: Suite 1700 - 155 University Avenue
Toronto, ON   M5H 3B7
Telephone: (416)947-1440 • Fax: (416)360-0010
Website: hrg.ca

HUNTER DICKINSON INCORPORATED
Stock symbol: (see companies)
Head Office: Suite 1020 - 800 West Pender Street
Vancouver, BC   V6C 2V6
Telephone: (604)684-6365 • Fax: (604)684-8092
Website: hdgold.com

IMA EXPLORATION INCORPORATED
Stock symbol: IMR - TSX
Head Office: Suite 709 - 837 West Hastings Street
Vancouver, BC   V6C 3N6
Telephone: (604)687-1828 • Fax: (604)687-1858
Website: imaexploration.com

IMPERIAL METALS CORPORATION
Stock symbol: III - TSX
Head Office: Suite 200 - 580 Hornby Street
Vancouver, BC   V6C 3B6
Telephone: (604)669-8959 • Fax: (604)687-4030
Website: imperialmetals.com

MINERA ANDES INCORPORATED
Stock symbol: MAI - TSX
Head Office: Suite A - 111 East Magnesium Rd.
Spokane, WA   99208
Telephone: (509)921-7322 • Fax: (509)921-7325
Website: minandes.com

NORTHERN ORION RESOURCES INC.
Stock symbol: NNO - TSE
Head Office: Suite 220 - 1075 West Georgia Street
Vancouver, BC   V6E 3C9
Telephone: (604)689-9663 • Fax: (604)434-1487
Website: northernorion.com

NOVAGOLD RESOURCES INCORPORATED
Stock symbol: NRI - TSE
Head Office: Suite 3454 - 1055 Dunsmuir Street
Vancouver, BC   V7X 1K8
Telephone: (604)669-6227 • Fax: (604)669-6272
Website: novagold.net

OREZONE RESOURCES INCORPORATED
Stock symbol: OZN - TSE
Head Office: Suite 201 - 290 Picton Street
Ottawa, ON   K1Z 8P8
Telephone: (613)241-3699 • Fax: (613)241-6005
Website: orezone.com

RUBICON MINERALS CORPORATION
Stock symbol: RMX - TSX
Head Office: Suite 1540 - 800 West Pender Street
Vancouver, BC   V6C 2V6
Telephone: (604)623-3333 • Fax: (604)623-3355
Website: rubiconminerals.com

ST. JUDE MINERALS LIMITED
Stock Symbol: SJD - TSX
Head Office: Suite 200 - 5405 48th Avenue
Delta, BC   V4K 1W6
Telephone: (604)940-6565 • Fax: (604)940-6566
Website: stjudegold.com

SPARTON RESOURCES INCORPORATED
Stock symbol: SRI - TSX
Head Office: Suite 605 - 55 University Avenue
Toronto, ON   M5J 2H7
Telephone: (416)366-3551 • Fax: (416)366-7421
Website: spartonres.ca

STEALTH MINERALS LIMITED
Stock symbol: SML - TSX
Head Office: 2382 Bayview Avenue
Toronto, ON   M2L 1A1
Telephone: (416)510-8397 • Fax: (416)510-8561
Website: stealthminerals.com

TUMI RESOURCES LIMITED
Stock symbol: TM - TSX
Head Office: Suite 1305 - 1090 West Georgia Street
Vancouver, BC   V6E 3V7
Telephone: (604)657-4058 • Fax: (604)685-1631
Website: tumiresources.com

VIRGINIA GOLD MINES
Stock symbol: VIA - TSE
Head Office: Suite 200 - 116 St.-Pierre
Quebec City, QC   G1K 4A7
Telephone: (418)694-9832 • Fax: (418)694-9120
Website: virginia.qc.ca

WOLFDEN RESOURCES INCORPORATED
Stock symbol: WLF - TSX
Head Office: Suite One - 309 Court Street South
Thunder Bay, ON   P7B 2Y1
Telephone: (807)346-1668 • Fax: (807)345-0284
Website: wolfdenresources.com

X-CAL RESOURCES LIMITED
Stock symbol: XCL - TSE
Head Office: Suite 750 - 666 Burrard Street
Vancouver, BC   V6C 2X8
Telephone: (604)662-8245 • Fax: (604)688-7740
Website: x-cal.com